A TEXTBOOK OF GEOLOGY

TEXTBOOK OF GEOLOGY

PUBLISHED BY

JOHN WILEY & SONS, Inc.

PART I

Physical Geology. By Chester R. Longwell, Professor of Geology, Yale University; Adolph Knopf, Silliman Professor of Geology, Yale University; and Richard F. Flint, Associate Professor of Geology, Yale University. Cloth; 6 by 9; 514 pages; 341 figures.

PART II

Historical Geology. By Charles Schuchert, Professor of Paleontology and Historical Geology, Emeritus, and Carl O. Dunbar, Professor of Paleontology and Stratigraphy, and Curator of Invertebrate Paleontology, Yale University. Third Edition, Rewritten and Reset. Cloth; 6 by 9; 551 pages; 332 figures in text, 34 plates.

Outlines of Physical Geology. By Chester R. Longwell, Adolph Knopf, and Richard F. Flint. Cloth; 6 by 9; 356 pages; 297 figures.

Outlines of Historical Geology. Third Edition, Rewritten. By Charles Schuchert and Carl O. Dunbar. Cloth; 6 by 9; 241 pages; 151 figures.

C. B. Waite.

ERUPTION OF COLIMA VOLCANO, MEXICO, IN 1906.

Billowy puffs issued from the crater at fifteen-minute intervals, and blended to
form the cloud shown near the top of the view.

A TEXTBOOK OF
GEOLOGY

PART I — PHYSICAL GEOLOGY

BY

CHESTER R. LONGWELL
Professor of Geology in Yale University

ADOLPH KNOPF
Silliman Professor of Geology in Yale University

AND

RICHARD F. FLINT
Associate Professor of Geology in Yale University

NEW YORK
JOHN WILEY & SONS, Inc.
London: CHAPMAN & HALL, Limited

Printed in U. S. A.

Printing	Composition and Plates	Binding	10–37
F. H. GILSON CO.	TECHNICAL COMPOSITION CO.	STANHOPE BINDERY	
BOSTON	CAMBRIDGE	BOSTON	

PREFACE

Three years ago the writers helped revise Part I of the " Textbook of Geology " by Pirsson and Schuchert. Extensive changes were made throughout, and several chapters were entirely rewritten; but as the revised book remained under the authorship of the late Professor Pirsson, the revisers felt an obligation to retain as nearly as possible the original method of presentation. The present volume, which embodies not only ideas of organization and presentation developed by the work of revision and by constant use of the revised text, but also much new material, is the avowed successor to Pirsson's book. Probably the most valuable inheritance is the balance between subjects for which the original book has been widely commended. The general order of the final revision is retained, and in a few chapters some parts of Pirsson's scheme of presentation have been used, but only where they could be effectively adapted to the general plan of the present authors.

The organization of the subject matter assumes that students who use the book begin their study by making an acquaintance with the common minerals and rocks. This approach to the study of geology appears to be fundamental, since the operation of geologic processes, for example weathering, can not be appreciated without some knowledge of the materials involved. In their elementary course the authors devote a considerable time to a practical study of minerals and rocks before taking up any of the processes. For such a preliminary study the student needs adequate descriptions arranged in convenient form. To meet this need the present volume offers in two appendices the definitions and elementary descriptions of all the minerals and rocks considered in the text. Another appendix gives an introduction to the study of topographic maps. Such a special arrangement does not in any way obscure the importance of highly essential subject matter. On the contrary, the device serves a twofold useful purpose: it brings together, in the form of a short manual, the elementary explanations needed for laboratory study; and it removes a considerable amount of bare definition and description from the body of the text, which can then be devoted more effectively to the discussion of geologic processes and problems.

Preparation of the introductory chapter has received particular attention, since physical geology usually is the introduction to geology as a whole and therefore the student needs an orienting statement to

iii

acquaint him with the scope and the general viewpoint of the subject. The historical aspect of geology needs emphasis, and this purpose is served by sketching briefly the astronomical setting of the Earth and by implanting at once the concept of the immense length of geologic time. A large advantage is gained if the student can be made to appreciate at the outset that geologic features are studied not merely for their own sake but more particularly for the history they reveal.

With this keynote in mind, the attempt is made throughout the book to keep to matters that have a direct bearing on geologic history. The authors consider it a mistake to use the limited space in an elementary text for the exposition of scientific matters not directly a part of geology, however interesting they may be in themselves. For this reason the discussion of weather, of which at best only a smattering can be given in a geologic text, has been abandoned. Similarly a detailed discussion of the mechanics of glacier motion, which has inherent interest but is not essential to an understanding of land sculpture by glaciers, is dispensed with.

In brief summary, some of the outstanding features of the new book are the following: Weathering is treated as a unit subject, and its relation to general erosion is made clear. The chapter is not entitled " Work of the Atmosphere," because all gradational processes, including stream erosion and glaciation, depend either directly or indirectly on the atmosphere. The importance of climate in determining soil types, as demonstrated by recent research, is emphasized. Wind action is discussed in a separate chapter, since the common practice of combining this subject with weathering leads to confusion. In the discussion of stream work the explanation of the erosion cycle under different climatic conditions is given more emphasis than in the final edition of the Pirsson textbook. The discussions of glaciation, igneous geology, and metamorphism are revised to take account of the most recent data. Modern researches in seismology, and particularly the late work on near earthquakes, are considered in the chapter on the Earth's interior. The relation of geologic processes to landscapes has been given special attention in nearly every chapter. As in the final edition of the Pirsson textbook, the treatment of the more complicated aspects of land forms is deferred until deformation and other processes have been explained in detail; but the old treatment has been entirely reorganized and much new material has been added. The final chapter gives a discussion of coal and petroleum, in addition to a short treatment of ore deposits, and it emphasizes that our understanding of these mineral resources depends on geologic principles developed earlier in the book.

Discussion of many major subjects in geology leads quickly into the fields of inference and theory. Some elementary textbooks, probably for the purpose of simplifying and shortening the treatment of debatable matters, make dogmatic statements not warranted by existing knowledge. In the opinion of the present writers this practice does a disservice to the science. The teacher loses nothing by stating frankly what is not known; on the contrary he can in this way gain the student's confidence and stimulate his interest. The cause of rock exfoliation has not yet been proved; we can not give any quantitative evaluation of wind erosion; the origin of igneous rocks and the causes of crustal movements are great mysteries. Since almost every aspect of geology teems with fascinating problems, why should an elementary text give the false impression that most of the Earth's secrets are known? It is the aim of the present volume not only to state the essential facts of physical geology, but also to indicate the limits of knowledge and to direct the student's attention to the vast field awaiting exploration.

Most of the illustrations used are new. Numerous block diagrams, specially drawn for this book, are employed to explain the genesis of structural features and land forms. None of the figures are used simply for embellishment; all have been chosen for their geologic significance. Duplication is avoided by referring both forward and backward to figures that illustrate more than one subject or principle. Special care has been used in preparing the legends of the illustrations, with the purpose of centering attention on significant features and making the figures intelligible without direct reference to the text.

With the idea of welding the chapters together and showing the interrelation of various subjects, cross-references are used freely throughout the book.

Direct responsibility of each author in preparing the text is indicated in the following division by chapters:

Chapter I by Knopf and Longwell.

Chapters II, VII, XII, XIII, XV, and XVI, and Appendix D by Longwell.

Chapters III, IV, V, VI, VIII, and XVII, and Appendix C by Flint.

Chapters IX, X, XI, XIV, XVIII, and Appendices A and B by Knopf.

The authors are under obligation to many individuals and organizations for the use of photographs. Proper acknowledgment is made with each halftone.

C. R. L.
A. K.
R. F. F.

New Haven, Conn.,
January 1, 1932.

CONTENTS

PHYSICAL GEOLOGY

CHAPTER I

A GENERAL VIEW OF THE EARTH

Man has a natural curiosity about the Earth, his home. Of what materials is it made? When and how did it come into being, and through what changes has it passed? What has been the story of life on the Earth, and exactly what part has man himself played in the drama? Inquiries such as these have engaged the attention of thinking people from a very early period, as evidenced by the mythologies of the ancients. Some of the old philosophers — Pythagoras, Aristotle, and others — caught brilliant glimpses of the truth; but the science of geology, which strives for the full answer to questions about the Earth and the record of life, had its first consistent development in modern times, with the growth of science in general. The practical exigencies of mining stimulated the development of modern geology, but the growth of the science to its present substantial proportions was largely the result of the intellectual curiosity of the human mind. The principles thus discovered have been applied to practical ends, and geology has repaid a thousandfold its early debt to mining.

Geology enlists the aid of other sciences in examining the various aspects of the Earth and its history. A fitting introduction to the study considers the Earth in its astronomical setting.

THE EARTH AS A MEMBER OF THE SOLAR SYSTEM

The Earth is one of a group of nine known planets that revolve around a common central orb, the Sun (Fig. 1). Some of them, like Jupiter, are much larger than the Earth; some, like Mercury, are smaller. Two are nearer the Sun, the others are farther away. They all revolve around the Sun in nearly a common plane, which is slightly inclined to the Sun's equator. The Earth and the other planets were born of the Sun, as has been recognized since the latter half of the eighteenth century when the nebular hypothesis of Kant and Laplace was formulated. According to the modern theory of cosmogony, which we owe to Chamberlin and Moulton, the substance of the planets was torn from the Sun

1

under the influence of the disruptive pull of a passing star several times more massive than itself; but how this incandescent matter from the Sun came to form the planets is a problem on which ideas are still far apart. According to the most recent development of the theory, by Jeffreys in 1931, the passing star actually collided with the Sun in grazing incidence, this collision being thought necessary to account for the existing rotation of the Sun on its axis. The matter torn from the Sun by the collision was pulled out as an incandescent filament, which condensed in detached separate masses to form the planets. In this version of the theory of the origin of the Solar System the Earth is supposed to have passed through a fluid stage. A further corollary

Fig. 1. — Planets revolve about the Sun almost in the same plane, and all in the same direction, as suggested by the orbits of three of them.   The orbits are nearly circular, but in the figure they appear strongly elliptical because the observer is supposed to look down upon them obliquely. The diagram is not drawn to scale.

of this theory is that the substance of which the Earth is built is a sample of only the outer layer of the Sun. The birth time of the Earth was probably at least 2000 million years ago, and since then the Earth has continued to have an eventful history, which it is the special task of geology to decipher. The record of a vast span of time is written in the rocks which make up the visible portion of the planet's outer shell. Just as in human history, so in the Earth's history the earlier records are scarce and nearly illegible, but the later records are much more abundant and more easily read. That portion of the Earth's history which is written in the rocks is referred to as *geologic time*. For this portion of the history we have positive information, and no matter how fascinating cosmogonic speculations may appear, the foundations of geology do not rest on them; on the contrary, the most probable cosmogonic fact concerning the origin of the Earth, that it was born 2000 million years ago, rests on the discoveries of radioactivity and geology.

The Sun is a star of very moderate size which has already lived three-fourths of the estimated time during which it will be self-luminous. Its surface temperature is approximately 6000° C. as determined observationally; the temperature at its center is estimated to be 40,000,000°. The geologic record shows that the Sun has been supplying light and heat to the Earth at a uniform rate during hundreds of millions of years. Up to the early part of the present century the other sciences could not adequately explain how the Sun has been able to maintain this prodigal expenditure of energy. It is now thought probable that its fires are stoked either by utilizing subatomic energy in the building up of the heavier chemical elements from hydrogen or by the annihilation of matter — the rushing together of electrons and protons, their mutual destruction, and transformation into radiant energy. The utilization of the energy within the atom would keep the Sun's fires going 10,000 million years, but the annihilation of matter would prolong its fires vastly longer. Sir James Jeans regards the destruction of matter as the most probable explanation and computes that the Sun is losing weight at the rate of 4 million tons a second. In time, therefore, the Sun's gravitational grip on the Earth will weaken and the Earth will recede farther into space; but on account of the enormous mass of the Sun this contingency is immensely remote.

The mass of the Sun is 332,000 times that of the Earth. Even counting in the masses of the other planets, practically all the mass of the Solar System is in the Sun, which therefore is the overwhelmingly dominant member of the system. Carrying with it the planets and their moons, the comets, and the asteroids, the Sun is traveling at the rate of 12 miles a second through space nearly toward the bright star Vega.

The path of the Earth around the Sun is not a circle, but an ellipse, one of whose foci is the Sun. The departure from circularity, termed the *eccentricity* of the orbit, is relatively small, however. The average distance of the Earth from the Sun is nearly 93 million miles, but because of its elliptic orbit, the Earth is 3 million miles nearer the Sun on January 1 than it is on July 1. Summer thus occurs in the northern hemisphere when the Earth is farthest from the Sun, and winter when it is nearest to the Sun. This fact causes summer to be somewhat cooler and winter somewhat warmer in the northern hemisphere than they would otherwise be. Summer, as measured from the vernal equinox on March 21 to the autumnal equinox on September 23, is at the present time 7 days longer than winter. In the southern hemisphere, however, winter is the longer season. Owing to the precession of the equinoxes, this condition will be reversed between the two hemispheres 10,500 years hence.

Because of the perturbing effect of the other planets, the eccentricity of the Earth's orbit is subject to secular variation — called secular because going on from age to age. The eccentricity of the orbit is now decreasing and will reach a minimum about 24,000 years hence. At maximum eccentricity the Earth is 13 million miles nearer the Sun in summer than in winter, thereby causing short hot summers and long cold winters. At that time the winter will be 35 days longer than summer.

Besides revolving around the Sun, the Earth is spinning on its polar axis, each rotation in 24 hours giving rise to day and night. The axis of rotation is not perpendicular to the plane of the Earth's orbit but is inclined to it at an angle of $66\frac{1}{2}°$, and this inclination causes the annual march of the seasons, summer and winter, alternately in the northern and southern hemispheres according as the axis is pointed toward the Sun or away from it. The angle between the Earth's equatorial plane and the plane of its orbit is called the inclination of the plane of the ecliptic; it is at present $23\frac{1}{2}°$ $(90° - 66\frac{1}{2}°)$, but is subject to a variation from $22°$ to $24\frac{1}{2}°$ during a period of about 40,400 years.

The variation of the three astronomic elements — eccentricity of the Earth's orbit, inclination of the ecliptic plane, and precession of the equinoxes — evidently must influence the climatic conditions on our planet, and must therefore influence the geologic processes that are affected by climate. At particular conjunctions of all three the effect will be most strongly accentuated, and it has been held that at such times they were able to bring about the several glacial epochs that have affected our planet during its long career.

The Earth, as we have seen, is a very insignificant fraction of the solar system, and for that matter the solar system itself is but an insignificant fraction of the universe. The Sun is a modest star in a stellar system whose members are numbered in thousands of millions. At immense distances beyond this system — the galactic system, or our " universe," as it is currently called in astronomy — are the spiral nebulae, which prove to be gigantic systems comparable to ours in size and number of stars. Some of these are so remote that their light takes over 100 million years to reach us. Each of them is an " island-universe," scattered in magnificent isolation through the immensity of space. Nevertheless, throughout this vast system of island-universes, each with its myriads of stars in various stages of development, the same general physical laws that we know on the Earth hold sway. Gravity operates in the same manner; light is transmitted everywhere by vibrations of the same kind; the spectroscope tells us that the same chemical elements occur in the Sun and the distant stars as on our Earth. Moreover, the meteorites which our planet gathers in its journey through space, and which are probably the disrupted fragments of comets, are made of substances identical with those found on the Earth. Differences in degree occur, owing to the enormously greater temperatures and pressures that Nature has at her command in the stars, but not in kind. Consequently there is a unity of law and a uniformity of material throughout space, and we feel justified in assuming that facts and reasoning derived by astronomical study of the other heavenly bodies can also be applied in our study of the Earth.

Larger Features of the Earth

Form of the Earth. — The Earth is not a true sphere but a spheroid flattened at the poles, so that the axis on which it rotates is shorter by 27 miles than the equatorial diameter. This equatorial bulging and resultant oblateness of the Earth, as well as that of the other planets, is fully explained by the principles of celestial mechanics. It depends on the centrifugal force due to rotation and on the internal constitution of the planet. By internal constitution is meant the composition, density, and distribution of the density within the planet (Chap. XV).

Continents and Deep-Sea Basins. — Of the 197 million square miles making up the surface of the globe, 71 per cent is covered by the interconnecting bodies of marine water; the Pacific Ocean alone covers

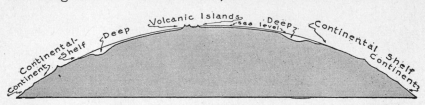

Fig. 2. — Segment of the Earth, showing major features of relief. The vertical scale is greatly exaggerated.

half the Earth and averages nearly 14,000 feet in depth. The *continents* — Eurasia, Africa, North America, South America, Australia, and Antarctica — are the portions of the *continental masses* rising above sea level. The submerged borders of the continental masses are the *continental shelves*, which extend with gentle seaward inclination out to the 600-foot isobath, where the slopes fall off, in many places abruptly, to the abyssal depths (Fig. 2). So vast is the volume of the sea that, if all the inequalities of relief of the globe were leveled off, the globe would be covered by a universal body of water 8600 feet deep.

The deep-sea basins attain their greatest depths not in mid-ocean, but in certain elongated furrows, or long narrow troughs, the so-called *deeps* (Chap. VIII). These profound troughs have a peripheral arrangement (Fig. 2), notably around the borders of the Pacific and Indian oceans. The position of the deeps near the continental masses suggests that the deeps, like the highest mountains, are of recent origin, since otherwise they would have been filled with waste from the lands. This suggestion is strengthened by the fact that the deeps are frequently the sites of world-shaking earthquakes (Chap. XIII).

The submarine topography of the oceans is none too well known, areas of a million square miles in the Pacific being represented by single soundings. The Atlantic, however, is fairly well known, especially as a result of the recent work of the German *Meteor* expedition. A well-defined ridge — the mid-Atlantic ridge — runs north and south between Africa and the two Americas. The soundings show furthermore that the topography of the floor of the Atlantic has considerable and abrupt relief, probably the result of mountain-making activities. In this respect the Atlantic seems to differ from the Pacific, and recent seismic evidence (Chap. XV) appears to show that the floors of the two oceans differ in constitution.

The continents stand on the average 2300 feet above sea level. North America averages 2300 feet; Europe averages only 940 feet; and Asia, the highest of the larger continental subdivisions, averages 3200 feet. The highest point on the globe, Mount Everest in the Himalayas, is 29,000 feet; and as the greatest known depth in the sea is over 35,000 feet, the maximum difference in elevation on the globe exceeds 64,000 feet, or more than 12 miles. Relative to the Earth's diameter of 7900 miles, however, the maximum relief is extremely small. The continental masses and the deep-sea basins are relief features of the first order; the deeps, ridges, and volcanic cones that diversify the sea floor are relief features of the second order. Topographic features of the continents — the plains, plateaus, and mountains — are also relief features of the second order. There is, however, a vast difference between the relief of the sea floor and that of the continents. The lands are unendingly subject to a complex of activities summarized in the term *erosion* (p. 14), which first sculptures them in great detail but ultimately reduces them to sea level. The modeling of the landscape by wind, weather, and running water is apparent to the keenly observant eye, and causes the more active minds to speculate on what must be the final result of the ceaseless wearing down of the lands. Long before there was a science of geology, Shakespeare wrote " the revolution of the times makes mountains level."

The origin of the continental masses and the deep-sea basins is still an unsolved problem. Have they existed in their present form and position since the beginning of geologic time? Have deep-sea floor and land changed places? These are moot questions. If the continents have been permanent features of the globe for some 2000 million years, or even for a much smaller span of time, why have they not been worn down to sea level? Instead, they stand high above sea level — 2300 feet on the average; manifestly there is some restorative force acting from within the Earth that counteracts the destructive effects of erosion acting from without the Earth. To these questions we shall return in later chapters.

Rocks, the Primary Documents of Geology

The outer zone of the Earth — the zone on which we live and the one directly accessible to our observation — is generally known as the *crust*. Because " crust " is an inheritance from the now obsolete nebular hypothesis of the origin of the Earth and is therefore thought by some to connote that the Earth has a molten liquid interior, the term *lithosphere* (from the Greek *lithos,* stone) has been coined in analogy with atmosphere, the gaseous envelope of the globe, in order to avoid this implication. We shall, however, use the simpler term crust, but without any implications as to the condition and origin of the core of the Earth.

Any understanding of the Earth must begin with some knowledge of the substances that compose it. We are permitted to see only a thin rind of the globe, and therefore all information about the vast interior portion must depend on indirect evidence. However, our most active interest lies in the part that can be explored directly; and this part in itself provides an almost limitless field of study. It is a zone composed of rocks and their constituent minerals. Even to the casual observer it is evident that these materials, exposed in cliffs or in road cuts, tunnels, and other artificial excavations, are highly varied in character; and accordingly it may appear that only a specialist can hope to gain any adequate acquaintance with rocks. Fortunately it has been found that comparatively few types are important quantitatively in the visible part of the Earth, and therefore any educated person can learn without great difficulty to recognize most of the rock masses he may see in the Alps, the Rocky Mountains, or elsewhere in his travels. A study of variations in rock types or of the more detailed features in minerals must of course be left to men specially equipped for the task.

The practical value of recognizing one rock from another is readily apparent from the viewpoint of the professional geologist or the mining engineer. In the search for petroleum and for ore minerals, in the selection of sites for great dams to make storage reservoirs, or in constructing an intricate subway system for a large city, knowledge of rocks and their peculiarities is a vital necessity. But there is a much broader interest in the subject, and the general key to this interest is within easy reach. A visitor to the slopes of Vesuvius or of Mauna Loa sees masses of dark, slaggy rock. It is fairly obvious, even without actually seeing fluid lava, that this dark material was once liquid and flowed down the slopes as a red-hot stream (Fig. 3). Continued investigation would convince the traveler that the " fire-made " or igneous rocks are common in many lands and have been formed at many different dates; they constitute an important part of the bedrock beneath us. Again, a brief examination in parts of the high Andes or Himalayas reveals layers of compacted sand and mud that include an abundance of sea-shells. Phenomena of this kind recall the conclusion of Aristotle, " The relation of land to sea changes, and a place does not always remain land or sea throughout all time."

If we group rocks according to the way in which they originated, they fall into three main classes: I, *igneous* rocks, formed by the solidification of molten material; II, *sedimentary* rocks, formed from material

Hawaiian Volcano Observatory.

Fig. 3. — Igneous rock in the making. The dark-colored rock is solidified lava; the white band is a stream of fluid lava, flowing toward the observer. The Alika flow, Mauna Loa volcano, 1919.

that has settled out of a transporting medium, generally water but more rarely air or glacier ice; and III, *metamorphic* rocks, formed by the impressment of new characters on preëxisting rocks by temperature, pressure, and other factors acting within the Earth's crust. Three-fourths of the land area of the globe is underlain by sedimentary rocks and the other fourth by igneous and metamorphic rocks. Although the sedimentary rocks thus preponderate in the visible part of the crust, they are essentially a veneer, a mile or less thick on the average. The foundation rock of the continents is largely igneous rock (granite). Metamorphic rocks are exposed in greatest abundance in the cores of mountain ranges deeply dissected by erosion.

THE SCOPE AND METHOD OF GEOLOGY

The grouping of rock masses according to the mode and place of their origin is not merely a dull classification for the convenience of scientists; it is the first step in the fascinating task of unraveling the ancient history of a region. In all of its many aspects, the study or practice of geology recognizes this fundamental interest in past events. But just as the proper understanding of human history requires some knowledge of present-day social, economic, and political conditions, so the deciphering of events in the geologic past is dependent on acquaintance with processes still operating on and within the Earth. Rocks are not inert monuments to conditions and forces that no longer exist. At active volcanoes we may observe all stages in the development of new rocks from molten material (Fig. 3). In the muds of river deltas and on sea floors we find the modern equivalents of ancient beds, now greatly distorted and eroded, which furnish the shells and other fossils so common in high mountains and plateaus. Rivers, glaciers, and other surface agencies are etching and slowly wearing away the lands. In some continents the land is being lifted up at a measurable rate, and there is evidence that some mountains are in process of active growth. Thus we are actual witnesses to a constant struggle between Titans: some that work at the surface, striving to tear down the rocky continents, and others within the Earth that persistently oppose the leveling process. Rocks are being destroyed and others are forming to replace them. Activities that can be seen and analyzed have been persistent throughout geologic time, and accordingly we may use the present as a key to the past. All processes now engaged in modifying the Earth are important in the preliminary study of geology.

From the geologist's viewpoint, therefore, the Earth is dynamic and changing; not static and inert. However, since most of the changes are very slow as judged by human standards, it is necessary to form some conception of geologic time in order to appreciate the continuity of Earth-history. The study of geology revolutionizes ordinary notions of time, just as a moderate knowledge of astronomy gives a new vision of space. Our Solar System has grand dimensions, and yet in its entirety it is but a point by comparison with the stupendous diameter of the starry galaxy. Similarly we think of the earliest human records as very ancient; but in a geologic sense the first appearance of man is a modern event. The oldest relics of primitive men are found only in the superficial soil or other rock débris formed in the latest geologic epochs. In all the time that has elapsed since the oldest civilizations existed, the major landscape features of the Earth have remained essentially unchanged; but we know from the immensely longer geologic record that, before any evidence of man appeared, generations of mountains were made and worn away by the same deliberate forces now at work.   The length of time required for such transformations has been almost inconceivably great.   How long has it taken for the Colorado River to excavate the Grand Canyon?   We are astonished at the realization that the slow action of water has carried away so many cubic miles of solid rock.   Nevertheless the Grand Canyon is a youthful feature.   The general record of earlier events is written plainly in the

E. C. LaRue, U. S. Geol. Survey.

Fig. 4. — The Grand Canyon of the Colorado.   The inner gorge is cut into granite and similar rocks; the upper part of the valley cuts through flat-lying layers of sandstone, shale, and limestone, most of which were formed on ancient sea floors.   Steep cliffs are developed on resistant layers and gentler slopes on weak layers.   Cutting of the canyon by stream erosion is a recent event geologically, although it required a long time measured by human standards.

rocks (Fig. 4) traversed by the trail in climbing the vertical mile from the inner gorge to the outer rim.   Mountains were made and worn down; then the land was submerged beneath the sea for long ages, and continued to sink slowly while mud and sand built up deposits thousands of feet thick; this loose material was converted into firm rock; and finally the rising of the wide plateau region high above the sea permitted the cutting of the canyon.   Minimum estimates fix the age of the lowest rocks in the gorge at hundreds of millions of years; and yet these rocks may be youthful in comparison with the total age of the Earth.   The closest study of the geologic record has revealed " no vestige of a beginning, no prospect of an end."

This broad, philosophical aspect of geology rests on a secure foundation only because of patient effort by generations of workers in all lands. Prior to the nineteenth century many natural philosophers formed their ideas on geologic subjects largely by deductive reasoning, in ignorance of the facts to be learned by observation in the field. Gradually it came to be realized that inductive study, based on all the facts obtainable, is essential for any safe conclusions. A vast array of field evidence has been accumulated. The great mountain ranges have been fruitful fields for geologic investigation, since they furnish the finest exposures of rock formations. But no sources of information are neglected. Geologic features everywhere are examined closely in the field and represented accurately on maps. Mines give opportunity to explore beneath the surface, and deep wells drilled for water or oil yield valuable data. Modern instruments devised to record earthquake waves and to measure the value of gravity have made it possible to draw important conclusions regarding the invisible interior. Slowly but surely the Earth is giving up many of its secrets to the inquisitiveness of man.

Of necessity, a field so broad as the study of the whole Earth calls for a division of labor among specialists. Some workers give their principal attention to the rock formations laid down in former seas, lakes, and streams; some to the volcanic and other igneous rocks; some to the mineral veins and other deposits of economic value. Other subjects of special study are the deformation of rocks by folding and fracturing, the various land forms sculptured by surface agencies, the fossils entombed in rocks, and the minerals that make up rocks of all kinds. All groups of investigators recognize unsolved problems, and by their united efforts continue to widen the frontiers of the science as a whole. Like any other growing subject, geology extends beyond the lighted zone of proved fact. It has also a large twilight zone of inference and probability into which the full light of investigation continues to spread slowly; and beyond this a region of shadow and complete darkness, relieved only by scattered flashes of speculation. The speculative side of the subject is in some respects the most fascinating, but it may also be dangerous to the uninitiated. A comprehensive discussion of geology takes account of fact, inference, and speculation, but distinguishes carefully between them. Careless broadcasting of hypotheses as if they were proved facts has given rise to numerous popular misconceptions about the Earth and its record of life.

The study of geology begins logically with an introduction to the important kinds of rocks and minerals. It proceeds to an examination of the forces that act on the outer part of the Earth, and the changes produced by these dynamic agencies. Finally, the keys provided by this preliminary study are used to explore the long geologic record contained in the rocks.

READING REFERENCES

1: The Fundamentals of Astronomy; by S. A. Mitchell and C. G. Abbot. 307 pages. D. Van Nostrand Co., New York, 1927.

2. Astronomy; by H. N. Russell, R. S. Dugan, and J. Q. Stewart. Vol. I, The Solar System, 470 pages; II, Astrophysics and Stellar Astronomy, 462 pages. Ginn and Co., Boston, 1926.

3. An Introduction to Oceanography, with special reference to geography and geophysics; by James Johnstone. 368 pages. 2d edition. Hodder and Stoughton, Limited, London, 1928.

CHAPTER II

ROCK WEATHERING AND ITS PART IN EROSION

Bedrock and Mantle. — It is a familiar fact that bedrock underlies all parts of the land surface, and although it is concealed in most places it can be reached by digging or drilling to sufficient depth. The cover, which ranges in thickness from a few inches to hundreds of feet, consists of soil, clay, sand, gravel, and other loose material. Obviously the coarser pieces are fragments of rock or of individual minerals; and a powerful microscope shows that rock particles, some fresh and others very much altered, make up a large part of the fine material also. This complex assemblage of rock débris that covers the bedrock is the *mantle* (Fig. 5).

Careful examination of the mantle in a wide region reveals that in some places all the recognizable particles consist of minerals found in the bedrock directly beneath. In other places, however, most or all of the constituents in the mantle have no apparent relation to the underlying rock. It is a logical inference that the mineral fragments in the mantle have been detached from firm bedrock, and that much of the débris has been removed from its place of origin. The part that remains essentially in place is *residual* mantle; the part that is carried away and dropped elsewhere forms *transported* mantle.

Weathering and Erosion. — Wherever the bedrock is exposed at the surface, as in a cliff, it has suffered obvious change. Usually some blocks or chips of the rock are loose and others can be detached with little effort. Many of these pieces are so rotten that they crumble in the fingers. By quarrying into the cliff we encounter firmer, fresher rock; but along joints or crevices some staining and softening are evident to considerable depths. Even the most casual observer recognizes that the outer part of the rock has been changed by exposure to the weather. Accordingly we say that the rock has been *weathered*, and the rather complex set of processes involved in the breaking up and decay is called *weathering*. Aside from its fundamental position among geologic processes, weathering is of vital importance to the human race because it results in soils which are the basis of all life on the lands.

Most cliffs also suggest plainly that they are remnants left by the disappearance of great quantities of rock around them (Figs. 4 and 17).

Regular layers end abruptly at a cliff face, and since identical layers can be recognized in neighboring cliffs or hills we can hardly avoid the inference that the layers once were continuous across the intervening space. It is difficult to imagine the removal of so much resistant rock; but the weathered condition of the rock now exposed at the surface suggests that this process of decay, continued for a very long time, has made it comparatively easy for running water and other agencies to fashion the present landscape.

The loosening and removal of rock material by any process at the Earth's surface is *erosion.* Since streams, glaciers, the sea, and the

A. P. Church.

Fig. 5. — A rounded mountain summit partly covered with mantle formed by weathering. Some of the more resistant rock layers make outcrops on the mountain side. Uinta Basin, Utah.

wind are the chief agencies involved in actually removing the débris, we recognize as separate processes *stream erosion, glacial erosion, marine erosion,* and *wind erosion.* In each of these processes considerable fresh rock is carried away in addition to more or less weathered material; but both directly and indirectly weathering increases enormously the rate and effectiveness of erosion. Therefore rock weathering is one of the most essential steps in erosion of the lands.

WEATHERING

Rôle of the Atmosphere. — The chief agent of weathering, as of the weather, is the atmosphere, which uses energy derived from the heat of the Sun. Although it is for the most part invisible, the atmosphere is responsible for vast changes on the Earth. By carrying moisture from the sea and precipitating it on the continents the atmosphere makes possible the formation of streams and glaciers, which are powerful eroding agents. Winds, by blowing dust and sand, accomplish some erosion directly, and by generating waves on the sea they cause marine erosion of the coasts. Therefore the greater part of erosion is chargeable either indirectly or directly to the atmosphere. For the present, however, we shall consider only its part in rock weathering.

The important geologic activities of the atmosphere depend upon its peculiar physical and chemical properties. Since it is a gas it penetrates readily into all crevices and other openings that lead down from the Earth's surface, and so comes into contact with much of the bedrock in addition to exposed surfaces. Air distributes heat, and hence is an important factor in causing temperature changes that affect rocks near the Earth's surface. At the same time, the atmosphere in general serves as a blanket to retard radiation and so tends to prevent extreme variations in temperature. About three-fourths of the atmosphere consists of the gas nitrogen, which is rather inert chemically, although with the aid of certain plants and bacteria it enters into some important reactions in the ground. Oxygen is enormously more active chemically and plays a large part in the attack on rocks. Carbon dioxide, which normally forms only 3 parts in 10,000 of the atmosphere by volume, has an importance out of all proportion to its rank in quantity. Aside from its vital function in supplying carbon to growing plants, carbon dioxide combines with some of the elements in rocks and so brings about radical changes. Water vapor is a highly variable constituent of the air, but its geologic rôle is large. Precipitated as rain or dew, it moistens the rocks, dissolves some of the minerals directly, takes an essential part in many chemical reactions, and assists in mechanical changes also.

Other substances form small fractions of the atmosphere, but oxygen, water vapor, and carbon dioxide are the only constituents that are of direct importance in rock weathering.

Other Factors Involved. — Temperature changes play a significant part in weathering. Such changes are influenced in an important way by the atmosphere, but are due primarily to daily and seasonal variations in heat received from the Sun.

Plants and animals help directly in the disruption of rocks, and indirectly but more effectively by producing substances that attack minerals chemically.

Water, after it is precipitated and is no longer part of the atmosphere, continues to be a prime factor in weathering so long as it remains on the surface or at shallow depths in the crevices of bedrock and in the pore spaces of the mantle.

Mechanical and Chemical Weathering. — It has been suggested (p. 13) that a twofold division is recognizable in the general effects of weathering. On the one hand, whatever the original nature of the rock, it is disrupted mechanically. This reduction of rock to smaller pieces, with or without some chemical alteration, is described as *disintegration*. On the other hand, the composition of the constituent minerals is changed by chemical attack, resulting in *decomposition* or " rotting " of the rock. Disintegration and decomposition usually proceed together and are so interrelated that they can not be distinguished clearly as due to wholly different processes. However,

G. K. Gilbert, U. S. Geol. Survey.

Fig. 6. — Fractures in the bedrock which aid weathering by allowing ready entrance of water, air, and plant roots. Sierra Nevada, California.

under certain conditions one effect predominates over the other. Disintegration and decomposition of bedrock are facilitated by the presence in nearly all rocks of numerous cracks and crevices (Fig. 6) which allow ready entrance of air, water, and other weathering agents. Even some of the mineral grains have cleavage planes or minute cracks which admit some moisture. By weathering processes these original openings are widened and others are formed. The loose arrangement and high porosity of the mantle make it especially susceptible to continued weathering.

Decomposition of Rocks

It is obvious that mechanical breaking-up of rocks makes decomposition much more effective, since the chemical agents can attack each newly made fragment from all sides simultaneously, and can descend ever deeper into bedrock as new cracks are formed or old ones are extended. However, since decomposition is directly responsible for some of the mechanical disruption, it is advisable to consider the chemical aspect of weathering first.

Effects of Oxygen, Water, and Carbon Dioxide. — A piece of bright new steel exposed to the weather becomes coated in a short time with yellowish-brown rust. If the exposure is continued for months and years scales of rust fall from the surface of the steel, and finally the entire piece can be crumbled into brown dust. In popular parlance, the steel has rusted away or decomposed; in chemical terms, the iron of which the steel was chiefly composed has reacted with oxygen and water to form a new mineral, hydrous iron oxide or *limonite*. This is an example of *oxidation* (chemical union with oxygen) and of *hydration* (chemical union with water).

A piece of bright copper treated in the same way keeps its original appearance longer than the steel, but eventually turns green from union of copper with carbon dioxide in the air, to form basic copper carbonate. This reaction is *carbonation*. Platinum exposed to the air remains unaltered indefinitely because it is chemically inert toward all constituents of the atmosphere. A lump of rock salt placed in the rain quickly disappears through *solution*, another process by which mineral substances are profoundly changed.

Rocks exposed at the Earth's surface consist of various minerals, and these react to the chemical agents of weathering differently and at very different rates. Iron in such minerals as black mica in a granite or pyroxene in a basalt unites slowly with oxygen and water to form limonite, which makes a brown stain on the surface of the rock. But the reaction is far more complex than the last statement suggests. Before the iron in pyroxene, for example, is released to form limonite, the entire original composition of the mineral is broken up, and then the various elements enter into new combinations, some containing carbon dioxide, some oxygen, and others water. The net result is softening and partial or total disruption of the mineral grains, not only at the surface but also along any crevices into which moisture can penetrate. In fact, the change may be more effective at a slight depth than on a bare surface, since moisture lingers in the shelter of crevices and enables the chemical work there to continue without interruption, whereas intermittent drying retards decomposition on surfaces exposed directly to the air.

Solution. — Chemical reactions do not proceed readily between dry substances, as we know from laboratory experiments. Therefore one of the most essential parts played by water in the changes described above is to serve as a medium in which other reagents can work. Besides performing this essential indirect function, and in addition to its union with other substances in the process of hydration, water aids in decomposing the rocks by removing certain minerals in solution. Only a few common minerals are soluble in pure water, but many others dissolve in carbonic acid (H_2CO_3) which forms when carbon dioxide (CO_2) unites with water. For example, the mineral calcite (calcium carbonate, $CaCO_3$) is only slightly soluble in pure water, but carbonic acid converts it into calcium bicarbonate [$CaH_2(CO_3)_2$], which goes into solution and is carried away by water percolating through the pores and crevices in the rock. Calcium carbonate is the chief constituent of limestone, and vast quantities of this rock have been carried away in solution (Chap. IV). Other less soluble mineral grains scattered through various rocks dissolve very slowly; their loss weakens the rock and provides additional openings to be used by chemical reagents.

The continued removal of soluble material by water percolating through the mantle or through shattered bedrock is termed *leaching*.

Decomposition of Feldspar. — Since feldspars are the most abundant rock-making minerals their response to weathering merits particular attention. When feldspar decomposes the chief product is clay, which is of great importance because it is one of the commonest materials in the mantle and also because it goes into the formation of shale, the most abundant type of sedimentary rock (p. 214). The chemical weathering of orthoclase, one mineral of the feldspar group, is outlined as follows:

Orthoclase ($KAlSi_3O_8$) + Water (H_2O) + Carbon dioxide (CO_2) ⇌ Clay (various hydrous aluminum silicates) + Silica (SiO_2) + Potassium carbonate (K_2CO_3).

Complete decomposition of feldspar requires considerable rainfall and a warm or temperate climate. The carbon dioxide involved in the reaction comes in part directly from the air and in part from decaying vegetation. Some of the potassium carbonate (potash) formed is dissolved by water and removed, but part of it is held by the clay and is used as plant food if the clay becomes transformed to soil (p. 28).

Chemical Weathering of Other Minerals. — Amphibole, pyroxene, and other common minerals that contain aluminum also yield clay when they are decomposed. Several of these minerals contain some iron, which commonly forms limonite, and thus the clay acquires a yellowish color.

Quartz resists chemical weathering more successfully than any other common mineral in the rocks. Therefore when feldspar and other minerals decay, the associated grains of quartz remain essentially unchanged. Since quartz is quite hard and has no cleavage to form planes of weakness, the grains also resist better than most other minerals mechanical wear by wind, streams, and waves, and therefore sand and gravel come to consist largely of quartz particles.   Much of the sand that now lies on beaches or in shifting dunes is made up of quartz grains that were weathered from granites during remote geologic periods.

Disintegration of Rocks

Effects of Freezing Water. — When water freezes it expands by about one-tenth of its volume, and if it is in a closed vessel the pressure on the walls is very great.   In the days of muzzle-loading cannon this principle

F. E. Matthes, U. S. Geol. Survey.

Fig. 7. — Blocks of granite sprung apart by frost action.   Sierra Nevada, California.

was utilized in disposing of captured enemy artillery.   Rocks in favored positions are disrupted by repeated freezing and thawing of water in cracks or pore spaces (Fig. 7).   The effect is confined to a shallow zone, and is most noticeable near the edges of cliffs where blocks are poorly supported.   In high mountains, freezing at night occurs even during the summer months, and there the results are especially conspicuous.   Probably the wedging apart of minute rock scales or mineral grains is as important in the long run as the dislodging of large blocks.

Direct Effects of Temperature Changes. — The heat of a forest fire causes large flakes and spalls to break from exposed surfaces of granite and other rocks.   Unlike iron and most other metals, rock is a poor conductor of heat; fire heats only a thin outer shell, which expands and is disrupted by the strains that result.

Theoretically the smaller changes in temperature between day and night also cause slow disintegration of rocks. Heating by the Sun is most extreme in arid regions, where rocks grow uncomfortable to the touch during a summer day. Rapid cooling at night is also character-istic of arid lands, the daily range in rock temperatures sometimes being more than 100° F. Disintegration is conspicuous in deserts. The unlike mineral grains in granite and similar rocks become loose and fall apart, and it is argued that this effect is produced by minute strains between mineral grains due to unequal expansion and contraction of feldspar, quartz, and other minerals when they are heated and cooled. The spalling-off of thin flakes and slabs from rock surfaces, an effect that is more common in moist than in dry climates, also has been as-cribed to expansion and contraction through repeated heating and cooling. This theory has been tested by laboratory experiments, in which temperature ranges considerably greater than those recorded in any desert have failed to cause the slightest breaking of rock samples. Such experiments, however, can not duplicate the time involved in weathering. Possibly the minute strains repeated by daily temperature changes through thousands of years finally cause *fatigue* in the rocks, with resulting disintegration. It is probable, however, that slight chemical changes, discussed below, are at least partly responsible for the effects commonly attributed to temperature.

Heating of sedimentary rocks causes local buckling and rupture of individual layers. This effect is especially noticeable in the floors of quarries where strata have been exposed recently to direct heating by the Sun.

Mechanical Effects of Chemical Weathering. — Many chemical changes cause considerable increase of volume. Hydration especially produces swelling of the parts of the rock affected and therefore sets up strains. The outer surface of an exposed rock dries rapidly; but moisture that penetrates into minute crevices remains until some decay is effected. Slow increase of volume at slight depth finally disrupts the rock, and pieces that are quite or nearly undecomposed are broken off. *Exfoliation,* the spalling-off of flakes and of comparatively thin concentric shells (Fig. 8), probably is due at least in part to such chemical effects, although many observers have attempted to explain it as caused en-tirely by temperature changes. It is significant that exfoliation is common only in regions where moisture is fairly abundant, and not in deserts where rapid changes in temperature are most extreme. How-ever, it must be admitted that the mechanism of exfoliation is something of a mystery.   Many of the great shells that separate from the granite domes near Yosemite Valley, California, are 10 to 100 feet in thickness (Fig. 8); and it is highly improbable that either temperature changes or hydration can be the original cause of the fracturing at such a depth below the surface.   It has been suggested that relief of load by erosion of material from the top permits the rock to expand, with the result that thick shells are detached, as in the Yosemite domes and in Stone Mountain, Georgia.   Exfoliated shells a few inches or a fraction of an inch thick are much more common, and these more logically can be

F. C. Calkins, U. S. Geol. Survey.

Fig. 8. — Exfoliation on a large scale. The top of the cliff is 500 feet above the foreground, and some of the curved shells are 10 feet thick.   Northeast side of Half Dome, Yosemite Valley, California.

attributed to chemical changes or temperature effects, or to both factors working together.

The slow disintegration of granite into its constituent mineral grains probably results in part from hydration in microscopic crevices, even in the driest regions.   In Egypt the surficial disintegration of granite blocks and monuments is more pronounced in shaded places where the moisture is conserved than it is on the sides most exposed to the Sun.

Mechanical Work of Plants. — The wedging-apart of rocks by the roots and trunks of growing trees has some importance in weathering.

Shrubs and smaller plants also send their rootlets into tiny crevices of the bedrock and slowly enlarge the openings. In the course of time, the amount of disintegration accomplished in this way must be large, but much of it is obscured by chemical weathering which takes advantage of the openings as soon as they are formed.

Factors Influencing the Rate and Character of Weathering

Influence of Climate. — Pronounced contrasts in climatic conditions are accountable for striking differences in the rate of weathering and in the effects produced. Since warmth and abundant water are essential to effective chemical change in rocks, this form of weathering proceeds

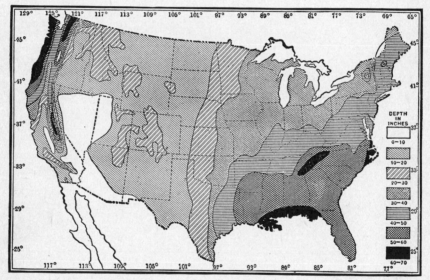

U. S. Geol. Survey.

Fig. 9. — Rainfall map of the United States. Conventions show average annual rainfall.

very slowly in polar regions even if moisture is plentiful, and in deserts even if temperature is high. Decomposition progresses most rapidly and reaches to greatest depth in moist tropical lands, although it is quite effective also in temperate regions that have abundant rain.

The controlling influence of rainfall appears convincingly in a comparison of the rainfall belts of the United States (Fig. 9). Soil and other decomposed mantle form a thick cover in most parts of the southern Mississippi Valley and of the South Atlantic States. In the southern Appalachians, where rainfall is exceptionally heavy, the mantle is remarkably deep, and decomposition of its constituents is extreme. At the same latitude but with only one-fourth as much rainfall, the " panhandles " of Texas and Oklahoma have thin, stony soils and numerous exposures of bedrock. In the arid region of southern Nevada and southeastern California, true soil is almost absent, and over great areas the bedrock actually appears at the surface or is veneered only with coarse rock débris which appears fresh or only slightly decayed. The coastal belt of Washington and Oregon has the heaviest rainfall in the United States, and the cover of decomposed mantle in that region is very thick, although the average temperature is considerably lower than in the southern Appalachians. In all moist regions of the temperate zones the luxuriant growth of vegetation is an indirect but powerful ally of the ordinary chemical processes. The dead plants build up in the soil organic matter, or *humus*, which forms acids that are very effective in leaching the soil and decomposing the bedrock. Arid regions are deficient in both soil and water for the growth of abundant vegetation, and therefore the scanty water that is available for weathering is not reinforced by organic acids.

It is evident that decomposition is dominant in the humid parts of the country, and disintegration in the arid regions. It is not to be inferred, however, that forces causing mechanical breakdown are absent or of small consequence in areas where rainfall is large. Disintegration is very effective in such areas so long as bedrock is exposed, but the results are partly obscured by chemical decay, and as a thick decomposed mantle develops the bedrock beneath becomes more and more immune to mechanical disruption. In an arid region the forces causing disintegration may be less powerful, but since no insulating mantle of soil or clay is formed the work continues unabated and the cumulative results are conspicuously displayed. Expansion and contraction due to changes in temperature are at a maximum in deserts, where the daily range in temperature is greatest. Frost action is very limited in such regions owing to the scarcity of water. Plants play an appreciable part in disintegration only in areas sufficiently humid to support abundant vegetation. Volume increase from chemical effects, which probably is one of the most important factors in mechanical weathering, is far more effective in humid than in dry climates.

Frost action functions at its best in high temperate latitudes or in corresponding climatic zones of high mountains, where alternate freezing and thawing occur during a considerable part of the year. The total effect of this process is less in polar regions because the continued cold during long seasons does not permit frequent repetition of the wedging action of ice.

Influence of Topography. — As a general rule, high altitude and steep slopes favor disintegration of rocks, for several reasons. The average temperature decreases with altitude, and hence frost action is effective

in high mountains even in low latitudes. Rainfall generally increases
with increasing height, and therefore even in a very dry region the
mountain peaks and ridges have sufficient moisture for some frost
action and for considerable hydration of minerals, with resulting disintegration of the rocks by scaling or spalling. The daily and seasonal
ranges of temperature are large in high mountains, and possibly expansion and contraction of the rocks from this cause result in slow disin-

Simmer Studio.

Fig. 10. — Talus at the base of a granite cliff. The natural slope at the base has been
disturbed by grading for the highway and railroad. The granite bedrock in the cliff
forms an *outcrop*. Valley of the Columbia River, Washington.

tegration. Because of the steep slopes most of the loosened débris
falls, rolls, or is washed to lower levels, and thus fresh surfaces are exposed to the attack of the weather. At the bases of high cliffs the fallen
blocks accumulate to form masses of " slide rock," known as *talus* (Fig.
10). Talus deposits develop below cliffs in nearly all regions that have
rugged relief, whatever the nature of the climate. Their presence is
evidence of fairly rapid disintegration of the rocks above them.

Mountains in humid regions ordinarily have their lower, gentler
slopes covered in large part with soil or other decomposed mantle.
Rolling topography at a moderate elevation offers the most favorable
opportunity for decomposition to great depth. Vegetation protects the
soil from rapid erosion, and as the upper part of the mantle decays more
and more the chemical reagents penetrate to greater depth. There is a

limit to this penetration, because below a certain level all the openings are filled with water which moves very slowly or is almost stationary. In a low plains country this level is not far below the surface, and weathering is confined to a rather shallow zone, even if climatic conditions are especially favorable for weathering and the rocks near the surface become thoroughly decomposed. Under areas that have moderate altitude, like some parts of the southern Appalachians, water in the ground drains downward, carrying carbon dioxide and organic acids to deeper zones and allowing the air to enter openings to considerable depth.

Influence of Rock Composition. — Rocks vary greatly in their susceptibility to weathering under different climatic conditions. Quartz

G. K. Gilbert, U. S. Geol. Survey.

Fig. 11. — Granite surface high on the mountain slope above Yosemite Valley, California. Movement of glacier ice during the last Ice Age gave the bedrock a high polish. Although the rock at this locality has been exposed since the ice disappeared, thousands of years ago, weathering has destroyed only part of the polished surface by loosening thin flakes and slabs of rock.

is one of the most stable minerals, and rocks composed almost wholly of it, such as quartzite or siliceous sandstone, are especially stubborn in their resistance. Granite yields much more easily in any kind of climate; in a humid region the feldspar decomposes to form clay, and in a desert the grains of feldspar and quartz fall apart owing to strains set up either by slight hydration of the feldspar or by unequal temperatrue effects. The actual rate at which these changes occur, however, is slow as judged by human standards. Granite has a long life in buildings and in monuments. In the Sierra Nevada some granite surfaces retain the polish and scratches formed by glacier ice at least 10,000 years ago (Fig. 11).

Limestone is dissolved wherever there is sufficient water; caverns and sinks are formed (Chap. IV), and the limestone finally disappears, leaving only the small amount of clay, sand, or other insoluble impurities that may have been contained in it. In a humid climate, therefore, limestones weather faster than most other rock formations and tend to form lowlands; but in arid lands extensive solution can not occur, and there limestone is one of the most resistant kinds of rock. In many parts of Nevada and adjacent States, thick series of limestone layers make the highest mountain ridges and peaks.

Ordinary shale consists chiefly of clay which was the product of chemical weathering in an earlier geologic period. Further weathering can not cause much additional change in composition, but shale disintegrates easily into soft clay, especially if it becomes thoroughly soaked with water. In regions of old mountains like the Appalachians, where the rocks are steeply tilted sedimentary strata, the resistant sandstones come to form the high ridges, whereas the weaker shales and limestones underlie the valleys and plains. Some sandstones, however, are not highly resistant. If the grains are cemented with calcium carbonate, solution removes the cementing material and the sand grains fall apart.

Products of Weathering

Residual Mantle. — Wherever weathering occurs, part of the resulting débris is carried away by running water, wind, or some other transporting agent. In some places the loosened material is removed as fast as it is formed, and the bedrock is exposed as *outcrops* (Fig. 10); in other places transported material is dropped and builds up a thick mantle; in many areas part of the weathered rock is removed, by solution or otherwise, but a residue accumulates. In regions with plentiful rainfall the upper portion of residual mantle normally consists of soil, and there is a gradual change downward through clay that contains some rock fragments into more or less rotten rock (Fig. 12). This evident relation to the underlying rock, shown by almost insensible gradation into it, is characteristic of mantle formed in place.

Residual Boulders; Spheroidal Weathering. — In some situations most of the fine-grained products of weathering have been removed, but rounded boulders made of rock like the underlying bedrock are scattered on the surface.   Usually such boulders have been fashioned from rectangular blocks bounded by joints or cracks (Fig. 13).   Since

G. P. Merrill, U. S. Nat. Museum.

Fig. 12. — Residual mantle on bedrock.   The material grades from firm rock below through rotten rock into pebbly clay, and finally into soil made dark by organic matter.

the corners of such blocks are attacked from all sides simultaneously they are rounded off, and continued exfoliation of thin shells finally makes the boulders nearly spherical or egg-shaped.   Some of these *residual boulders* have an onion-like structure, with partly detached thin shells several layers deep. This type of weathering is sometimes called *spheroidal weathering*. It takes place only in fairly moist climates, and since the minerals in the shells show the effects of hydration and other chemical changes they lend support to the belief that chemical effects are more potent than temperature changes in accomplishing exfoliation (p. 20).

F. E. Matthes, U. S. Geol. Survey.

Fig. 13. — Residual boulders forming by weathering of jointed granite. Quarter Dome, Yosemite Valley, California.

Soils. — The term *soil* is sometimes applied erroneously to mantle of any kind, but properly it refers only to the part of the mantle which has been so decomposed and otherwise modified that it supports rooted plants. Development of a good soil is an extremely slow process. First the upper part of the mantle, whether residual or transported in origin, becomes sufficiently decomposed to yield some plant food, and a little vegetation takes root. Ordinarily the soil at this stage is scanty and poor in quality; it contains large quantities of disintegrated rock, little altered, and may be called a *skeletal* soil. As the plants die and are partially decayed they contribute some organic material, which contains carbon extracted from the air by the growing plants. Bacteria multiply in the soil, and some of these serve highly important functions such as taking nitrogen from the air and combining it with other elements to make available food for plants. The decaying vegetable matter furnishes acids that help to decompose the mineral particles in the mantle and leach out some substances, carrying them to lower levels. Thus the composition of the soil changes continuously, though slowly. If erosion does not disturb progress, and if there is plenty of rainfall to carry on chemical weathering and to support vegetation, the building of the soil accelerates for a time, since each step in the development increases plant growth and the resulting contribution of organic matter in turn speeds the development. Gradually the soil grows deeper, and as it loses all except the most insoluble of the original mineral particles it becomes *mature*. Usually it has a darker color than the underlying *subsoil*, which contains some materials carried down in solution but lacks the most vital ingredients developed in the true soil.

So long as a soil developed on residual mantle is skeletal or immature it reflects the character of the underlying bedrock. An immature soil on granite (Fig. 12) is rich in clay formed from the weathered feldspar; it contains numerous bits of quartz and other constituent mineral grains of the granite, set free but unaltered; iron derived from biotite or from hornblende has been oxidized, and the resulting limonite colors the clay yellow; and the clay contains certain soluble substances such as potash which suggest the composition of the original feldspar. A soil formed from weathered shale and limestone contains clay and is rich in calcium carbonate. However, as these unlike soils mature under similar climatic conditions the differences disappear, and eventually it is difficult to distinguish between them. Therefore such terms as *granite soils, sandstone soils*, or *limestone soils* have real value only in classifying soils so immature that they show a strong relationship to the parent rock formations. There are only a few distinct types of mature soil, and these types reflect the climatic conditions under which they were developed.

Soil Types Determined by Climate. — To illustrate the effects of climate, let us consider the development of two strongly contrasted soil types. In the latitude of the northern United States, good mature soils are dark from their high content of humus, the organic matter derived from plants (Fig. 12). In tropical countries, on well-drained ground at low or moderate altitudes, soils contain no humus whatever, even if they support a heavy growth of vegetation; humus in the low-altitude tropics exists only in swamps. The reason for this striking contrast between the tropical and the cool temperate zones is simple. Bacteria destroy humus in the soil; bacteria are numerous in all soils, but their maximum development is prevented by the comparatively low temperatures in high latitudes, and therefore in those parts of the world humus develops faster than it is destroyed wherever plants grow abundantly. In the tropics the high average temperature stimulates bacterial growth to a maximum and humus is destroyed as fast as it can form. In swamps, however, bacteria can not thrive because the water excludes air from the soil, and therefore humus accumulates in tropical swamps. It is found also in high mountains in the tropics, where lower temperature checks the development of bacteria.

But the difference in humus content is not in itself the principal point in the contrast between typical soils in the two zones; the final consequences of the presence or absence of humus are very important indeed. With the aid of humus, water percolating through the soil gradually leaches out certain substances, especially iron oxide and aluminum oxide, depositing them at lower levels in the mantle. If no humus is present the water can not remove these substances, which therefore become concentrated in the soil as other materials are removed. Therefore the common soils of tropical countries are rich in alumina, and in many regions are colored brick red by oxidized iron. Such a soil is called *laterite* (from the Latin *later*, brick; the soil is sometimes cut and used as building-bricks). In very old laterites these oxides are so concentrated and plant food is so deficient that plants grow poorly even with a high rainfall. Such soils cover large areas in India, Brazil, and other countries whose rainfall is controlled by the seasonal monsoon winds.

Humus-laden soils are not entirely devoid of iron and aluminum oxides, but the quantity of these substances continuously diminishes in such soils as they mature. The presence of some iron in nearly every soil is demonstrated by heating a sample to a high temperature in a kiln or oven. All the organic matter is burned out, and the iron compounds disseminated through the soil become *ferric oxide* (Fe_2O_3), which gives the whole mass a reddish color. Before the heating the iron was kept *reduced* by the organic matter to the *ferrous* condition, in which form the iron compounds have no conspicuous color. In the warmer parts of the temperate zones the mature soils are intermediate in character between those of more northern regions and the tropical laterites. In the southern Appalachians the deep soils on well-drained foothill slopes are distinctly red, indicating that bacterial action is vigorous in destroying humus and thus permitting accumulation of iron oxide. However, in the stream valleys of the same region, where the mantle is more continuously wet and plant growth is more vigorous than on the slopes, the soil is prevailingly gray or black. Evidently in these situations the humus, if it does not actually leach out the iron, at least keeps it reduced to the ferrous state and so obscures it.

Movements of the Mantle

Weathering is essentially a static process, and any removal of weathered material from its place of origin is accomplished by other agencies, of which the most prominent are rain wash, streams, glaciers, waves, and the wind. However, there are important movements of the mantle, for the most part slow and of small or moderate extent, which are independent of the ordinary transporting agents and are closely related to the continued action of weathering. These movements, which are controlled directly by gravity, are an essential part of erosion.

Movements of Talus. — When rock fragments are loosened on the face of a disintegrating cliff they fall to the slope beneath and by rolling or sliding reach a place in the accumulating talus (Fig. 10). The upper part of a talus slope is as steep as the angle at which coarse fragments can lie; the slightest disturbance, such as the falling of a large block from the cliff, starts sliding in some part of the mass. Breaking up of blocks by continued weathering removes the support of pieces higher up the slope, and more readjustment by sliding is necessary. Thus there is slow but general migration downward. In a humid region the older blocks in the lower part of the slope are decomposed, and the talus merges gradually into a soil-covered slope set with grass or other vegetation.

Creep. — It is evident that water from rain falling on talus washes the fine weathered particles to lower levels and thus contributes to the soil accumulating below. By this action as well as by the gradual sliding of the débris the older material in the talus slowly encroaches on the lower plant-covered slope, and this encroachment is continuous because fresh fragments from the cliff keep feeding the upper part of the sliding mass. But does the plant-covered slope also move, to make way for the material crowding into it from above? As we look at such a slope it is difficult to believe that it loses anything by erosion except for some mineral matter taken into solution by water percolating beneath the surface. Perhaps every part of the soil is covered closely with grass or held by a close mat of roots, and without first breaching this protective armor to form gullies, running water can not begin an attack. Nevertheless the mantle under every such slope as this is moving downward, carrying the cover of vegetation with it. Usually the movement is so slow as to be imperceptible, and the entire sheet of soil moves essentially as a unit so that no breaks appear in the surface. The moving force is gravity. On even a moderate slope the weight of the loose material gives a tendency to slide downward. When the soil is soaked with rain the water in the pore spaces adds to the weight and also lubricates the mass, thus decreasing the friction. The force acts continuously, and even if movement is almost infinitesimal in the course of a year, the final result is inevitable. In regions that have cold winters, freezing of water in the soil causes expansion, and the surface of the ground is lifted slightly at right angles to the slope. When thawing occurs each point tends to drop vertically instead of returning exactly to its former position (Fig. 14), and this process

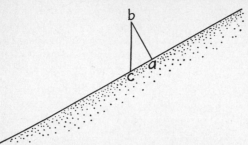

Fig. 14. — When the soil on a hillside expands by freezing, a boulder on the surface at *a* is carried outward at right angles to *b*; when thawing occurs and the surface subsides the boulder tends to drop vertically to *c*. (Vertical scale exaggerated.)

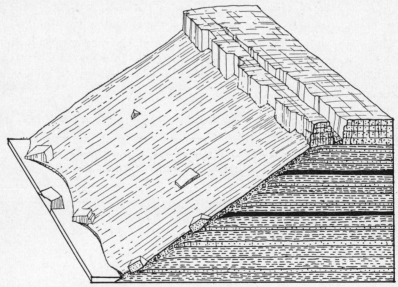

Fig. 15. — Segment of one side of the Cheat River valley, West Virginia. The valley is youthful and deep, and the steepness of the slope causes exceptionally active creep of the mantle. The thick sandstone layer at the top is weakened by vertical joints parallel with the valley. As the mantle moves away from the base of the cliff and the weak shale directly beneath is softened by water, long blocks of the sandstone separate along joints and move slowly outward, tilting more and more with the slope. Smaller blocks are detached from time to time, and many of them roll down to the stream. Due to the active creep, little talus accumulates. As the creeping mantle reaches the foot of the slope it is carried away by the stream. The slope is not gullied because it is protected by a dense cover of vegetation, not represented in the sketch. (Not drawn to scale.)

adds to the slow downward movement or *creep* of the mantle. In a general way the entire mantle of weathered material on all parts of the continents is creeping steadily from higher to lower altitudes; but of course on very low slopes the movement is so slight as to be unimportant. On each side of a valley the slow movement brings weathered material within reach of the stream at the bottom, and the stream carries it away (Fig. 15). The cliff at the top of the slope retreats as material is weathered from its face, and therefore the slope grows longer and less steep. Thus weathering and creep are important factors in the widening of valleys.

The discussion above considers the common case of a slope that has a cliff at its upper margin. In such a situation the cliff supplies part

G. K. Gilbert, U. S. Geol. Survey.

Fig. 16. — Small landslide on a grass-covered slope, Berkeley Hills, California. Sliding was started by an earthquake, but the principal movement took place later, after the ground was thoroughly soaked with rain.

of the loose material in the downward movement; but if no cliff is present the creeping mantle is derived wholly from weathering of the bedrock beneath the slope itself.

Landslides and Rock Glaciers. — Not uncommonly the movement of the mantle on slopes is rapid and even catastrophic. Where the slope is unusually steep or the mantle is exceptionally thick and incoherent a heavy rain may weaken resistance and start a *landslide* (Fig. 16). A sharp earthquake shock usually sets many landslides in motion, especially in a mountainous region (p. 343). Movements of this type differ considerably in their behavior. In some cases a mass of débris weighing thousands or millions of tons rushes precipitately down the valley side, carries away timber and everything else in its path, and makes a huge dam across the stream with the result that a lake is formed. Some landslides of this nature in the Alps and elsewhere have destroyed entire villages. On the other hand, some slides move slowly and spasmodically; when frost goes out of the ground in the spring, or after an exceptional rain, there is irregular movement for a few feet or hundreds of feet followed by a period of quiet. Timber continues to grow on the top of such a slide, but trees are tipped about at various angles and some are uprooted. Movement of this kind resembles creep but the rate is vastly greater.

Great landslides that involve the bedrock as well as the mantle are in a different category. They are discussed in Chapter XII.

On high mountains made of weak rocks, talus accumulates rapidly, and not uncommonly a mass of the débris moves slowly but perceptibly, under its own weight, down a slope or a narrow valley. Freezing and thawing of water in the mass helps the work of gravity. From the resemblance of the movement to glacier motion these streams of rock fragments are called *rock glaciers*. In the San Juan Mountains of southwestern Colorado such features are numerous, and some of them are thousands of feet long.

Effects of Weathering on Landscape Features

Major Effects. — In a journey from the eastern United States to the arid Southwest the traveler is impressed with the striking contrasts in the landscapes. These differences reflect complex causes, but among the most important factors are rate and kind of weathering under the different climatic conditions. The abundant vegetation of the Eastern States in itself creates a strong contrast with the barrenness of New Mexico and Arizona; but there is a more fundamental difference in the actual land forms. In the East the hills and slopes are characterized by rounded curves and smoothed profiles; in the Southwest the profiles are angular.

Disintegration as the dominant type of weathering tends to produce angularity. Forces that break the rocks take advantage of original joints which form square-cornered blocks, and as these natural units loosen and fall the cliffs from which they are displaced remain rugged and unsoftened. Ridges and hills made of flat-lying strata remain flat topped and steep sided as they grow smaller through disintegration and recession of the cliffs. These are the *mesas* and *buttes* of western landscapes (Fig. 17). Wherever the structure of the rocks favors development of sharp peaks and jagged ridges, these features tend to keep their irregular forms as they waste away. Divides between adjacent valleys are either flat topped (where strata are horizontal), or sharp and rugged, and valley sides are steep and commonly step-like, with a succession of cliffs (Fig. 4). These are some of the typical forms of the arid Southwest, where there is little decomposition and soils form scantily.

Vigorous chemical weathering rounds off sharp corners in both large and small features of the landscape. Vertical cliffs and angular ridges in a humid region are exceptional rather than the rule; their presence indicates either brief exposure to the atmosphere or extremely resistant rocks. Sharp peaks and serrate ridges tend to disappear under the influence of decomposition. Mantle forms on valley sides, and as it

W. T. Lee, U. S. Geol. Survey.

Fig. 17. — A butte near Billings, Montana. The capping is a horizontal layer of sandstone resistant to weathering; horizontal layers of shale beneath it weather easily, and the débris moves down by creep and slope wash. Undermining by this process, aided by frost action and other factors, causes blocks to fall from the cliff at the top. Thus the butte slowly grows smaller.

accumulates and moves by creep from higher to lower levels the slopes take on smooth curving profiles (Fig. 18). With the formation of soil and the spreading of vegetation, decomposition becomes more effective and the slopes grow still smoother, because the cover of vegetation protects the slopes from gullying by running water, and the roots tying the soil together make the process of creep more uniform. On opposite sides of a ridge cliffs retreat, grow lower, and disappear, and the top of the ridge becomes smooth and rounded under a cover of soil. Thus divides between adjacent valleys tend to become broad and smooth in contrast to the sharp, rugged divides of arid regions.

Differential Weathering. — The unequal resistance of rocks to weathering is responsible for many details in topography under any climatic conditions, but particularly in arid and semiarid regions. In lands that have abundant rainfall the soil and other mantle conceals most of the bedrock and tends to obliterate small irregularities. Wherever there are cliffs or other outcrops, however, the rocks are sculptured into irregular forms by more rapid disintegration or decay in some parts of the rock than in others. This unequal yielding due to the nonuniform character of rocks is called *differential weathering*.

The scale of differential weathering has a wide range; the nonuniformity of bedrock is responsible for some of the largest features in a landscape and also for minute irregularities of microscopic size. It has been pointed out (p. 26) that thick sandstone formations tend to make ridges while adjacent shales are worn down to form lowlands; that great thicknesses of limestone disappear by solution under humid

E. W. Shaw, U. S. Geol. Survey.

Fig. 18. — Rounded hilltop and smooth slopes characteristic of a region in a humid climate. The bedrock has been exposed by quarrying. Note that the mantle is thin at the summit of the hill; it is moved downward by creep and slope wash, and accumulates to a greater thickness on the lower slopes.

climates but show superior resistance by forming mountain ranges in arid regions. Of course other important factors besides weathering are involved in producing these major landscape effects. Most rocks that are susceptible to rapid weathering also yield easily to cutting by streams or other eroding agents, and therefore the final results have a complex origin. However, the part played by unequal weathering in producing uneven topography is fundamental.

The fashioning of many smaller features depends more directly on weathering effects. Alternating layers of sandstone and shale exposed in a cliff yield at different rates; gradually the shale gives way to form reëntrants between the projecting sandstone strata. If shale lies beneath thick sandstone an overhanging cliff results. Grotesque effects are produced from various combinations of resistant and weak beds, especially in semiarid regions. Jointed rocks are fashioned into irregular pillars, some of which have fantastic forms and are known as *hoodoos*. There are numerous excellent examples in the Garden of the Gods, Colorado, and in Bryce Canyon, Utah. In many places large residual boulders are left delicately balanced, with only a small surface in contact with the rock beneath.

Quartz veins and small dikes of resistant igneous rock stand in relief as the surrounding rock is etched away. Veinlets that intersect in

F. E. Matthes, U. S. Geol. Survey.

Fig. 19. — Pits in granite caused by decomposition, hastened by the presence of shallow depressions in which standing water promoted local decay. Some of the pits coalesce as they enlarge. Sierra Nevada, California.

an intricate network form patterns that resemble lace or filigree work. Some sandstones that look quite uniform on fresh faces weather into a maze of pits and ridges that suggest honeycomb. This effect indicates irregular cementation of the sand grains.

Under certain conditions rock of uniform composition also weathers irregularly. Shallow depressions on exposed surfaces promote local decay by holding rain water and thus keeping small areas moist. As weathering proceeds the depressions deepen and the effect is intensified (Fig. 19).

RELATION OF WEATHERING TO OTHER ASPECTS OF EROSION

In the discussion above it has been necessary to point out repeatedly the interruption or modification of weathering effects by streams, the wind, or other agencies. Weathering is not an isolated process; it is intimately related to other activities at the Earth's surface, all of them striving toward the same end — the wearing away of the continents. Weathering attacks the rock in cliffs, and as tiny particles are loosened they are washed off by rain or blown away by the wind. Larger pieces fall to the ground, where weathering continues to reduce them while gravity and running water urge them down the slope. Beneath the surface, weathering proceeds with less interruption and produces a considerable thickness of soil and other mantle; but as this cover forms it moves down slopes by creep and landslides; continuously the water soaking through the mantle robs it by dissolving various substances; water at the surface forms gullies and washes the material into larger streams; and as the creeping mantle arrives at the bottoms of valleys the streams take their toll directly. Thus weathering and transportation of rock materials proceed together. Streams and the wind carry pebbles or sand grains along the ground, and by the friction other particles are worn from the bedrock or from the moving débris; but this process of frictional wear is not a part of weathering.

Some of the mantle in transport is dropped temporarily at the bases of mountains, on the floodplains of streams, on beaches, or in sand dunes; but in the upper parts of these deposits disintegration and chemical decay continue. There is no escape from the unrelenting attack until the débris is deeply buried on land or spread out in lakes or upon the sea floor, and there enters into the formation of new sedimentary strata (Chap. IX).

READING REFERENCES

1. Rocks, Rock Weathering, and Soils; by G. P. Merrill. 400 pages. Macmillan, New York, 1906.
A comprehensive treatment of weathering processes and effects.

2. Studies on Weathering and Soil Formation in Tropical High Altitudes; by M. W. Senstius. Proc. Am. Phil. Soc., Vol. 69, 1930, pp. 45–97.
An excellent discussion of the influence of climate in determining soil types.

3. The Evolution and Classification of Soils; by E. Ramann. Translated from the original German by C. L. Whittles. 118 pages. W. Heffer and Sons, Limited, Cambridge, 1928.
A concise up-to-date explanation of soil formation.

CHAPTER III

RUNNING WATER

ORIGIN AND SIGNIFICANCE OF STREAMS

Geologic Importance of Streams. — Every observer who stands on the brink of the Grand Canyon of the Colorado (Fig. 4), and looks down at the winding ribbon of the river a mile below, is impressed with the vast size of the rock-walled valley and with the puny appearance of the stream at its bottom. The earliest observers thought that the Colorado had found this low-level course already prepared for it by a great gash or rift in the Earth's crust. But the visitor of today, if he knows some of the principles of geology and understands streams and their behavior, is convinced that the river once flowed through a shallow trough at the level of the canyon's brink, and that very gradually the sediment-laden water cut down into the underlying rocks, sawing ever more deeply until in the course of time it dug a trench a mile deep. This same visitor surveys from an eminence the intricate pattern of canyons and subcanyons which, arranged symmetrically like the veins in a leaf, join the main valley, most of them entering at the level of the main stream. He realizes that they were developed not by chance but as members of a unified and interrelated system, obeying a common law and having a common destiny. And when he sees this same pattern repeated again and again in stream systems large and small throughout the world, he concludes that all streams act according to certain definite rules imposed on them by their surroundings.

Streams return to the sea the water evaporated from it, carried by the atmosphere over the lands, and there precipitated as rain and snow. Furthermore, because they are so widespread, streams as a group are the most important single agent of erosion on the face of the Earth. Constantly excavating valleys and as constantly washing the excavated rock fragments from the land toward the sea, they must continue to operate in this way as long as there are lands with rain falling upon them. The process of excavation and washing away, although complicated, is controlled by a series of laws which enable us not only to follow intelligently the intricate detail with which running water sculptures the land but even to predict the way in which the land will be carved in the future. We must begin with the rainfall.

39

Rainfall. — Probably there is no part of the Earth's surface on which rain or snow does not sometimes fall. Even the most arid spots in the Libyan Desert receive a little rain once every few years. Death Valley in southeastern California, one of the driest areas in North America, has about 2 inches of rainfall annually. Whereas the thickly populated temperate regions such as eastern North America and western Europe have 20 to 60 inches of rain, some parts of India receive as much as 500 inches. Such great differences in rainfall exert a strong influence on streams and valleys and so account in a large measure for differences in landscape in various parts of the world.

Runoff. — The rain water that reaches the surface of the land has a varied history. A part is trapped by surface depressions and remains in lakes and ponds. A part evaporates, a part sinks below the surface and becomes *subsurface water* (Chap. IV), and a part flows down the slope of the surface, forming the *direct runoff*. Some of the water that sinks below the surface later emerges, adding to the runoff as a whole.

About one-third of all the rain that falls forms runoff directly or indirectly. At any one place, however, the amount contributed to runoff depends on several factors such as (1) surface slope, (2) permeability and solubility of the local rocks, (3) character and amount of vegetation, (4) temperature and humidity of the atmosphere, and (5) distribution of the rainfall throughout the year. Therefore runoff varies greatly from place to place. Certain areas of very porous limestones have essentially no runoff, since all the rainfall sinks below the surface. On the other hand, in the Appalachian Mountains nearly all the water from rains in the early spring flows off because the ground is already saturated with melted snow.

Formation of Streams. — No land area is either perfectly flat or perfectly smooth. As a result, the runoff, though it may start to flow as a thin sheet of water spread evenly over an area, is quickly concentrated by converging slopes into fairly definite channels, taking the shortest and steepest routes downward, and following the lowest courses that present themselves. Thus, continuously augmented by seeps and springs representing the reappearance of the water that has sunk into the ground at higher levels, the runoff, unorganized at first, takes the form of organized *streams*, and becomes a *fluvial* agent of erosion.

FLUVIAL PROCESSES

Analysis of Factors Involved

Since about one-third of all rainfall becomes runoff, much of which flows seaward from areas many thousands of feet high, the power of the resulting streams to do work is very great. The work accomplished consists of loosening and removal of rock material, and *deposition*. These operations are accompanied by weathering, which is so closely related that it is difficult to separate from them in practice.

Weathering as an Accompanying Process. — The various operations, minute in detail but of huge cumulative importance, that combine to disintegrate, decompose, and comminute the rocks, and that are embraced in the general term *weathering* (p. 13), combine to play a highly significant part in the general process of erosion. Without continuous weathering, erosion would occur at but a fraction of its actual rate, for loose material is many times more easily worn away than is solid rock. Not only does weathering quicken the other processes of erosion by furnishing an abundance of loose material, but these processes in turn quicken weathering by removing weathered rock from the surface, thereby making more fresh rock available for attack.

Fluvial Erosion. — The process of fluvial erosion is not simple, but consists of four subprocesses, each of which operates in its own way. These are *hydraulic action, abrasion, solution,* and *transportation*. We must consider each separately before examining their combined effect.

Hydraulic Action. — The force inherent in the flow of water is able to lift and move away loose material with ease. The impact of water from a garden hose playing upon turned-up soil is a case in point. The soil is churned up and washed away, leaving tiny gullies excavated by the escaping water, and for the entire operation hydraulic action is almost solely responsible. Every rainfall accomplishes the same result in plowed fields and on steep slopes. And in all streams hydraulic action operates as an important factor, although the effects attributable exclusively to it are masked by the effects of other processes that are going on at the same time.

Abrasion. — Abrasion is the mechanical wear of rock on rock. Fluvial abrasion is brought about (1) by friction between rock fragments moving with the stream and rock fragments or solid rock in the stream bed, and (2) by friction between fragments moving through the stream at different rates. Rubbing, knocking, bumping, scraping, scouring — all these terms are applicable to fluvial abrasion. It is true that this process depends on the presence of rock fragments in the stream, whereas hydraulic action can be accomplished by clear water. On the other hand, no stream free from rock fragments remains free for long, since it automatically acquires them through its own hydraulic action, through contributions from tributaries, and through slumping of its banks. Both hydraulic action and abrasion operate in all streams and work in close association with each other. Not only does abrasion wear down bedrock exposed in the stream; it wears down the rock fragments themselves, making them smaller and rounding them more and more.

Solution. — No stream water is free from substances in solution, inherited in part from the subsurface water that issues upstream in springs and seeps and in part directly from the rain water, which contains acids dissolved from the atmosphere and from decaying vegetation. The rock most susceptible to the solvent action of stream water is limestone (calcium carbonate). But even rocks relatively insoluble are affected by acid-bearing stream water that passes over them, removing certain soluble minerals and thereby loosening the adjacent insoluble mineral grains and preparing them for mechanical seizure by the current.

Transportation. — Transportation is not sharply set apart from the other processes of fluvial erosion, but is inherent in all of them, since hydraulic action, abrasion, and solution can not take place without change of position on the part of the material involved. To make the connection even closer, fluvial transportation itself is accomplished largely by hydraulic action. The rock waste (*detritus*) and dissolved substances carried by a stream constitute its *load*. Whether the load is rolled along the bottom, carried in mechanical suspension, or moved forward in chemical solution, it is nevertheless being moved by the hydraulic force of the stream current.

The character of the current itself is the chief factor controlling transportation by most streams. Stream water does not have a uniform and constant flow. The middle moves faster than the sides, and the top moves faster than the bottom. In addition, every bend in the stream's course and every irregularity in its bed set up additional currents and eddies moving in various directions. In the resulting tangled mass of twisting currents, loose rock particles on the stream bed are quickly lifted and kept in suspension by repeated tossing into the body of the stream as they are carried forward. Because of this mode of operation, transportation is selective. The particles smallest in size and lightest in weight are tossed up most easily and most frequently, and so remain longest in suspension. The larger and heavier fragments are rolled or pushed along the stream bed, but movement of this kind is necessarily much slower than that of suspended particles. The result is that the distance through which a rock fragment is transported by a stream depends chiefly on its size and weight. For this reason, fluvial deposits are sorted according to size and specific gravity. This fact constitutes one of the reasons why the beds of some streams are pebbly near their heads and sandy or muddy near their mouths.

Factors Controlling Erosion. — The capacity of a stream to erode depends on its volume and velocity. The velocity in turn depends on

(1) the slope down which the stream is flowing, (2) volume of water, (3) the shape of its channel, and (4) weight and volume of its load.

The rate of descent of the bed of a stream is the *stream gradient*. It is ordinarily expressed as so many feet per mile. The gradient changes from place to place along the course of the stream. Velocity increases rapidly with increase of gradient. Thus mountain streams with high gradients erode their valleys much more quickly than lowland streams of comparable size with low gradients. It follows that streams wear high gradients down to low ones by continued erosion, and that as the gradients are worn down the rate of erosion must decrease.

Volume of water is a variable factor in all streams, largely because of fluctuations in rainfall. Velocity and rate of erosion in any stream are therefore always changing. As a rule, these changes are too slight to be readily noticeable, but in some regions they are great enough to cause streams to dry up at certain seasons, and to rise in floods at others. In other regions fluctuations are less extreme. Every spring the lower Mississippi has a normal rise in water level of 15 to 20 feet. The Nile normally rises 24 feet and the Ganges 32 feet. The erosive effect of such floods is considered below.

The shape of the stream channel as seen in cross-section also influences velocity. Since friction between water and channel slows a stream down, velocity is greatest in channels with the smallest area in proportion to volume of water. Deep, narrow channels therefore give greater stream velocity than broad, shallow ones.

A stream continues to acquire a load until it is carrying the greatest possible amount permitted by the gradient, volume of water, and kind of material available.

Laws of Erosive Power. — Having examined the factors that control stream velocity, we can now turn to the effect of increased velocity on erosive power. Two relationships are important here. The first concerns transporting power or " competence." If the velocity of a stream be doubled, the diameters of rock fragments it can move are increased 4 times. In other words, *the maximum diameter of the individual rock fragments a stream can move varies as the square of the velocity.*[1] The second concerns abrasive power. Calculations have shown that doubling the velocity of a stream increases its abrasive power at least 4 times, and under certain conditions as much as 64 times. In other words, *abrasive power varies between the square and the sixth power of the velocity.*

These laws not only explain the vastly greater erosion accomplished by swift streams than by slow ones under normal conditions, but they

[1] Assuming that all the fragments have the same specific gravity.

show clearly why exceptional floods, greatly increasing velocity by increasing volume, have such tremendous destructive power. The volume of the Colorado River measured at Yuma, Arizona, during a flood in 1921, was 155 times its normal volume. Again, when the St. Francis dam near Los Angeles gave way in 1928 and flooded the valley below, huge blocks of concrete weighing up to 10,000 tons each were moved by the escaping water. In India, during the Gohna flood of 1895, which lasted just 4 hours, the water picked up and transported such quantities of gravel that through the first 13 miles of its course the stream made a continuous gravel deposit from 50 to 234 feet thick.

Fluvial Deposition. — The constructive process of fluvial deposition goes forward side by side with fluvial erosion. This is a result of the complexity and variability of the stream currents, which constantly drop some rock fragments to the bottom while they pick up others. When a stream is actively eroding its bed at a certain point, it is merely picking up and carrying away more rock material than it is depositing there, and when it is actively depositing the reverse is going on. Therefore, whereas fluvial erosion and deposition are processes physically opposed to each other, they can be separated in practice only by recognizing the preponderance of one over the other.

Application of Fluvial Processes to the Stream Valley

Development of the Stream Valley; the Consequent Stream. — On a land surface newly exposed to the atmosphere, the impact of raindrops washes away (by hydraulic action) loose rock particles and carries them down the nearest slopes in little temporary rills. Joining at the bases of converging slopes, two or more rivulets combine, and the increased velocity resulting from increased volume causes increased erosion in more than direct proportion. With progressively increasing erosion, the rills become larger, and the larger they become the more runoff they carry, automatically gearing up the process. Each rill first excavates a *gully*. Erosion at its head, accelerated because the gradient is steepened there, causes the gully to lengthen headward, and the runoff washing down its side slopes widens it after each successive rain. At the same time the rill flowing through the gully deepens it. Thus undergoing continued enlargement, the gully grows into a ravine and eventually into a valley.

The slopes down which the runoff flows in this early stage are *initial slopes*, and the streams following or " consequent upon " these slopes are *consequent* streams.

Intermittent Streams and Permanent Streams. — At a very early stage the valley is likely to carry water only during and after rains.

Under these conditions, the stream is said to be *intermittent*. As erosion deepens the valley, however, more and more of the rainfall that enters the ground directly has opportunity to emerge again along its sides, and to contribute to the runoff through it long after the rains have ceased. Eventually the valley is excavated to the depth at which all openings in the rocks are permanently filled with water (p. 84). From this time on, water seeps steadily and uninterruptedly into the valley bottom, and the resulting stream is said to be *permanent*.

Longitudinal Profile. — The continuous curve formed by the slope of a stream from source to mouth is its *longitudinal profile*, whereas the *gradient* is its inclination in any one part of its course. The profile of a stream newly formed by runoff down the slope of a land surface must begin by being coincident along its line of flow with the profile of the land surface itself. Erosion and deposition soon change the profile, however. Near its source the stream receives only the runoff from local rainfall, its volume is slight, and its erosive power is therefore not great. With increasing distance downstream it receives not only the local runoff, but, through tributaries, an increasing volume of runoff from wide areas farther up the slope. Volume therefore increases from source to mouth, and the erosive power, which varies with volume, also increases in more than direct proportion (p. 43). On the other hand, increasing erosive capacity increases the load also, up to the maximum carrying capacity of the stream. Thereafter, its energy being fully taxed by carrying the load it has already acquired, it can not pick up more. Hence at some point between source and mouth erosion is at a maximum, and below this point it declines. For this reason the profiles of most streams approach a curve concave upward (Fig. 20). The curve is never perfectly smooth, since the rocks over which a stream flows are not homogeneous and some are therefore more easily eroded than others.

Baselevel. — When a stream reaches the sea it loses its velocity and consequently can erode no more. The sea level therefore is a level below which streams can not cut.[1] The level of the sea, projected inland as an imaginary plane below the surface of the land, is called *baselevel*, because it is the controlling base and ultimate lower limit of erosion by streams. Since capacity to erode varies with velocity, it is evident that the longitudinal profile of a stream is steepest in the early stages of its history and that it progressively decreases as baselevel is approached. In Fig. 20 the base line represents the baselevel toward which the profile is steadily being lowered.

[1] The fact that the lower channels of certain streams lie well below sea level does not invalidate the application of the baselevel principle to broad areas.

The general conception of baselevel is not invalidated by the fact that sea level is not permanently fixed. Fluctuations caused by widespread glaciation (p. 153), by deformation of the crust (p. 292), and by deposition of detritus in the sea (p. 292) are not large in proportion to the heights of the continents, and most changes of this kind are either so temporary or so slow that the idea of baselevel is not seriously affected.

Fig. 20. — Longitudinal profile of the Lehigh River and its continuation through the lower Delaware River to the sea, illustrating the general concave form of its curve. Base line = sea level. Horizontal distance = 120 miles. Elevation of stream at top of profile = 820 feet. Vertical exaggeration = 132 times. The irregularities in the profile are caused by unequal resistance of the rocks to erosion and possibly by other factors.

If a stream empties into a lake, its downcutting is limited by the level of the lake for as long a time as the lake exists. The lake therefore acts as a local baselevel for the stream, but because every lake above sea level must be drained ultimately, the baselevel that it represents is temporary as well as local. For these reasons the level of the lake, projected inland, may be regarded as a *local and temporary baselevel* controlling the region upstream from it. Similarly, the floors of lakeless basins in arid regions (p. 79) act as local and temporary baselevels for the streams tributary to them. Barriers of resistant rock across the path of a stream limit the downcutting upstream in the same way. All local and temporary baselevels, however, disappear eventually, and the areas they formerly affected pass into the control of the ultimate baselevel.

Transverse Profile. — The transverse profile of a stream valley is shaped by three factors: downcutting, movement of loose material down the sides of the valley into the stream, and lateral cutting.

Since the first factor, downcutting, is controlled by velocity, it takes place most rapidly in the earlier stages of valley development. The second factor, movement of loose material down the valley sides, is accomplished by direct rainwash, and by gravity, which promotes slow creep of the mantle (p. 31), the formation of talus, and occasional landsliding. As the incoherent rock-matter is shifted down the side slopes by these agencies, more is made by continuous weathering of the bedrock. In this way a constant movement of newly manufactured mantle takes place, feeding the stream with additional débris. This movement is greatest while downcutting is greatest, since downcutting

keeps the valley sides steep and maintains a high rate of creep and
landsliding. Most valleys that are being actively cut downward by

Fig. 21. — Transverse profiles of a stream valley, developed successively during the
progressive erosion of the valley. *1, 2, 3,* = V-shaped profile. *4, 5* = broadly flaring
profile.

their streams have a V-shaped transverse profile (Fig. 21, *1, 2, 3*; Fig.
22). This is a general indication that weathering and gravitative

Simmer Studio.

Fig. 22. — Very young V-shaped gorge of Chelan River, Washington,
being excavated in resistant rocks.

movements on valley sides take place rapidly enough to keep pace with
downcutting by the streams.

The third factor, lateral stream-cutting, occurs continually as the
stream undermines its banks, but it is greatly augmented by the fact

that since no stream valley is straight, the bends throw the main current with full force alternately against the banks of the stream, seriously eroding them. This lateral swinging begins as soon as the first rill is formed, and is a factor in the erosion of the resulting valley. Its effects, however, are masked by the more obvious effects of downcutting, which, constantly lowering the stream, prevents the laterally swinging current from cutting long at any one level.

On the other hand, as the stream lowers its longitudinal profile toward baselevel, this relationship changes. Decrease in gradient reduces velocity and thereby reduces erosion in more than direct proportion. Downcutting is slowed up, and the currents thrown from side to side are permitted at last to work at one level for a considerable period, so that they cut effectively into the valley walls. Valley widening therewith surpasses valley deepening, and accordingly the transverse profile gradually widens out from a V-shape to a broadly flaring shape (Fig. 21, *4, 5*).

Grade. — We have seen that the load is closely related to the material on the stream bed, that rock fragments are dropping out while others are being picked up. Under normal conditions, during the earlier stages of valley excavation, more rock material is being picked up and carried away than is dropped out. In other words, the transporting power of the stream exceeds its load. The net result is degradation of the valley. But, as downcutting reduces the gradient, the accompanying decrease in erosive power slows down the rate of degradation until transporting power and load are about equal. When any part of a stream reaches this condition of near-equilibrium, that part is said to be *graded* or *at grade*. The various reaches of a stream commonly attain the graded condition at different times, until finally the whole stream may become graded. The length of time required for reaching grade is determined by the resistance to erosion of the rocks along the valley, since this in turn controls the ease with which the load can be acquired.

The fact that a stream has reached grade does not imply that degradation of its valley has ceased. Indeed, most streams become graded throughout considerable parts of their courses long before they approach baselevel. Once this condition is attained, a very slow gradual decrease in load allows the stream to continue degrading its valley at an almost imperceptible rate.[1] In the course of time, however, this must result in the reduction of the valley to baselevel.

[1] Slow degradation of the valley floor by a swinging stream (p. 56) may result in the temporary development of discontinuous rock-defended terraces (p. 423).

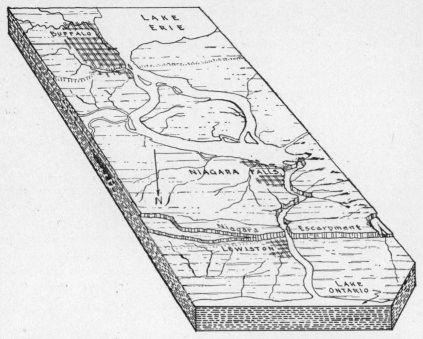

Fig. 23. — Bird's-eye view of Niagara River and Falls. Greatest length of block = 35 miles. Vertical exaggeration 2×.

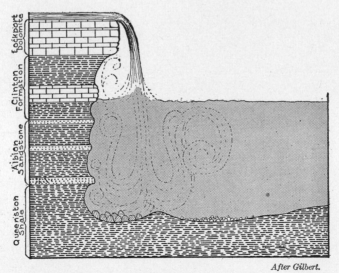

After Gilbert.

Fig. 24. — Relation of Niagara River to bedrock at the Falls. Depth of pool at base of Falls is greater than height of Falls above river surface.

Accordance of Tributaries with Main Streams. — As a rule, each tributary enters its main stream at the level of the main, and is therefore said to be *accordant*. The reason is that as the main stream cuts downward the increased gradient imparted to the tributaries enables them to keep pace in downcutting in spite of the smaller volume of water they contain. This increases the ratio of downcutting to lateral cutting in the tributary valleys, and if the increase is sufficient they develop into narrow canyons. Examples are afforded by some of the tributaries of the Colorado River which, in their effort to keep accordant relations with the main stream, have cut precipitous, slot-like canyons.

Disturbance of the Graded Condition. — Any change in gradient, volume, or load would upset the graded condition by altering the rate of erosion. Abnormally heavy rains, for example, might initiate a flood whose greatly enlarged erosive power would convert the graded stream into one actively degrading. Such changes, however, are temporary, for upon the subsidence of the flood the graded condition would be gradually restored. Again, great increases in load are known to have converted graded streams into actively aggrading ones, for example when glaciers appearing in their headwater regions poured great additional quantities of rock débris into them.

Slower changes of longer duration occur when a movement of the Earth's crust (p. 297) warps a land area drained by streams and so alters their longitudinal profiles. The streams begin at once to adjust themselves to the new profiles, and sooner or later again reach a graded condition that is also adjusted to the altered position of the land. All streams therefore work toward the equilibrium implied by the graded condition; if thrown out of it, they slowly but surely return to it, and if left unmolested by interruptions they would maintain it not only until they reached baselevel but as long as they continued to flow.

Falls and Rapids. — Niagara Falls, probably the most widely known cataract in the world, affords a clear example of how a common type of falls is formed. The Niagara River, originating as the outlet to Lake Erie at Buffalo, and thereby draining the four upper Great Lakes, flows over a plateau that ends near Lake Ontario in an escarpment (Fig. 23). At the surface of the plateau is a layer of resistant dolomite, and underneath this are weak, easily eroded shales (Fig. 24). When the river came into existence by the overflow of Lake Erie, it flowed across the plateau and tumbled over the escarpment at Lewiston, forming a falls. As the falling water gradually undermined the weak shales, the resistant dolomite above was left projecting as a " lip," which, left unsupported and penetrated by cracks and fissures, fell block by block and was swept away. Through long continuation of this process the falls perpetuated

Cliff Paper Co., and Meriden Gravure Co.

Fig. 25. — American Falls before the break of Jan. 17, 1931. View from Goat Island.

Cliff Paper Co., and Meriden Gravure Co.

Fig. 26. — American Falls after the break, viewed from the same point.

itself and gradually retreated upsteam, leaving a great gorge downstream to mark its path.   It has now moved 7 miles back from its original position and is still retreating.   On January 17, 1931, a large mass of rock at the lip of the American Falls was undermined and fell, leaving the lip greatly altered (Figs. 25, 26).

G. K. Gilbert, U. S. Geol. Survey.

Fig. 27. — Gully with tributaries developing through headward erosion by small consequent streams.   Mt. Tamalpais, California.

Application of Fluvial Processes to the Stream Pattern

Development of Tributaries. — A main stream and its tributaries constitute a *stream system*.   We have seen that many of the tributaries of a consequent stream system are formed simultaneously with the main stream, by runoff down previously existing convergent slopes.   Additional tributaries, however, grow by branching off from the main stream. The tributary streams themselves, of course, flow toward the main, but the valleys they excavate grow headward, *away* from the main.

Any irregularity in the side of a valley, however slight, is sufficient to concentrate the runoff at that point and so to begin the excavation of a tributary gully (Fig. 27), which enters the main stream at an acute angle. This is true even when the general slope of the land is parallel with and not toward the main valley. Fig. 28 represents a main valley with a point *o* on one of its sides where the runoff is concentrated. Runoff at this point is affected by gravity in two directions, *oa*, the direction of general slope of the land, and *ob*, the direction of slope of the valley side.

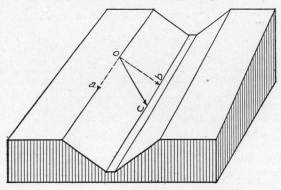

Fig. 28. — Ideal main valley with sloping sides, showing why tributaries grow headward from it at acute angles. *oa* = slope of land surface; *ob* = slope of valley side; *oc* = resultant course of local runoff.

In consequence it takes a course down the steepest available slope, *oc*, intermediate between the two. For this reason, and others, the pattern of a consequent stream system is usually[1] dendritic (branching like a tree).

Divides. — The watershed between two valleys or stream systems is a *divide*. In an early stage of growth of a stream system, some of the small divides are destroyed by lateral cutting as a large gully in process of being widened engulfs a smaller one lying parallel with it. Even the more important divides that separate two stream systems flowing in opposite directions are gradually lowered as the slopes leading away from them are cut down by erosion. As a major divide is lowered it is also shifted laterally. This takes place because no two stream systems have exactly the same erosive power, and because even a very slightly greater rate of erosion on one slope shifts the divide slowly away from the more vigorous stream system, causing it to lengthen, and correspondingly shortening the weaker system (Fig. 29). Because of progressive decrease in gradients as the streams approach baselevel, a divide shifts ever more slowly, until its shift becomes imperceptible.

Since each of the various headwater tributaries of both stream systems

[1] See p. 413.

has a rate of erosion that differs from its neighbors', the intervening divide is shifted unequally along various parts of its course, and so assumes a zigzag pattern (Fig. 29), no matter how straight it may have been at the outset.

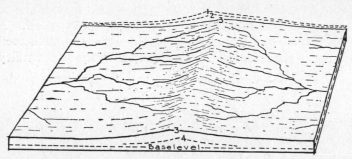

Fig. 29. — Divide between two stream systems, showing zigzag pattern, and progressive shifting caused by unequal erosion. Dashed lines *1*, *2*, indicate former profiles of the divide; dashed line *4* indicates future profile. The horizontal shift from *1* to *4* is very noticeable.

Application of Fluvial Processes to Stream Deposits

Types of Stream Deposits. — The flattened curve of the longitudinal profile of a typical stream shows that erosion greatly exceeds deposition in the upper part of the stream's course and that it becomes relatively less important in the lower part. This does not imply that deposition exceeds erosion in the lower reaches of a stream; it implies merely that extensive stream deposits are developed commonly in the lower rather than the upper part of the longitudinal profile, because gradients are there relatively low, reducing the velocity and decreasing the power of the stream to transport its load.[1] The dropping of excess load by the stream is an effort to maintain the graded condition. On a basis of form and mode of accumulation three general types of stream deposits are recognized. These are the *floodplain*, the *delta*, and the *fan*. The material of which all stream-deposited forms are built is commonly referred to as *alluvium*.

The Floodplain; Meanders. — Given time enough, all streams deposit alluvium extensively along their valleys, forming long continuous flats or *floodplains*. The first step in the development of a floodplain occurs early in the history of the valley. The lateral swinging (p. 47) of a stream, set up by initial irregularities in its course, throws the main current from side to side of the valley, and causes lateral cutting of the valley wall on the outer sides of the curves (Fig. 30). At the same time

---

[1] In arid regions deposition commonly occurs also as a result of decreased volume caused by evaporation and by disappearance of water into the stream bed.

the water becomes slack on the inner
sides of the curves and slips off the
adjacent valley side. With continued
erosion the curves grow smoother and
more regular and each valley side is
sculptured into alternating steep undercut walls and gentle *slipoff slopes*, corresponding exactly with the widening
curves of the stream (Fig. 31). At the
same time deposition occurs in the slack
water along the insides of the curves,
and the deposits are left high and dry
in alternating crescent-shaped patches
of alluvium (Fig. 31) as enlargement of
the curves while the stream cuts downward causes the current to edge away
from them both laterally and downstream. As the curves grow wider the
alternating patches of slack-water deposits coalesce, making a continuous
alluvial flat which is crossed and re-
crossed by the swinging stream (Fig.
32). The undercut walls that face upstream are slowly planed away (Fig.
33), and are followed downstream by
the curves themselves. This process
results in the widening-out of the valley to a width great enough to accommodate the curves (Fig. 34). The valley walls are now more or less parallel,

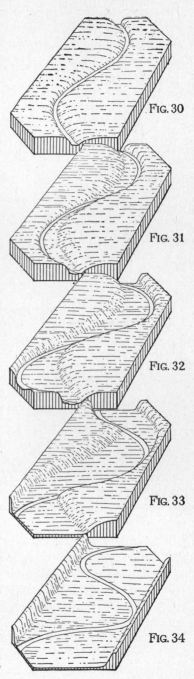

Figs. 30–34. — Evolution of the floodplain, and
development of stream curves into meanders.

Fig. 30. — Stream valley in an early stage of
development, with bends inherited from the initial slopes. Stream channel coincident with axis
of valley.

Fig. 31. — Later stage. Stream forming undercut walls, slipoff slopes, and crescentic patches
of alluvium.

Fig. 32. — Later stage. Stream has widened
its valley and built a continuous alluvial flat.

Fig. 33. — Later stage. Stream is undercutting the spurs that face upstream.

Fig. 34. — Later stage. The valley has been
widened to the width of the curves (now *meanders*), which sweep down-valley.

but the stream is no longer parallel with them as it was at the outset; its curves sweep downstream unchecked. When the curves have reached this condition they are termed *meanders*.

The valley walls are neither straight nor quite parallel except through short distances. Irregularities in the course of the valley walls (Fig. 35) throw the whole belt of meanders from side to side, causing under-cutting, just as with single curves at an earlier stage (Fig. 32). The

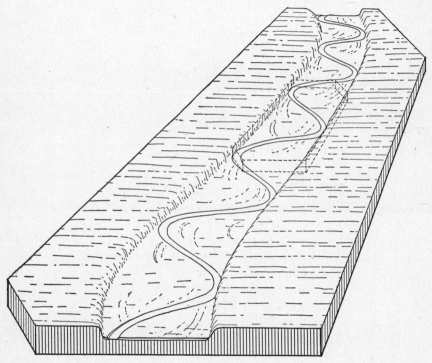

Fig. 35. — Valley of Figs. 30–34, showing broad curves in the course of the valley. The position of the block shown in Figs. 30–34 is indicated by dashed lines.

result is that the meanders slowly continue to cut back the valley walls, still further widening the valley itself (Fig. 36). In this way the belt of meanders itself develops curves, forming a pattern admirably repre-sented by the lower Mississippi River.

The individual meanders sweep continuously down the meander belt and as a cumulative result the meander belt still sweeps continuously down the valley, by the simple process of erosion on the outer and downstream sides of the curves and slack-water deposition on the inner and upstream sides, just as in Fig. 33, except that the material being

eroded is alluvium instead of solid rock.   The steepest bank and deepest
water are always on the outer sides of the meanders (Fig. 38).

Cutoffs; Oxbow Lakes. — As the arc of a meander becomes more pronounced a loop is cut through, leaving an island, the main current takes
the shorter route afforded by the cutoff, and the entrances to the abandoned channel are silted up, leaving a shallow crescentic *oxbow lake*
(Figs. 39–41, 47).   Ordinarily oxbow lakes do not form until the valley

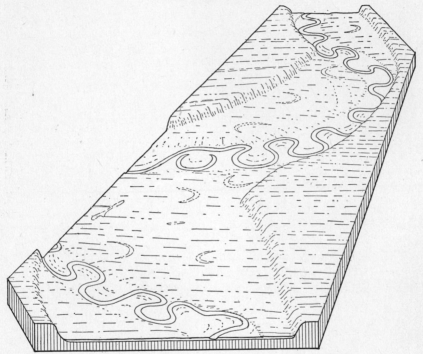

Fig. 36. — Further widening of the valley of Fig. 35, by lateral swinging of the *belt*
of meanders.   Formation of cutoffs and oxbow lakes.

has been made considerably wider than the meander belt.   Fig. 36
shows a valley floor dotted with oxbow lakes.   These will be gradually
destroyed as they are undercut by the downstream sweep of the meander
belt, and new ones will form.

Effect of Floods; Natural Levees. — In temperate latitudes increased
stream volume commonly occurs in the spring, when melting snows and
heavy rains swell the tributaries.   If the increase, concentrated in the
main stream, is great enough to raise the water level until it overtops
the channel and spreads out over the bordering flats, the stream is said
to be *in flood.*   This rise of the water increases the volume, velocity, and

erosive power *in the channel*, the bottom of which is therefore deepened. On the other hand, the velocity of the surface water, suddenly forced out on to a shallow flat, is quickly and effectively checked, causing

Alaskan Aerial Survey, U. S. Navy.

Fig. 37. — Stream valley with wide floodplain. The tributary entering from the left foreground has repeatedly shifted its course, leaving scars in the plain marking its former meandering course. Stikine River, Alaska.

concentrated deposition of alluvium along the immediate borders of the flooded channel gradually growing less in an outward direction, away from the channel. The deposits therefore take the form of very low but

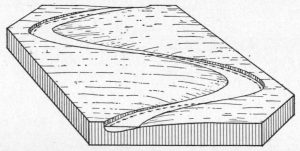

Fig. 38. — Small segment of floodplain traversed by a meandering stream channel. Arrows indicate course of current and location of deepest water. Undercutting on outer banks and continuous deposition on inner banks result in giving to the floodplain surface the alternate interlocking slopes clearly visible in the diagram.

distinct ridges known as *natural levees* (Fig. 42), bordering the channel. These ridges have a height of from 4 or 5 feet up to 20 feet or more, and are the most pronounced relief features of some valley floors.

They remain after the flood has subsided and the stream has shrunk to its old dimensions. As a result of this flood deposition the alluvial floor, originally built up bit by bit through deposition on the inside curves of meanders slowly moving down-valley, is capped by a thin veneer of fine alluvium deposited all at once in somewhat lake-like shallow

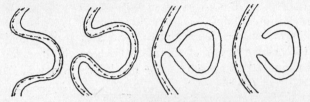

Fig. 39. — Development of cutoffs and oxbow lakes. Compare Fig. 36.

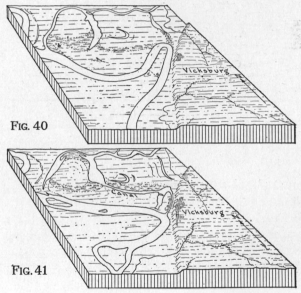

Figs. 40–41. — Formation of a cutoff and oxbow lake on the Mississippi at Vicksburg, Mississippi. Length of front of block = 11 miles. Vertical exaggeration 2×.

Fig. 40. — Situation in 1863. During the siege of Vicksburg, Grant tried to isolate town from river by attempting an artificial cutoff along the line c–c. The cut could not be completed.

Fig. 41. — Situation in 1914. The river later accomplished what military strategy failed to do, and left Vicksburg on an oxbow lake. This situation was remedied by the cutting of canals, which diverted the tributary Yazoo River and kept a channel open to the Mississippi.

flood water. It is from this surface coating that the valley flat derives its name of *floodplain*. The floodplain of the Mississippi, including the natural levees and the low swampy lands beyond their outer slopes, covers an area of 30,000 square miles.

Sloughs. — Where natural levees are inconspicuous or absent, flood-water overflowing a meandering channel often excavates shallow short-cut channels across the tongue of land formed by the meander. Some of these channels are enlarged, permanently cutting off the meanders they span; most, however, are abandoned as the flood subsides and are left as *sloughs* (Fig. 36), which are slowly undercut as the meander shifts downstream.

Floodplain Terraces. — If an uplift of the land or other major change increases the erosive power of a stream that has built a floodplain, it incises its channel and abandons the floodplain, which is thereby left

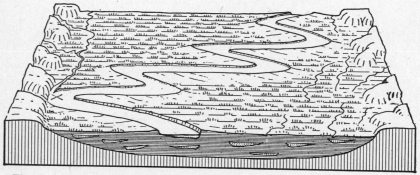

Fig. 42. — Segment of floodplain with natural levees. The tributaries entering the main valley are prevented by the levees from joining the main stream until it impinges against one of the valley walls, as at *x*.

in the form of terraces flanking the newly excavated channel. This process is discussed in Chapter XVII.

Economic Problem of Floods. — As a flood subsides the decrease in volume of water stops erosion of the channel bottom and renews deposition on it, so that during low water (between floods) the channel grows shallower, but the water is held in it by the levees. With continued additions to the levees during floods and to the channel bottom during low water, many streams rise until they flow at levels actually above the greater parts of their floodplains, and are restrained only by the levees from deserting their channels and following lower courses near the floodplain margins. This situation (Fig. 43) represents the condition of the lower Mississippi when in normal flood.

Before the settlement of the lower Mississippi Valley, the river overflowed its banks periodically, the flood-water reaching the sea through the low flats beyond the natural levees. As early as 100 years ago attempts were made to confine the flooded river to its channel in order to reclaim for agricultural purposes the rich and fertile alluvial lowlands. These attempts took the form of artificial levees (Fig. 43) which were built upon the natural ones, thus deepening and heightening the channel at the same time. If a given amount of water is confined to a narrowed course and thus prevented from normal spreading, its channel must necessarily be deepened. A part of this added depth is attained locally by increased erosion of the bottom, but much of it is attained by rise of the water surface. Hence whenever a new levee is put in, all those already in existence must be raised. The first artificial levee, built at New Orleans, was 4 feet high. Today the average height is more than 13 feet. In 1902 there were 1300 miles of these levees along the Mississippi; in 1927 there were 2500. The river level is gradually rising higher above the adjacent basins, and when floods occur, they are correspond-

U. S. Weather Bureau.

Fig. 43. — The Mississippi in flood near Pilcher Point, Louisiana, nearly overtopping the artificial levee.

ingly more destructive, as witness the disastrous flood of 1927, in which the swollen river broke through the levees and inundated thousands of square miles of inhabited land. The building of levees is therefore not in itself an adequate method of preventing floods. The extensive flood-control plan now under consideration recognizes the need of additional means of combating floods, among which are the straightening of the river and the establishment of permanent overflow channels to act as safety-valves for regulating the height of the stream.

The scheme of building artificial levees has been followed in many parts of the world. In the floodplain of the Po in northern Italy the stream bed is above the housetops. Breaks in the levees on the Hwang-Ho at various times have resulted in enormous loss of life. In the flood of 1887 more than a million people were drowned.

Braiding. — During low water, many streams heavily loaded with fine sediment on low gradients, and steadily losing volume through evaporation or through seepage into their beds, choke up their channels

with alluvium, overflow, and cut new channels, which in turn become
rapidly choked.   This process, termed *braiding,* results in the development of an intricate network of shallow channels forming a complex
pattern on the floodplain.   Many streams in arid and semiarid regions,
and streams of glacial meltwater heavily loaded with detritus, are
intricately braided (Fig. 108).

The Delta. — When the current at the mouth of a stream is checked
by a body of standing water such as a lake or the sea, its load is promptly
dropped, building up an embankment with a front that grows outward
like a railroad or highway fill in process of construction across a valley.
As the deposit is built up close to the water surface, the floodplain
usually encroaches upon it from upstream and gradually covers it so
that it is built above water in a crudely triangular shape with one apex

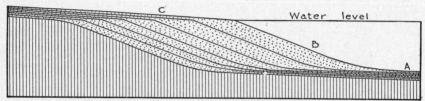

Fig. 44. — Section through a delta, idealized to show relation of foreset beds, *B*, to topsets, *C*, and bottomsets, *A*.   Topsets are shown thickened relatively to foresets and bottomsets.   (After Barrell.)   In a large delta such as that of the Mississippi the angle of
inclination of the foresets is vastly less than that shown in the figure.

pointing upstream.   From this shape, resembling the Greek letter Δ, the
deposit derives its name of *delta.*   This name is applied regardless of
whether the embankment remains submerged or whether the encroachment of the floodplain has raised it above the water surface.

The bulk of the delta-forming material is dropped on the frontal slope
of the growing embankment, forming thick *foreset beds* (Figs. 44–46).
Some of the finest sediment, however, remains longer in suspension and
is carried farther out and dropped as fine *bottomset beds,* thinning outward
away from the stream.   Along the top, where erosion and deposition
alternate as the stream current fluctuates, thin horizontal *topset beds*
are laid down.   The thickness of the whole mass is in some cases very
great.   Borings put down in Venice, on the delta of the Po, reached a
depth of more than 500 feet without attaining the bottom of the delta
beds.

Whenever the stream in flood overtops the natural levees, it breaks
through at weak points and flows seaward through new channels, leaving
a diminished volume of water in the old channel.   In the case of large
streams unhampered by artificial levees, new outlets are broken through
soon after they have been formed, and a branching system of *dis-*

tributaries grows up, giving shape to the delta. Between the distributaries lie shallow basins which gradually fill with sediment during floods and thus become low land (Fig. 45).

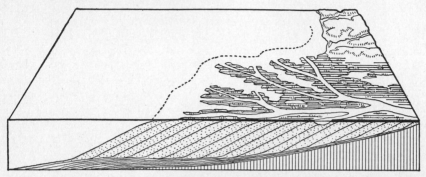

Fig. 45. — Delta in 3-dimensional view. At the surface appear "delta fingers" formed by deposition from distributary streams. On the face of the block are seen thick, inclined foreset beds underlain by bottomsets and overlain by topsets. The topsets are represented only by the thickness of a single line, because they are commonly very thin. Vertical scale greatly exaggerated.

The shifting of the main channel through the development of new distributaries is strikingly illustrated by the Hwang-Ho, which for approximately 700 years prior to 1852 had discharged eastward into

R. F. Flint, Conn. Geol. Survey.

Fig. 46. — Section of delta deposited in an ice-dammed lake now extinct. Shows foresets and topsets only. Bottomsets are concealed by sliding sand. Waterbury, Connecticut.

the Yellow Sea. In 1852 it broke its banks at a point more than 300 miles above its mouth, formed a new channel northeastward across the great alluvial flats of the province of Shantung, and finally emptied into the gulf of Chihli, almost 300 miles north of its old mouth. The Hwang-

Ho has occupied this new course with minor distributaries since 1852, and the old channel has largely dried up.

American Geographical Society.

Fig. 47.—Small stream seen vertically from the air, meandering on its floodplain and building a delta at its mouth.   Note the oxbow lake in mid-course.   The delta is largely under water.   Hampton, Virginia.   (W. T. Lee, "The Face of the Earth as Seen from the Air.")

The Mississippi attempted a similar change in April, 1890, breaking its banks at the Nita Crevasse[1] between New Orleans and Baton Rouge,

[1] The term *crevasse* in the region of the lower Mississippi refers to a break in a levee.

at a point well over 100 miles from its mouth. From here it flowed eastward through Lake Maurepas, Lake Pontchartrain, and Lake Borgne into Mississippi Sound, inundating a wide area, causing great damage, and halting railroad traffic for two months. The river at length resumed its old course, after having taught local engineers that in the vicinity of the Nita Crevasse the level of the Mississippi stood normally about 21 feet above the level of the bordering swamps and flats.

Rate of Delta Growth. — Through the growth of deltas the land at the mouths of large streams is constantly being added to at the expense of lakes and the sea. The rate at which advance of the land takes place and the form of the delta itself are variable, depending upon such factors as depth of water offshore, volume of detritus, and power of waves and longshore currents to sweep away the newly deposited material. It is estimated that the delta of the Mississippi is growing out into the Gulf of Mexico at the rate of more than 250 feet each year, and the Po pushes into the Adriatic at nearly as great a rate. Since 400 B.C., the Rhone has been encroaching on the Mediterranean at the rate of 36 feet annually, whereas the deltas of the Danube and the Nile are growing only 13 feet yearly. The obstructions to navigation caused by deposition have been successfully removed by the building of extensions of the natural levees out beyond the mouths of two distributaries. These *jetties* confine the current and force it to keep its channel scoured out and at the same time to carry its load into deep water before dropping it.

It follows from their rapid growth that the deltas of large rivers form extensive areas of land. The Nile delta is nearly 100 miles long and 200 miles broad on its seaward front. The combined delta formed by the Ganges and Brahmaputra is 200 miles long and has an area of 40,000 square miles. The Mississippi delta is likewise 200 miles long, but is much narrower, having an area of not much more than 12,000 square miles. The Po delta, which was large at the beginning of the Christian Era, has increased by nearly 100 square miles since that time.

The Fan. — When a swift tributary stream emerges from high land into a wide and nearly level valley, the abrupt change in its gradient may cause it to deposit immediately the greater part of its load on the valley floor. In this way a low semi-conical *fan* is built up, radiating outward from the point at which the tributary emerges (Fig. 48). In one sense the fan may be regarded as a delta formed on land, but it differs from the delta in having a sloping rather than a flat top, since its upbuilding is not controlled by the surface of a body of standing water.

The fan acquires its shape because of the nearly uniform distribution of alluvium over its surface by the parent stream. The stream repeatedly silts up its channel, overflows, and forms new distributaries, just as in the braiding process (p. 61). When one radius of the fan has been built up, the stream shifts to another radius and builds that up. In this way the entire surface is covered eventually by the stream, and the deposit as a whole is remarkably symmetrical.

The deposition of the fan is an attempt by the stream to reach the graded condition rapidly. Fans are therefore much larger and more common in regions of high relief at points where streams emerge from very steep slopes on to plains, than in regions of low relief and gentle slopes. For this reason fans occur more commonly in the mountainous

C. R. Longwell.

Fig. 48. — Fan built at the mouth of a small valley in the Pintwater Range, Nevada.

parts of western North America (Figs. 61, 66) than farther east. They are also more common in regions of dwindling streams than in regions of through-flowing streams, even if slopes are comparable. East of the Rocky Mountains, fans are very small and are confined chiefly to the bases of such steep slopes as valley sides laterally cut by streams.

Character of Stream Deposits. — Pebbles and sand grains transported by streams become rounded, whatever their original shape, through the bumping and smoothing they suffer as they are rolled and tumbled by the shifting currents. Furthermore, because of the delicate adjustment of transporting power to the size and weight of the rock fragments forming the load, stream deposits, whether in floodplains or deltas, invariably exhibit sorting according to size and weight (and therefore composition) of rock fragments (p. 42). Layers of pebbles of various sizes are separated from layers of sand, and these in turn are sorted out from layers of silt and clay. No one layer extends far, however, because the extreme irregularity of stream currents, repeatedly changing the conditions of deposition, results in thickening and thinning of the layers, and causes them to lie at angles inclined to each other.

THE FLUVIAL CYCLE

Since streams steadily enlarge their valleys and gradually reduce the divides that separate them, and since stream erosion is limited downward by baselevel (p. 45), the question arises: What will be the ultimate conceivable result of the long-continued erosion of a land mass by streams? Theory and the study of stream-sculptured lands both lead to the same answer: the wasting away of the land to a low surface from which the water drains sluggishly to the sea. This process, the complete destruction of a land mass, involves an enormous amount of time, but if no interruption occurs the final result is inevitable. The series of changes involved in the complete fluvial reduction of a region to baselevel constitutes a *fluvial cycle of erosion*. The time required necessarily varies with varying circumstances such as initial elevation above the sea, resistance of the underlying rock to erosion, and amount of rainfall and runoff.

As we have seen, the rainfall factor exercises an important control over the process of fluvial erosion, by controlling both the rate of erosion and the places where erosion and deposition occur. For example, in regions where runoff is very slight the streams dry up before they reach the sea, and all their detritus is deposited inland. For this reason the characteristics of the cycle under various types of climate must next be considered.

The Fluvial Cycle in Humid Regions

Although the progressive changes that constitute the cycle are continuous, the cycle is divided for convenience into stages. It must be remembered, however, that each stage grades into the next, and that all are parts of one unbroken chain of events. The following description of a typical cycle is illustrated by Figs. 49–54.

Initial Stage. — It is probably true that no part of any continent has escaped inundation by the sea at one time or another during the Earth's history. Not infrequently parts of the shallow sea floor (such as the floor of Hudson Bay) have been warped up above sea level and have become dry land. As soon as such an area appeared above water in a humid climate, it would have received rainfall, and the runoff would have been shed from the high places toward the low, and so into the sea. All the conditions necessary for fluvial erosion would be fulfilled — a quantity of water being pulled downward by gravity, loose mantle constantly being formed by weathering processes, and the débris picked up, carried away, and deposited at lower levels by running water.

An upwarped sea floor, then, appears above the sea, bearing on its

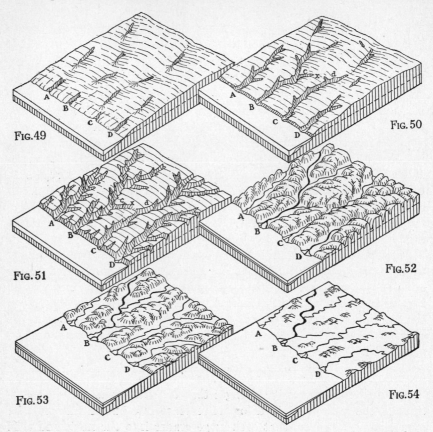

Figs. 49–54. — Ideal fluvial cycle under a humid climate and in homogeneous rocks.

Fig. 49. — Initial stage, showing gullies developing at points where the runoff is concentrated.

Fig. 50. — Early youth, showing integration of main drainage lines and growth of the stronger at the expense of the weaker streams.

Fig. 51. — Later youth, showing the reduction of the initial surface to irregular flat-topped ridges.

Fig. 52. — Early maturity, showing dissection of divides into flowing slopes and development of floodplains.

Fig. 53. — Later maturity, showing decrease in relief, lowering of slopes and widening of valleys.

Fig. 54. — Old age, showing development of peneplane with monadnocks.

surface initial irregularities. For the sake of simplicity let the material composing the mass be broadly homogeneous, with only local variations in its resistance to erosion. Gullies develop as consequents upon this surface (Figs. 27, 49) and grow headward. Adjacent gullies join down-slope and form connected chains, which gradually become valleys. In the early stages of the cycle gradients are so steep that downcutting is dominant over lateral erosion; hence the valleys and gullies are steep-sided and sharply V-shaped. Any irregularity of slope or material in the side of a gully concentrates runoff and thus gives opportunity for the start of a tributary stream. Since no gully is uniform in these respects, tributaries rapidly develop, lengthening themselves headward from the parent gully. The extensive development of tributaries breaks up the continuity of the initial slopes, and the land area passes from the *initial stage* into *youth*.

Stage of Youth. — The land area is now drained by an integrated stream system developed upon the preëxisting initial slopes. These slopes were so arranged that more concentration of drainage took place along the lines of the infant streams B and C (Fig. 50) than along the streams A and D. In other words, the sum total of depressions in the areas of B and C made those areas lower than those of A and D. The chain of cause and effect was thus set up most rapidly and thoroughly along B and C, and these streams sent out more tributaries and grew headward more swiftly than did A and D. Briefly stated, a struggle for existence takes place among adjacent streams in the competition to grow big and therefore to absorb larger drainage areas. In this case, the streams (B and C) favored by the initial slopes have won and are maintaining their lead over their less-favored, weaker neighbors (A and D).

The contest is illustrated by the situation at x (Fig. 50). Two streams, c and d, tributary respectively to B and to C, have lengthened their valleys headward toward each other, narrowing the broad divide that formerly separated them. Stream c has a shorter route to the sea than has stream d; hence the gradient of c is steeper; hence its power to erode is greater; hence it cuts its valley both downward and headward more rapidly than does d. This inequality in rate of erosion results not only in lowering the divide x but in shifting it away from c toward d. (See also Fig. 29.)

The streams in youth have gradients as steep as the height of the land above sea level permits; the valleys are V-shaped and steep sided (Figs. 22, 51), and their courses are crooked, with irregular bends determined by the initial irregularities of the land surface. Tributaries develop rapidly, their valleys working headward from the main streams like branches growing from the trunks of trees. The whole system is delicately balanced and adjusted throughout its extent. As the numerous tributaries dissect the initial surface, the broad divides contract into narrow and irregular ridges. The time of youth is the time of scenic grandeur in a landscape. Deep canyon-like valleys (Fig. 22), precipitous cliffs, and high ridges are characteristic, although later they are destroyed by the same processes that sculptured them.

Stage of Maturity. — When the tributaries have lengthened their valleys so far headward that the narrow ridge-like divides have been dissected into short hills and spurs, and when the growing valleys have destroyed all the initial surface by converting it into slopes, the land-

American Geographical Society.

Fig. 55. — Land mass high above sea level in maturity of the fluvial cycle. Between Ancon and Lima, Peru. Note intricate stream-dissection and arrangement of the divides. (G. R. Johnson, "Peru from the Air.")

scape imperceptibly takes on a new aspect and the region is said to be *mature* (Figs. 52, 55). The intricate network of drainage is complete and all the interstream areas have been carved into slopes. The main streams have cut downward far enough to decrease their own gradients appreciably. As decreasing gradient progressively decreases each stream's downcutting power, and thus causes it to linger at each successive level, the force of the current deflected from side to side of its valley cuts more effectively. Each valley is therefore widened with increasing rapidity, and each gradually develops a floodplain (Figs. 30–34).

As valley widening increases and valley deepening decreases the main streams reach grade through long stretches and meander over their newly developed floodplains, while the upland (initial) surface, so prominent during youth, has merged into slopes. Since downcutting has been checked, the mantle on the slopes is not swept away as rapidly as it is formed by weathering. It therefore accumulates, and moves slowly down the slopes under the influence of gravity. In this way, hollows in the slopes are filled in, irregularities are smoothed out, and the profiles of the valley sides are converted into smooth flowing curves (Fig. 57, *Left*). It is for this reason that the period of maturity is the time of restful beauty in such a landscape. The rugged splendor of youth has been modeled into sweeping curves.

Stage of Old Age. — Because of the low and ever-decreasing gradients of the main streams, the heights are now wasted by the steeper tributaries much more rapidly than the larger valleys can be cut down. The result is a gradual decrease in relief as the divides are worn down to successively lower levels (Fig. 53). Lateral cutting by the main streams widens the valleys and thus helps to cut away the adjacent higher land. The streams are sluggish, and the meander belts wander across the floodplains (Fig. 36). Natural levees bordered by swamps are built up in their lower courses. As the bottoms of the main valleys slowly approach baselevel, abrasion by the main streams gradually diminishes, and only the divides, where the gradients are still appreciable, are notably lowered. In this way the hills of maturity merge downward into low elevations in old age, shedding the runoff feebly in sluggish streams. Erosion takes place more and more slowly. The last few feet of vertical cutting might require a longer time than the entire amount of preceding excavation.

The Peneplane. — The resulting surface of low relief, very gently undulatory, is called a *peneplane* (" almost a plane," Fig. 54). The highlands have been brought low; the rocks that composed them have been carried bit by bit to the sea and have been there deposited in beds as sediment. Only a few residual remnants of the former high land remain. Here and there isolated hills (Fig. 56) rise above the general surface, like islands above a sea. They are composed either of very resistant rock or of masses so far from the main streams that they only stubbornly allow themselves to be eroded down to the general level of their surroundings. Such island masses are called *monadnocks* after Mount Monadnock in New Hampshire which rises in this manner above the level of the surrounding country.

The formation of a peneplane is by no means due entirely to lateral cutting by streams. Toward the close of the cycle, when gradients have been worn low and streams have grown sluggish, chemical weathering becomes relatively very important. The hills that remain are lowered partly by the removal of rock material in solution and partly by gentle creep of the mantle down the low slopes to the nearest streams.

The terms *youth*, *maturity*, and *old age* do not refer to periods of years, or to any absolute age. They denote merely stages defined by the amount of work done in proportion to the total amount of work involved in the cycle. Thus a region of very soft rocks might reach old age while an area of resistant rocks was still in youth as far as the amount of erosion accomplished is concerned. It follows that an extensive valley system might exist in various stages in different localities, depending on supply of water and on the nature of the underlying rocks. As a matter of fact this is commonly the case.

Geological Survey of Georgia.

Fig. 56. — Stone Mountain, 16 miles east of Atlanta, Georgia, a monadnock composed of resistant granite rising 650 feet above a peneplane that bevels weaker crystalline rocks.

This synthesis of stream sculpture is not mere theory. Every stage of the process is illustrated in some part of the world. The only stage of which we have no undamaged example is the one represented by the peneplane. Many peneplanes exist, but none are any longer at base-level. All have been lifted up to higher levels, and this has resulted in their dissection by a new generation of valleys. In spite of these valleys, however, the peneplane is still plainly recognizable in that remnants of it are preserved on the divides.

Time Involved in the Cycle. — The time required for the fluvial reduction of a land mass to a peneplane depends on the height of the land above the sea, on the resistance of the rocks composing it, and on the climate. Because of the variability of these factors, we can not make accurate estimates, but we can gain an idea of the order of magnitude of the amount of time required. Through the compilation of data on the loads being carried by the larger streams, it has been estimated that the whole area of the United States, embracing a number of large stream systems, is being lowered *on the average* at a rate of 1 foot in 7000 to 9000 years. At this rate more than 15 million years would be required to reduce it to the present level of the sea, taking no account of the slowing-up of erosion in the stage of old age as a result of decreased gradients. The actual time required would be vastly longer.[1]

The Fluvial Cycle in Semiarid Regions

Effect of Vegetation on Erosion in Humid Regions. — In humid regions the surface is commonly covered with an almost continuous blanket of sod, supplemented locally by brush and forest. This mat of vegetation occupies uplands, slopes, and locally valley floors. Through weathering aided by gravity the mantle creeps down the slopes, carrying the vegetation with it (p. 31). The movement is so slow and imperceptible that the mat of sod is rarely breached. Fresh gullying is hindered for several reasons: (1) Because roots hold the soil firmly together and enable it to resist the pressure of the moving water. (2) Because the mat of vegetation acting like a sponge absorbs the water and permits it to drain off so slowly that the erosive effect of sudden rushes of water after storms is prevented. (3) Because in the spring the melting of snow is retarded by forest shade, and the meltwater seeps through the ground to the nearest stream-head instead of gullying the immediate surface. The profiles and contours resulting from this essentially unbroken protective covering, especially in the mature stage of the cycle, are a series of smooth flowing curves (p. 71; Fig. 18). Moreover, it is noticeable that in forested regions the flow of the streams is less irregular than in non-forested regions, and the stream waters are relatively clear.

If the forest cover is removed, erosion proceeds rapidly and great damage may be done. The regulative action of the forests on erosion and the flow of streams is a matter of great importance, not only from the geologic standpoint, but as vitally affecting civilization. In some regions, of which parts of northern China and of Spain are examples, deforestation has so intensified erosion that large areas have become sterile wastes, subjected alternately to droughts and sudden floods. Smaller areas in the southern United States have been ravaged in this way. Continuous loss of valuable soil is one of the great wastes of modern civilization and should be checked as much as possible by careful forest regulation.

Vegetation and Erosion in Semiarid Regions. — The importance of the vegetation common to humid regions has been outlined in the pre-

[1] Isostatic uplift (p. 372) during the cycle would probably increase it still more.

ceding paragraphs.   In semiarid regions (regions where the annual
rainfall is roughly 10 to 20 inches and evaporation is great), such as the
Great Plains region east of the Rocky Mountains, vegetation is less
abundant and conditions somewhat resemble those in the deforested
areas of the more humid land farther east.   Trees are rare, the sod mat
is present but not generally strong, and the soil is loose, dry, and porous.
Moreover, rainfall is likely to occur in sudden bursts.   The results are
rapid runoff and rapid erosion.   Gullying occurs wherever the soil is
laid bare, as on cattle trails and in wheel ruts.   The streams are subject
to sudden and heavy floods, their waters are muddy, and in months of
little rainfall they become low or run dry.   Because of the slow rate of
weathering of their side walls, and rapid downcutting by their streams,
the valleys are steep sided.   Many are also flat bottomed because of
extensive deposition on their floors.

Effects of Rock Composition. — The steep-sided and commonly flat-
bottomed valley profiles resulting from scanty protection by vegetation

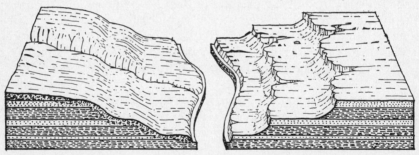

Fig. 57. — Contrast between landscape profiles in humid and arid regions.   Left —
resistant rocks largely masked by mantle of chemically weathered residuum creeping
down the slopes.   Right — resistant rocks exposed as broad platforms and steep cliffs.

are accentuated by the dominance of mechanical over chemical processes
of weathering (pp. 16, 22).   The smooth flowing slopes that characterize
the mature landscape in humid regions are absent here.   Mechanical
weathering accentuates instead of minimizing the effect of rock resistance on landscape profiles.   There is no creeping mat of chemically
weathered mantle to obscure the contacts between weak and resistant
rock.   The Grand Canyon affords an excellent example.   More than
200 miles long, 10 miles wide from rim to rim, and in some places more
than a mile deep, it has been excavated by the Colorado River in nearly
horizontal rocks arranged in alternating weak and resistant layers.
The more resistant layers form broad platforms and gaunt cliffs whose
taluses (derived from mechanical weathering) partly cover the weaker
beds (Figs. 4, 57).

Weak materials such as clays and shales exposed to erosion are rapidly carved into networks of gullies and ravines separated by sharp-ridged spurs (Fig. 58). This intricate gullying, which progresses visibly with every rain, is common along parts of the Missouri, Platte, Cheyenne, and other streams that drain the Great Plains region, most of which is built of these weak materials. Areas so gullied are termed *badlands*.

Summary. — The influences wrought by slight rainfall and consequent scanty vegetation impose themselves on the process of erosion in semiarid regions. The drainage pattern remains the same as in humid regions save that the tributaries are scanty instead of numerous and that in many of them the flow is intermittent. In maturity angular

Fig. 58. — Badlands, Custer County, South Dakota. *S. W. Williston.*

mesas and buttes (p. 34) are developed instead of the rounded hills and rolling plateaus of the humid region. The ultimate product, however, is a peneplane.

The Fluvial Cycle in Arid Regions

Some authors classify arid regions roughly as regions that receive less than 10 inches of rainfall annually; others classify them as areas in which drainage does not reach the sea. On the latter basis, one-quarter of the land area of the globe is arid, if exception be allowed for long through-flowing streams such as the Nile and the Colorado. These streams maintain themselves through arid regions in spite of great evaporation and lack of many tributaries because their headwaters in distant mountains give them a large and steady supply.

Chief among these areas of *interior drainage* are the Sahara, the Libyan

Desert, and the Kalahari in Africa, parts of the great Basin and Range region between the Wasatch Mountains and the Sierra Nevada in the western United States, the desert of western Australia, certain basins high in the Andes, and wide areas in central Asia, such as the Gobi Desert and the Takla Makan basin. All these regions are alike in that their streams lose themselves in the interior (Fig. 59). But they differ

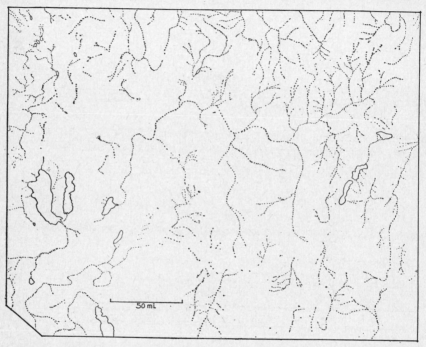

Fig. 59. — Outline map of a large part of northern Nevada showing interior drainage. The long stream in the center is the Humboldt River; like the smaller streams it ends in an interior basin. Compare with the drainage of a humid region of somewhat similar size shown in Fig. 309.

in many respects. In some the streams, while they last, are active agents of erosion and deposition; in those with least rainfall, the wind apparently is the chief agent of gradation.

No single example can illustrate them all. The set of conditions embodied in the more arid parts of the southwestern United States, however, gives rise to a characteristic and definitely recognizable fluvial cycle in which interior drainage is the underlying factor.

Processes Controlling Erosion. — Sculpture of arid regions is accomplished by several processes, the most noteworthy of which are described below,

(*A*) *Mechanical Weathering.* — Mechanical weathering (p. 19) is dominant over chemical weathering in arid regions, and is instrumental in maintaining bold rugged cliffs and steep slopes throughout the cycle.

(*B*) *Landslides.* — Landslides (p. 33) are important in some places where slopes are steep, where rocks are jointed so as to form heavy talus, and especially where shales make a slippery base for loose surface débris. The most favorable conditions for landslides are not found in arid regions, but locally they play a part in erosion.

(*C*) *Stream Erosion and Deposition.* — Rainfall over the mountain ranges of arid regions sends down torrents of water through dry valleys

E. Blackwelder.

Fig. 60. — Marginal part of a fresh thin mudflow. East base of the Stillwater Range, Nevada.

out on to the plains below. The heavy load of loose material acquired in the steep mountain valleys is rapidly deposited in broad fans (p. 65; Fig. 48) as stream velocities are abruptly checked and as the streams lose volume through evaporation and through percolation into their beds. Fans at the mouths of adjacent valleys coalesce and form a long piedmont slope fronting the mountains. The fan is the universal unit of stream deposition in arid regions *wherever steep slopes flatten out suddenly.* Aridity aids fan development, but is not essential to it (p. 66).

(*D*) *Mudflows.* — Another normal though infrequently operative process in arid regions is the *mudflow.* It occurs only where fine rock material becomes water-soaked on steep slopes after heavy rains, and moves downward as a slippery mass (Fig. 60). It advances in waves, stopping when it becomes too viscous to flow and damming the water behind it until it liquefies and again proceeds like an advancing flow of lava. Mudflows can carry boulders many feet in diameter. Observers have seen these great rocks bobbing " like corks in a surf." Successive mudflows play a part in the building up of fans.

(E) *Deflation.* — Deflation (p. 156) is the picking up and exportation of fine material by the wind. Rapid mechanical weathering and scanty vegetation in arid regions are factors favorable to deflation; and in some deserts, as in the Sahara where sandstorms are frequent and violent, deflation plays an important rôle. The numerous sand dunes indicate the temporary resting place of the material in transit, and falls of dust on ships in the South Atlantic testify to the amount of fine material blown into the sea by the prevailing winds. Deflation is not, however, of prime importance in the arid regions of North America, because its effects are greatly exceeded by those of other processes.

Outline of the Cycle. — The typical cycle described below is illustrated by Figs. 61–65. The conditions represented are somewhat specialized, but are analogous to those obtaining in the Basin and Range region of the United States.

Initial Stage. — Let an initial land surface consist of high ridges separated by broad, trough-like closed basins. Under a sufficiently arid climate this arrangement results in interior drainage. As the ridges are uplifted, streams develop consequent upon the newly formed slopes, and carry drainage from the new highlands down into the adjacent troughs (Fig. 61). They flow only after infrequent storms and are represented at other times only by dry valleys. Most of them evaporate or sink beneath the surface before they reach the bottoms of the troughs, depositing their loads in the form of fans (Fig. 48) built up along the bases of the highlands. Growth and coalescence of the fans result in the narrowing of the intermont basins. The central parts of the floors of these basins are *playas* (p. 106, Figs. 82–83); and the water that reaches them is impounded as shallow *playa lakes*, only to evaporate soon afterward. Fig. 61 shows the initial surface, initial consequent valleys, and playas in the troughs.

Stage of Youth. — Instead of being increased as in the normal cycle, the relief is slowly diminished by the removal of waste from the highlands and its deposition on the growing fans and in the playas. The centers of the two basins are occupied by playas, and their sides are flanked by ragged mountains much dissected by short deep valleys (Fig. 61). Since the streams do not reach the sea, sea level can exercise no control over them as it does over the streams in a humid climate.

Here the baselevels that limit downcutting by the streams must be formed by the basins themselves. The floor of each basin becomes the

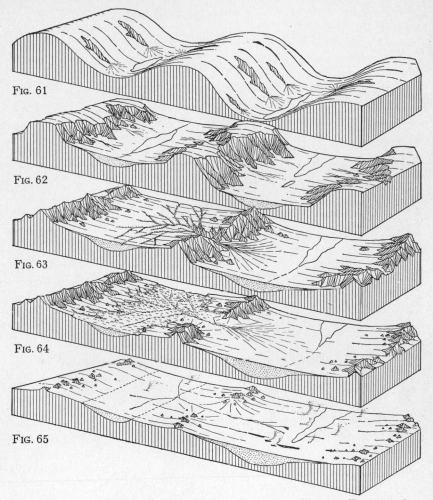

Figs. 61–65. — Ideal fluvial cycle under an arid climate. (Compare Figs. 49–54.)

Fig. 61. — Initial stage, showing ranges, basins, and early development of fans and playas.

Fig. 62. — Youth, showing decrease of relief as the basin floors rise by filling.

Fig. 63. — Maturity, showing capture of the higher basin by the lower.

Fig. 64. — Later maturity, showing dissection of the higher basin, transfer of the waste to the lower, and the exposure of pediments.

Fig. 65. — Old age, showing disintegration of the drainage and low relief. Climax of deflation is indicated by small whirlwinds carrying dust.

local baselevel for the streams tributary to it, and as the basins are slowly filled with waste from the mountains, each baselevel necessarily rises (Fig. 62). This decreases the stream gradients. As the streams approach the condition of grade and begin deposition progressively farther up their valleys the heads of the fans migrate backward toward the divides formed by the mountain crests. All the streams are intermittent, flowing only after rains. Strong winds sweep fine material from the playas upward and outward over the inclosing ranges so that it escapes from the region entirely.

Stage of Maturity. — As the mountain divide between the two basins is cut down and the basin floors are built up, the higher basin in time is able to drain downward *across* the old divide into the lower. The drainage of the higher basin is said to have been *captured* by the lower.

C. R. Longwell.

Fig. 66. — Basin between Desert Range and Sheep Range, Nevada, showing coalesced fans. Stage of maturity.

When the drainage in the basins has thus become integrated into a unit the mature stage is said to have been reached, and drainage passes from the upper basin to the lower in times of rain (Fig. 63). The capture results in the dissection of the higher basin by a consequent system of gullies working headward from the new channel, and the waste from their excavation is deposited in a great fan in the lower basin, hastening its filling. With the capture, the surface of the lower basin automatically becomes the master baselevel controlling both its own streams and those of its neighbor.

Full maturity is reached when the upper basin is so thoroughly dissected (usually into badlands, since they are composed of loose unconsolidated deposits) that every part of it drains down into the master basin (Figs. 64, 66). The initial highland surface is gone, and the mountain flanks are covered ever more completely with waste.

Stage of Old Age. — With the lowering of the mountains, the rains, infrequent at the outset, become even more rare since condensation decreases with decreasing elevation. The whole process outlined above is correspondingly retarded, but the wind, its erosive activity less interrupted by the periodic wetting of the remaining playa, blows away more rapidly the fine loose material of the basins. The higher basin, stripped of most of its earlier mantle of waste by transfer to the lower, is largely floored with bare rock planed to a platform or *pediment* by combined lateral cutting by the debouching mountain streams (Figs. 64, 65). The wind becomes an increasingly important agent of erosion, picking up the finest material, blowing it away, and thereby slowly lowering the whole surface, which now resembles a plain more nearly than a pair of basins. Only the rock masses that are most resistant to mechanical weathering remain as monadnocks projecting island-like above the surface of the plain. Since the wind can work at will over the entire area, the surface is slowly worn down to essentially the same level (Fig. 65). The final floor is thinly veneered with waste and dotted with monadnocks.

This last stage does not exist in any arid region at present, perhaps because sufficient time has not elapsed since the Ice Age (apparently a time of widespread humidity) to allow it to develop. It has been argued, however, that in the arid cycle the surface could be worn down by deflation to a depth well below sea level, providing the sea were kept out by surrounding highlands. The wind, however, can not pick up rock particles from wet ground, and so ultimately deflation would be stopped by the water table, below which the rock is kept permanently moist. The water table therefore probably constitutes the baselevel for the cycle in such a region.

Conclusion. — Given any kind of land mass acted upon by streams under specified climatic conditions, it is possible to foresee the general sequence of events that will take place and thus to reconstruct the past and predict the future by a careful study of the present. The organization of our knowledge of fluvial processes into a continuous chain such as is represented by the cycle concept is an invaluable aid in the study of the sculpture of the land by streams.

READING REFERENCES

1. The Geographical Cycle; by W. M. Davis. *In* Geographical Essays, Ginn & Co., Boston, pp. 249–278, 1909.

The first statement and complete explanation of the cycle here termed the *fluvial cycle.*

2. The Geology of the Henry Mountains; by G. K. Gilbert. 160 pages. Washington, pp. 99–150, 1877.

A classic work, dealing with the principles of fluvial erosion.

3. Rate of Recession of Niagara Falls; by G. K. Gilbert. 31 pages. U. S. Geol. Survey, Bull. 306, 1907.

A study of the bearing of the recession of Niagara Falls on the duration of time since the Ice Age.

4. Exploration of the Colorado River of the West and Its Tributaries; by J. W. Powell. Washington, pp. 149–214, 1875.

An account of a remarkable trip down the Colorado by boat, entertaining in style, and including an important discussion of features of fluvial erosion.

5. Rivers of North America; by I. C. Russell. 327 pages. Putnam, New York, 1898.

A popular discussion.

CHAPTER IV

SUBSURFACE WATER

Functions of Subsurface Water. — That most wells find water, that the majority of mines and caves are damp, and that constant pumping is necessary in many mines to keep them dry enough for operation, are indications of the nearly universal presence of water beneath the Earth's surface. This *subsurface water*, in addition to furnishing the chief water supply for human activities, works insidiously and very effectively to erode the land. It soaks through the rocks, dissolving some of the substances of which they are composed and delivering them to streams for transport seaward. The rocks, weakened by the removal of these constituents, are more readily broken up by other weathering processes. In some regions the rocks are so soluble that the subsurface water is able to excavate caverns and to pit the surface of the land with cavities, giving rise to highly characteristic landscape features. On the other hand, the deposition of substances dissolved by subsurface water is a major factor in cementing loose sediments to form rocks.

SOURCE, EXTENT, AND MOVEMENT

Source. — The subsurface water is varied in origin. Part of it ascends directly from the reservoirs of fluid rock within the Earth, and has not previously been at the surface. Another part is water that was included in great deposits of sediment later consolidated into rock. A third and by far the greatest part is rain water that has seeped downward from the surface. This water, once it has penetrated into the ground, behaves in many different ways. Part of it finds its way back to the surface as springs and joins the runoff; part of it is drawn to the surface by capillary attraction through the pores in the soil and is evaporated; some of it is sucked up by plants and evaporated through their leaves; some of it reaches the sea through underground channels without returning to the surface; some of it is held for indefinite periods within pore spaces at various depths; and some of it unites with the molecules of certain minerals and so becomes fixed in the rocks.

Extent. — The subsurface water occupies a comparatively shallow zone within the Earth's crust. Our actual knowledge is limited by our observations of the deepest wells, which, penetrating two miles of the

83

crust, show that water can occur at least at those depths. But laboratory experiments made to simulate conditions at much greater depths tell us that several miles below the surface the weight of the overlying matter exceeds the crushing strength of rocks, and that open spaces and subsurface water therefore can not exist at such depths.

Within the zone in which subsurface water occurs, the chief factors that control its distribution are climate and the character of the rocks. Climate, through rainfall and evaporation, governs the amount of water contributed to the ground. Rock character governs the amount the rocks will absorb.

Amount of Water below the Surface; Porosity. — All the rock material that composes the outer part of the Earth's crust is porous in some degree, but the porosity at any one place depends on the character of the material. Loose unconsolidated sand and gravel such as are found in the deposits of many streams and lakes have porosities as high as 30 per cent of their volume. When such deposits are cemented to form sandstone and conglomerate, their porosity is reduced to about 15 per cent, whereas the average shale has a porosity of about 4 per cent, and the average igneous rock less than 1 per cent. Open fractures and other partings present in all rocks greatly increase their porosity. The total amount of water in the ground depends largely on this factor of porosity.

Water Table Separating Vadose Water from Ground Water. — In most regions the rocks are saturated below a depth that depends largely on the porosity of the rocks, the amount of rain water that is allowed to sink into them, and the topography of the land. In permeable rocks this surface (it is not a " level " because it is very irregular) below which the rocks are saturated is the *water table*. The subsurface water that lies below the water table is *ground water*; that which lies between the water table and the Earth's surface is termed *vadose water*. In the vadose zone the water content fluctuates rapidly, and generally the available openings are very incompletely filled.

If all rocks were equally porous, and if rainfall never ceased, there would be neither water table nor vadose water; the outer part of the Earth's crust would be perpetually saturated, and the surplus rainfall would run off over the surface. But since the porosity of rocks varies greatly within short distances both horizontally and vertically, and since rainfall varies not only from place to place but from time to time, the water table is both irregular in form and fluctuating in position. It is a subdued replica of the land surface beneath which it lies (Fig. 67), rising somewhat beneath hills, and in some places intersecting the surface, forming springs and merging with streams, swamps, and lakes.

In times of rain it rises and becomes more irregular; in times of drought, it subsides and flattens out, as the water seeks its level. In general, the lowest part of the water table in any region is closely controlled by the surface of the largest stream present. As the stream gradually lowers its valley by erosion, the water table of the whole region is forced to subside, until in the ultimate peneplane it lies scarcely above the level of the sea.

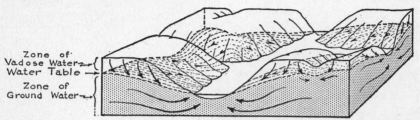

Fig. 67. — Ideal diagram showing the relation of the water table to the land surface, the movement of the subsurface water (indicated by arrows), and the zones of vadose water and ground water.

For simplicity, the area shown is regarded as underlain by homogeneous rock of uniform porosity. The ground above the water table is drawn as if it were transparent, to show more clearly that the water table is a subdued replica of the land surface. Note that the ground water tends toward the stream valleys, in which part of it emerges.

Perviousness. — *Perviousness* in a rock is its capacity to allow water to pass through it, or, as it is often stated, to "yield water." This property depends not on porosity but on the size and continuity of the pore spaces themselves. Clay has a high *porosity*, but when saturated it becomes *impervious*, because the water contained in its pores is held firmly by the molecular attraction of the clay particles. On the other hand, a compact granular rock such as granite, penetrated by a few scattered fractures, is much less porous than clay, but it readily yields its water because of ease of flow through its fractures.

Movement of Subsurface Water in Homogeneous Rocks. — The movement of the vadose water (the water above the water table) is for the most part directly downward (Fig. 67). The ground water (the water below the water table) moves in the same direction as the surface runoff, but more slowly, because of the friction caused by its passage through the interstices of the rock. It is probably most rapid beneath stream channels in sandy and gravelly floodplains that veneer the bedrock floors of many valleys. The continuous contribution from this whole great underground reservoir to springs, streams, and lakes is the cause of the continuous flow of streams. Were it not for the restraining influence of friction, the subsurface flow would be as rapid as that at the surface, every rain would cause a flood, and every stream would run dry between storms.

In general, the movement of ground water decreases as depth increases, because of loss of gradient and diminishing porosity. At the greatest depths to which ground water can penetrate, movement virtually ceases.

Springs and Wells. — Wherever the surface of the land intersects the water table, ground water emerges. When the water oozes out along the line of intersection a *seep* results, but if the water flows out with a distinct current a simple *spring* is formed (Fig. 68). A well excavated to a depth below the water table (*A*, Fig. 68) is assured a continuous supply of water, replenishing itself automatically as water is drawn out. The rate at which water is withdrawn, however, has to be adjusted to the perviousness of the rock, because wells in very per-

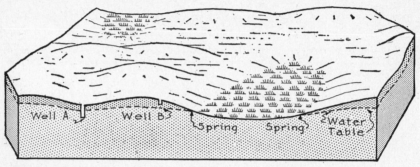

Fig. 68. — Conditions controlling locations of springs (along lines of emergence of the water table) and wells. Well *A*, reaching below the water table, has a continuous water-supply, whereas Well *B*, too shallow to reach it, is supplied uncertainly by vadose water.

vious rock replenish themselves much more rapidly than wells in rock of low perviousness. A well not reaching the water table, however (*B*, Fig. 68), must depend entirely on vadose water, a highly irregular and uncertain supply.

Movement of Subsurface Water in Heterogeneous Rocks. — In areas underlain by several kinds of rock of differing porosity, the movement of the subsurface water is less simple. If impervious layers are present, descending water is stopped at their upper surfaces. In areas where the water table lies well below the surface, an irregularly shaped bed of impervious rock in the zone of vadose water may hold an isolated body of ground water suspended above the normal ground-water zone. The isolated body has its own local water table — a *perched water table* — below which local shallow wells can obtain water (*A*, Fig. 69). Conversely, impervious strata may extend below the regional water table. A well (*B*, Fig. 69) penetrating such a stratum would be dry even after it had passed below the general level of the water table in the surrounding region.

Again, in a series of tilted sedimentary rocks consisting of alternating porous sandstones and impervious shales, for example (Fig. 70), water can enter the ground in quantity only along the outcrops of the sandstones. It descends through the sandstones, traveling perhaps no

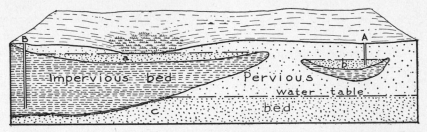

Fig. 69. — Perched water bodies (*a*, *b*) caused by irregular impervious beds lying above the main water table, and yielding water to a shallow well (*A*). A deeper well, (*B*), ends in an impervious bed and fails to obtain water.

faster than 2000 or 3000 feet per year. The sandstone beds, being the water conduits, are termed *aquifers*. Wherever a fissure cuts an aquifer and reaches the surface, a *fissure spring* results (Fig. 70). The hydrostatic pressure of the water as it seeks its own level forces it up through the fissure and out upon the surface. The difference in level between the point of intake and the point of emergence (the *hydrostatic head*), together with the size of the pore spaces in the aquifer, determines the velocity with which the water emerges at the surface. There is always

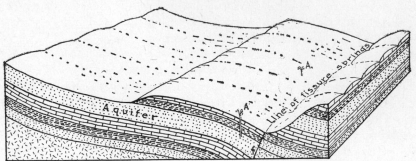

Fig. 70. — Conditions necessary for fissure springs and artesian wells. An aquifer outcropping at a high level at the left of the block descends toward the right, where it is capped by impervious shale. It is cut by the fissure *f*, along which the water may rise at various points, emerging as fissure springs. Holes bored at points such as *A, A* would upon tapping the aquifer become artesian wells. These wells are essentially independent of the fissure and would flow whether the fissure were present or not.

some loss of head as a result of friction. The conditions necessary for the development of fissure springs, then, are (1) an aquifer lying below an impervious stratum and outcropping in a region of sufficient rainfall, (2) an inclination high enough to cause the water to move through the aquifer,

and (3) a fissure cutting the aquifer and leading to the surface at a point
far enough below the intake to give the required head.   Actually a row
of springs would probably result, emerging along the line of intersection
between the fissure and the surface.   Such springs are usually steady in
their flow and are less affected by droughts than ordinary hillside springs.
They are generally cold, but the water while in the aquifer may come
into contact with heated rocks and issue as warm springs.   This is
probably the explanation of such warm springs as those at Hot Springs,
Virginia.   In some regions the water dissolves unusually large amounts
of mineral matter and gives rise to *mineral springs*, as at Saratoga,
New York, Hot Springs, Arkansas, Carlsbad in Czechoslovakia, Bath
in England, Wiesbaden in Germany, and Vichy in France.   Strictly
speaking, all springs are mineral springs, since all contain mineral matter
in solution, but the term is applied in general to springs that differ
markedly from ordinary water in the quantity or character of the mineral matter in solution.

Hot springs and *geysers* (which are merely intermittently eruptive
hot springs) are characteristic phenomena of the last dying phase of
volcanism, and are therefore considered in more detail in Chapter
XI.

Artesian Wells. — Some regions are underlain by suitable aquifers
receiving rainfall at their outcrops and inclined sufficiently to give
the necessary head, but lack fissures and therefore have no springs.
In such regions, those in search of a water supply have overcome the
difficulty by drilling holes and thereby tapping the aquifers.   The
successful holes are *artesian wells*, many of which flow with great
force because of the considerable head that governs them (Fig. 70).
Some of the most important aquifers that supply artesian wells in the
United States are: (1) The *Dakota sandstone*, which outcrops at the
surface and takes in water along the flanks of the Colorado Rockies and
the Black Hills, and underlies large parts of Kansas, Nebraska, the
Dakotas, and Saskatchewan.   (2) The *St. Peter sandstone*, which outcrops in central Wisconsin and underlies much of Iowa, Illinois, Indiana,
Ohio, Missouri, and Arkansas.   (3) The beds of poorly consolidated
sand that underlie the Atlantic Coastal Plain from Long Island to Texas.
In New England, northern New York, and much of eastern Canada,
conditions are generally unfavorable for artesian wells, since the underlying fractured metamorphic and igneous rocks afford no continuous
aquifers.

Artesian wells can not be made simply by boring deeply unless the
requisite geologic conditions are present.   Deep wells bored into rock
so as to intercept the water table are often called artesian wells, but this

is an incorrect use of the term; there is no difference in principle between wells of this kind and ordinary shallow wells.

In some districts wells must be bored very deep before encountering artesian water. In Berlin, St. Louis, and Pittsburgh, for example, the necessary depth is about 4000 feet, and depths of 1000 feet are not uncommon. Along the Atlantic coast, on the other hand, most of the artesian wells are only 100 to 300 feet in depth. The volume of water developed by some is large; the great 12-inch well of St. Augustine, Florida, with a depth of 1400 feet, supplies 10,000,000 gallons a day.

Where many wells are put down close together the withdrawal of water lowers the pressure to such an extent that the water will no longer rise above the level of the aquifer. The force of flow of many artesian wells tapping the Dakota sandstone in South Dakota and Nebraska has been gradually diminishing during the last few years. The matter is serious, since artesian water forms the chief source of supply. The water yielded by wells in this region represents the accumulation of ages, and at the present rate of yield serious depletion is inevitable.

Geologic Work of Subsurface Water

Factors Involved

Subsurface water erodes mineral matter, transporting much of it through considerable distances, and redeposits a part of it. The erosion accomplished by subsurface water includes *abrasion, solution,* and *transportation.* Abrasion (p. 41) takes place only where there are streams, and is therefore unimportant, being confined to the underground streams flowing through caverns in limestone regions. Solution, on the other hand, takes place wherever the rocks contain water, and is of enormous importance in spite of the fact that in most places its effects do not become apparent until after a long lapse of time. Transportation likewise is an important factor. The transportation of dissolved substances by subsurface water is a universal process of far-reaching significance.

The importance of solution in the weathering process has been discussed in Chapter II. All the soluble mineral matter in the rocks of the outer part of the Earth's crust is being slowly eaten away and carried off by the subsurface water. Some of it is redeposited in other parts of the crust and so helps to build up new rocks. Another part is carried off by streams and poured into the sea or into salt lakes. With the evaporation of the lakes it is precipitated as salts of various kinds, but a large part of the dissolved matter contributed to the sea has remained in solution, making the sea more salty every year. In some parts of the sea some of the calcium carbonate it contains is precipitated to form beds of limestone. The quantitative importance of solution is strikingly brought out by the calculation that the whole land area of the globe is being lowered at the rate of 1 foot every 30,000 years by the process of solution alone.

Rôle of Subsurface Water in Weathering

Pure water dissolves mineral matter, but water containing oxygen, carbon dioxide, and acids is a vastly more efficient solvent. The rain water that enters the rocks is not pure. In falling through the atmosphere it acquires oxygen and carbon dioxide, and in percolating through the mat of vegetation and the underlying soil in humid regions it absorbs more carbon dioxide as well as various organic acids formed in the decomposition of plant matter.

Hard sandstone breaks down into loose sand when the cementing substance, such as calcium carbonate, is dissolved from between the grains. Similarly the feldspars and iron minerals of an igneous rock such as granite are gradually decomposed by subsurface water, the interlocking crystalline texture of the rock is destroyed, and the once firm rock crumbles away. By decomposing and aiding in the disintegration of partly soluble rocks, subsurface water is merely performing one phase of weathering, and thus it speeds up enormously the process of erosion by streams.

Solution in Carbonate Rocks

Limestone (calcium carbonate) and dolomite (calcium-magnesium carbonate) are among the common sedimentary rocks, and together they underlie many millions of square miles of the Earth's surface. Both are soluble in water charged with carbon dioxide, and therefore in humid regions, where rainfall is plentiful and evaporation relatively slight, these rocks are vigorously attacked by subsurface water with striking results. Great holes are formed in the surface, caverns are hollowed out below ground, and surface streams are undermined and led away through subterranean channels. That subsurface water is responsible for this work is shown by the fact that the water of springs and wells in regions of limestone and dolomite is " hard "; that is, it contains much calcium carbonate in solution.

Sinks. — In compact, well-stratified, and strongly jointed limestones and dolomites, the avenues of easiest descent for vadose water are vertical joints and bedding-planes. Those avenues most favorably situated with respect to supply from above and free circulation below are readily enlarged by solution as the descending water passes through them.   Enlargement is most effective at the surface, where movement of the water is most rapid and where the water is freshly charged with carbon dioxide from the atmosphere and from decaying vegetation, and decreases rapidly downward.   In consequence, the point of intersection of two joints near the surface becomes a funnel-shaped depression. As the depression widens, the overlying mat of insoluble mantle and vegetation collapses into it, and a *sink* is formed (Fig. 71).

Probably the majority of sinks are of this (funnel) type, excavated *above* the water table.   Not uncommonly they form definite patterns on the surface, controlled by the structural planes along which they

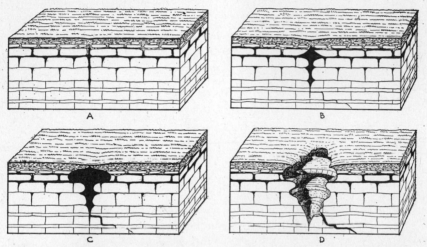

Fig. 71. — Development of a funnel sink in compact, jointed limestone overlain by a thin residual mantle of insoluble weathered material covered with sod.   The water table lies approximately at the base of the block.   Length of front of block 150 feet.

A, enlargement of a vertical joint plane by solution.   *B*, irregular widening of the enlarged joint chiefly by solution along stratification planes.   *C*, continued enlargement, most effective near the surface where the capacity of the descending water to dissolve is greatest.   *D*, collapse of the insoluble mantle, forming a funnel sink.

develop.   They range in size from small openings only a few inches in diameter to great depressions hundreds of feet wide.   Many are remarkably symmetrical, whereas others exhibit irregularities resulting from differences in the composition and structure of the rocks.

Another type of sink forms in massive and porous limestones and dolomites little affected by definite planes of weakness.   Under these conditions solution is less sharply localized and occurs irregularly throughout considerable volumes of rock, probably both above and below the water table.   Solution cavities of irregular shape are gradually excavated (Fig. 72).   As these enlarge into sizable *caverns*, their unsupported roofs collapse, and great depressions in the surface result.

These, like the funnel-shaped forms, are termed sinks, but they differ from them in their asymmetry, in the débris of the collapsed roofs with which their floors are strewn, and in a sagging of the beds of rock around their rims, testifying further to the failure of their roofs. Some sinks of this type are very large. One near Mammoth Cave, Kentucky, is said to have an area of 5 square miles. Probably this size has been attained by the coalescence of a number of adjacent caverns or sinks.

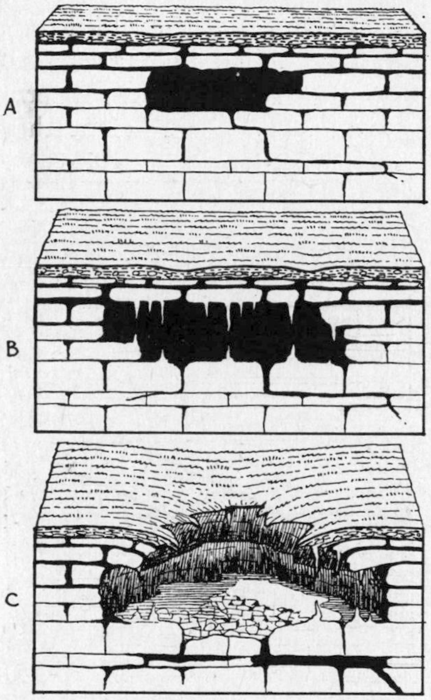

Sinks excavated below the water table usually contain lakes that persist as long as the water table is not lowered below the floors of the sinks. Most of the small lakes of northern Florida are of this kind. On the other hand, the funnel sinks, having been excavated above the water table, drain downward through openings in their floors, and therefore are usually dry. The outlets of some, however, are clogged by clay, humus, and other insoluble matter washed into them, allowing the development of small lakes whose levels are above the water table and independent of it. In some sinks the water leaks away slowly; in others the insoluble stopper is suddenly broken through and the lake disappears with a rush.

Fig. 72. — Development of a sink of irregular shape through collapse of a cavern roof. The water table lies approximately at the base of the block.
A, formation of a small cavern in the more soluble strata of a limestone series. *B*, enlargement of the cavern and development of dripstone deposits in the form of stalactites and stalagmites. *C*, collapse of the cavern roof, forming an irregular sink. The débris of the roof litters the sink floor.

Caverns. — Caverns of many shapes and sizes occur in limestones and dolomites in all parts of the world. Notable among them are the caverns of the limestone districts of Kentucky, Tennessee, and southern Indiana, the Shenandoah Valley in Virginia, northern Florida, Cuba, Yucatan, parts of the Philippines and Indo China, the Karst region in Yugoslavia, and the Causses of southern France. Although most caverns are of small size, there are notable exceptions. The Carlsbad Cavern in southeastern New Mexico extends downward to a depth of nearly 1000 feet and contains one chamber half a mile long and more than 200 feet wide. A single passage in Mammoth Cave, Kentucky, is said to be more than 8 miles in length, and individual chambers reach heights of 75 feet and widths of 150 feet. Certain vertical shafts in the Causses of southern France are more than 300 feet deep. Some caverns are linked up in connecting networks of galleries and shafts underlying areas of many square miles. Mammoth Cave has 30 miles of continuous passages. Some show the effect of solution only; others are ornamented with calcite deposited from solution. The variety is great, but all have been excavated by subsurface water at the points locally most favorable for solution.

N. H. Darton, U. S. Geol. Survey.

Fig. 73. — Sink in limestone near Cambria, Wyoming.

Here and there swinging subterranean streams have widened them by abrasion, but solution is overwhelmingly the dominant process in their formation.

In past times caverns often served as refuges for primitive man and as dens for animals now extinct. Because of this the bones of men and animals, stone implements, and other objects have accumulated in them and have been sealed up beneath deposits of calcium carbonate slowly accumulating on their floors. Relics of this kind, especially in certain parts of Europe, have revealed much concerning the life and culture of the times before the beginning of recorded history.

Solution Valleys. — The growth of a series of closely spaced sinks connected by a subterranean stream-channel (Fig. 79) gives rise to a series of unreduced areas between the sinks. Enlargement of the sinks narrows the areas between them and reduces them to mere natural bridges. As the bridges are undermined one by one, an open valley is formed. Although perhaps they have a general resemblance to valleys excavated by surface streams, such valleys are in reality the product of solution, a fact usually evident upon careful inspection. These *solution valleys* are recognized by their highly variable width, by their originating (and in some cases ending) in steep-walled sinks, by natural bridges that may still span them, and by tributary valleys left hanging above them through having lost their water to subsurface drainage.

Solution Independent of Sinks and Caverns. — Limestones free from sinks and caverns are not uncommon. In arid regions these masses ordinarily stand up sharply above the surrounding rocks because under

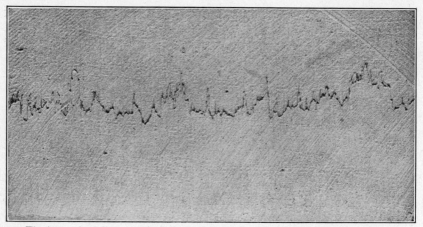

Fig. 74. — Stylolite seam in Indiana limestone. The seam lies parallel with the stratification of the rock. Length of seam = 12 inches.

dry climates they are nearly free from solutional attack. In humid regions, however, they form pronounced lowlands, indicating that they are being reduced more rapidly than the surrounding less soluble rocks.

In places, solution is localized along planes separating two beds of limestone or dolomite. The percolating water dissolves the more soluble parts of one bed so that the less soluble parts of the other bed project into it in the form of teeth or columns. Rows of these columns, usually seen on a vertical face of rock, are termed *stylolites* (Fig. 74). Once the process is started, the rock opposite the end of each column continues to be dissolved more rapidly than the rock between the columns because the pressure is greatest there and solution increases with increased pressure. The insoluble matter in the limestone (usually clay) collects on the end of each column, where it forms a cap of ever-increasing thickness. Where many rows or " seams " of stylolites occur only a few inches or a few feet apart, the total amount of solution they record is large. It has been estimated that the limestone strata in some districts may have had their thickness reduced 40 per cent by this process alone, although no openings exist to suggest the loss.

Deposits Below the Surface

The presence of thin layers of clay on the floors of caverns and subterranean passages shows that insoluble matter is deposited from mechanical suspension in underground streams and ponds. Such deposits are insignificant, however, compared with the great volume of precipitation from solution that takes place where subsurface water is at work.

The most important causes of precipitation of mineral matter from solution in subsurface water are (1) evaporation, both in caverns and in minute pores, (2) loss of carbon dioxide, (3) reduction of temperature, (4) reduction of pressure, (5) chemical reaction between the mineralized water and the rock through which it is passing, and (6) precipitation through the action of minute plants (*algae*).

Cavern Deposits. — The process of precipitation by subsurface water is most clearly evident in the deposits of calcite in the form of *dripstone*, with which most caverns are ornamented. Dripstone is formed only in caverns that are above the water table and are therefore filled with air. Vadose water charged with calcium carbonate percolates downward from the surface of the ground to the roof of a cavern, where, clinging to the ceiling, it forms drops. While at rest it evaporates a little, loses some carbon dioxide, and therefore deposits some calcium carbonate. Then, as more water is added from above, it is forced to drop, and falling on the floor below, it evaporates still further, leaving another minute deposit. As the drops slowly but endlessly succeed each other, long " icicles " of calcite (*stalactites*) grow downward from the roof, while broader accumulations (*stalagmites*) grow upward from the floor. If the process goes on long enough each pair coalesces and forms a column. Dripstone likewise develops in irregular sheets on roof and floor, and assumes many fantastic shapes curious to the cavern visitor, but all of it is formed in this simple way (Fig. 75).

Cementation. — Percolating water under the proper conditions precipitates mineral matter in the pores of rocks just as dripping water deposits it in the large spaces we call caverns. It is by this process that some of the loose and unconsolidated sediments are gradually *cemented* into sedimentary rocks (Chap. IX). Calcite, silica, iron compounds, and other substances dissolved from the rocks at and near the surface are carried away and precipitated as a cement at lower levels and in other regions.

Cavity Fillings. — Open spaces larger than pores are very commonly filled with mineral matter precipitated from solution in subsurface water, usually below the water table. The most striking example of this process is the filling of fissures, forming *veins*. Calcite and silica in various forms are among the most common vein-forming minerals, but gold, silver, copper, and other metals occur in some veins in quan-

Kentucky Geol. Survey.

Fig. 75. — Great Onyx Cave, Kentucky, showing dripstone deposits. Stalactites are forming at points where water emerges along cracks in the roof, broad-based stalagmites are growing upward, and some stalactite-stalagmite pairs have grown together to form massive columns.

tities great enough to constitute *ores* (Chap. XVIII). A number of these metallic vein deposits are brought up presumably by water ascending from hot rock-material at great depths.

Many cavities of various sizes and shapes, formed by solution, are filled at a later time with minerals precipitated from subsurface water. Deposits of amorphous silica are formed in this way, layer after layer. Upon crystallization, these become *agate*. If the mineral filling the cavity occurs as crystals (as quartz or calcite), with the crystals pointing inward toward the center of the cavity and only partially filling it, the resulting form is a *geode*.

Replacement. — The deposition of dissolved mineral matter from subsurface water does not always take place in openings already present. Commonly the water makes room for the substance deposited by dissolving matter already present. But it leaves behind an equal volume of another substance deposited from solution. Thus a buried tree trunk is slowly converted into *petrified wood* (Fig. 76) by the solution of its vegetable matter and the simultaneous deposition of silica. The fact that such replacements take place volume for volume is shown by

N. H. Darton, U. S. Geol. Survey.

Fig. 76. — Logs petrified by replacement while buried in shale. Petrified Forest, Arizona. The logs have since been exposed through erosion of the shale and have been broken up into segments.

the amazingly complete preservation of the fine texture of the original material.

Concretions. — The capacity of subsurface water to dissolve and redeposit is well illustrated by the formation of some of the oddly shaped nodules termed *concretions,* that occur in sedimentary strata. These forms, gradually built around definite nuclei by deposition from solution in subsurface water, are described in detail in Chapter IX.

Deposits at the Surface

Deposition by Springs. — The material in solution that is not deposited in the rocks is carried away by the drainage. It sometimes happens that on its way to the sea it comes to the surface and is deposited. Springs that deposit calcium carbonate furnish a good illustration. Many springs, especially if they rise from deep sources, contain much carbon dioxide under pressure. When this water passes through beds of limestone on its upward journey it dissolves large quantities of calcium carbonate. On arriving at the surface the calcium carbonate, partly because of evaporation and partly because of loss of gas through relief of pressure, is deposited in mounds and terraces, some of which are very picturesque. Some of the best-known deposits of this type occur at the Mammoth Hot Springs in Yellowstone Park. Other examples are Hot Springs, Virginia, Colorado Springs, Colorado, Banff Springs, Alberta, and the springs at Carlsbad in Czechoslovakia.

Thermal Springs. — Many springs that come from great depth are warm, and some are hot. Abnormally warm (*thermal*) springs ordinarily occur in regions of active or recently extinct volcanoes such as the Yellowstone Park region (p. 284). In such warm waters the deposition of both calcium carbonate and silica is greatly increased by the action of algae, which secrete these substances from the water. In many places deposition takes place so rapidly that articles suspended in the water become completely coated within a few days. It is probable that the warmth and chemical activity of the waters of some springs, particularly hot springs in volcanic regions, are greatly increased by gases and vapors that rise from masses of hot rock below.

Spring Deposits; Travertine, Tufa. — The substance most commonly deposited by springs is calcium carbonate, because it is the most soluble of the common rock-making substances. The physical character of the deposit depends chiefly on the rate of deposition. Deposits formed by slow evaporation are hard and compact. The dripstones formed in caverns are of this type. *Travertine*, from the Roman name for Tivoli, a town in Italy where an extensive deposit of the substance exists, is a general name for such deposits. " Mexican onyx " or " onyx marble " is a travertine with a banded structure brought out by varied tinting by iron and copper oxides. Calcium carbonate formed by rapid deposition from thermal springs, on the other hand, is likely to be porous and spongy. This less compact material is *calcareous tufa* (or *calcareous sinter*).

Many springs precipitate several substances in addition to calcium carbonate, and a few deposit almost none of the latter material. Limonite (hydrous iron oxide), iron carbonate, silica (Fig. 203), sulphur, and gypsum are the chief additional substances deposited by springs.

" **Alkali.**" — The soluble substances formed by the decay of the rocks in humid regions are quickly dissolved out of the mantle and carried off toward the sea. In regions where rainfall is scanty and where there is not sufficient water to perform this function, the salts remain in the mantle. At times of rainfall they dissolve, and during periods of drought they are precipitated as the water moves to the surface and evaporates, forming a white surface incrustation known as *alkali*. This is a common feature in many parts of the western United States.

The common salts that compose alkali are sodium sulphate (Na_2SO_4), sodium chloride ($NaCl$), and sodium carbonate (Na_2CO_3). The name alkali is due to the alkaline reaction and taste of the latter. Magnesium sulphate ($MgSO_4$) and gypsum ($CaSO_4.2H_2O$) are commonly present as well. In arid regions with interior drainage the concentration of all these substances gives rise to salt and alkaline lakes (p. 107). The irrigation of alkali lands must be carried on with care, for if water is used too freely it may bring the salts to the surface in such quantities as to ruin the land for agriculture.

The Cycle of Erosion in Soluble Rocks

Two distinct processes are visible in limestone caverns — excavation by solution, and replenishment with dripstone. There is nothing anomalous, however, in the fact that two fundamentally opposed processes have occurred in the same place, for the evidence shows that in most caverns excavation ceased before the deposition of dripstone began. The fact that dripstone manifestly is deposited by dripping water indicates conclusively that it is always formed above the water table. As to whether cavern excavation occurs above or below the water table, however, the evidence is conflicting. It is probable that caverns are excavated both above and below, but that those excavated above are more numerous.

The evolution of the surface of a limestone region through solvent erosion involves a continuous chain of cause and effect, whose operation forms a cycle parallel with the cycle of erosion by streams. The following description of a typical cycle is built up on the assumption that the effective solution occurs above the water table.

Initial Stage. — Assume a region underlain by thick horizontal beds of compact, strongly jointed limestone resting upon impermeable shale, both limestone and shale lying well above sea level. The limestone has been protected by a thin impermeable capping such as well-cemented sandstone, which, however, is now stripped away at two or three points, laying bare the limestone surface. The region is drained by surface streams, and the water table stands at a considerable depth below the surface (Fig. 77).

Stage of Youth. — At those points where jointed limestone is exposed at the surface, sinks of the funnel type begin to develop (Fig. 71), and the water that drains through them finds its way along a network of joints and bedding planes to one of the major valleys, where it reappears at the surface.

The water draining downward from the funnel sinks finds its way along joints, enlarging them by solution into vertical shafts. At some levels it moves laterally along bedding planes, enlarging them into horizontal galleries. In this way a network of shafts and galleries is formed, whose

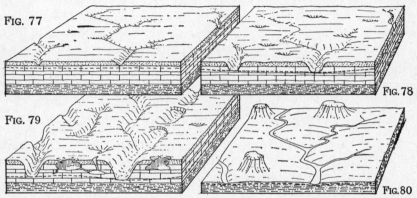

Figs. 77–80. — An ideal cycle of erosion in soluble rocks. Dashed line = water table.

Fig. 77. — Initial stage. An area of jointed limestone underlain by surface streams.
Fig. 78. — Stage of youth. Formation of funnel sinks, leading part of the surface drainage underground.
Fig. 79. — Stage of maturity. Formation of caverns and additional sinks, some of which coalesce and form solution valleys. The greater part of the drainage is now underground.
Fig. 80. — Stage of old age. Most of the limestone has been removed by solution, leaving only a few residuals resembling monadnocks. The drainage has worked down to the surface of the shale. From this time onward the area will be eroded still further through a fluvial cycle.

development is limited downward by the water table. One by one the surface streams are diverted downward into this network, forming permanent subterranean streams, which, meandering, widen the galleries somewhat by abrasion. The galleries are enlarged into big caverns in the places where solution is most rapid, and the roofs of some of the higher caverns collapse, forming irregular sinks at the surface. The gradual formation of closely spaced sinks leading downward into galleries gives rise to intervening natural bridges, which collapse one by one, converting the rows of sinks into solution valleys (Figs. 78, 79).

Stage of Maturity. — The stage of maturity is reached when subsurface drainage begins to exceed surface drainage and the greater part of the initial surface has been destroyed by the growing sinks and solution valleys (Fig. 79). The resulting topography is often referred to as *karst topography*, because of its striking development in the Karst region of Yugoslavia (p. 92). Below the surface the limestone is honeycombed with caverns. One after another the streams flowing through higher galleries are tapped and diverted downward through new openings into lower ones, as the subterranean streams gradually work down to the water table and merge with the ground water. Up to this time no drip-stone has been deposited in the caverns because the cavern streams have kept the air too moist to allow evaporation of the water filtering down from above. But with the diversion of the streams from the highest galleries, putting an end to their excavation, the air in those galleries becomes dry enough to permit evaporation of the water dripping from their ceilings, the building of stalactites and stalagmites begins, and this ornamentation of the caverns progresses downward level by level as successively lower galleries lose their streams.

Stage of Old Age. — As the last remnants of the initial surface are dissolved away and the galleries partly filled with dripstone are destroyed by successive cave-ins, maturity merges imperceptibly into old age. The surface is now a wilderness of irregular ridges and mounds separated by sinks (unroofed caverns) and solution valleys, dry with the exception of those which reach down to the top of the underlying shale. More and more caverns collapse, the sinks continue to enlarge, and bit by bit the surface is reduced to the surface of the shale. As the last caverns are unroofed, the débris is gradually dissolved and the insoluble residue is washed away by the streams which, formerly draining the now vanished caverns, have become well developed on the surface of the shale (Fig. 80). The cycle approaches its close. The shale beneath the limestone is laid bare over much of the region, but here and there isolated monadnocks of limestone, honeycombed with cavities, remain as witnesses to the nearly complete destruction of the thick strata of which they once formed a part.

Cycles of this kind are usually confined to much more restricted areas than are fluvial cycles, because they depend on rock composition, and therefore are limited to areas of soluble strata controlled by specialized conditions. Within certain areas, such as parts of Kentucky, Indiana, and the Karst of Yugoslavia, cycles somewhat similar to the one described are in progress, although none of them has yet attained the stage of old age.

READING REFERENCES

1. The Occurrence of Ground Water in the United States, with a Discussion of Principles; by O. E. Meinzer. 321 pages. U. S. Geological Survey, Water-Supply Paper 489, 1923.

Accurate and authoritative discussion of principles, the kinds of rock and their water-bearing properties, the influence of rock structure on subsurface water, and the chief aquifers of the United States.

2. Domestic Water Supplies for the Farm; by M. L. Fuller. 180 pages. John Wiley & Sons, Inc., New York, 1912.

A non-technical account of the problem of water supply with special emphasis on the location and construction of wells. Brief general treatment of the principles of occurrence of subsurface water.

3. Underground Water Resources of Connecticut; by H. E. Gregory; With a Study of the Occurrence of Water in Crystalline Rocks; by E. E. Ellis. 200 pages. U. S. Geological Survey, Water-Supply Paper 232, 1909.

A full discussion of subsurface water in fissured crystalline rocks.

4. Celebrated American Caverns; by H. C. Hovey. 228 pages. Robert Clarke & Co., Cincinnati, 1896.

A colorful account, written in popular style.

5. Formation of Travertine and Siliceous Sinter by the Vegetation of Hot Springs; by W. H. Weed. U. S. Geological Survey, Ninth Annual Report, Washington, pp. 613–676, 1889.

A very readable description and explanation of the famous hot-spring deposits of Yellowstone Park.

6. Origin of Limestone Caverns; by W. M. Davis. Bulletin of the Geological Society of America, Vol. 41, pp. 475–628, 1930.

An incisive inquiry into the various possible modes of cavern origin, with an excellent summary of the results of earlier studies of this problem.

CHAPTER V

LAKES AND SWAMPS

LAKES

Lakes are inland bodies of standing water; expanded portions of streams are sometimes also referred to as lakes. Small water bodies, particularly if shallow, are called *ponds*, but there is no fixed usage as to these terms. From the smallest pond there exists every gradation up to Lake Superior, the world's largest freshwater lake, and the Caspian " Sea," the largest salt lake. The great majority of lakes stand above sea level; some, including all coastal lagoons, are at sea level; a few, like the Salton " Sea " and the Dead " Sea," are below sea level. Lakes occur in all parts of the world, but since most of them are a direct result of glaciation, there are more lakes in high latitudes and at high altitudes than elsewhere. There would be no lakes if the surface of the lands everywhere were drained by graded streams, for then drainage to the sea would be perfect. Only where drainage is obstructed do lakes occur. Since all streams tend to destroy obstructions and to fill depressions in their ceaseless effort to reach grade, it follows that lakes are ephemeral and that sooner or later the existing ones must disappear.

Origin of Lake Basins

Basin-making processes are in progress in many parts of the continents, resulting in the constant formation of new hollows. In humid regions these basins catch water and form lakes; in many arid regions, however, they commonly remain dry. Nearly every major geologic process makes basins in one way or another, and these features therefore can be classified according to the processes that bring them into being.

Basins Formed by Crustal Movements. — Lake basins formed by broad movements of the crust have existed at many times during the Earth's history, and many of them have been large. We can be sure of this because their shore and bottom deposits are preserved long after the water that stood above them has been drained away.

Great lake-bearing depressions caused by fracturing and dislocation of the crust (*faulting*) are more common than those caused by bending of the rocks. The 4000-mile chain of valleys and lakes that includes the

River Jordan, the Dead Sea, the upper Nile, and the African lakes such as Tanganyika and Nyassa, was formed by the sinking down of narrow blocks of the crust between high steep walls. These great "rift valleys" contain more than 30 lakes, several of which are notably large and deep. Lake Tanganyika is 5100 feet deep, and since its surface is only 2500 feet above sea level its bottom is 2600 feet below. The Platten See of Hungary, 50 miles long, the Warner Lakes of Oregon, and some of the larger lakes of southern Sweden likewise owe their basins to faulting. Some structural basins have been formed within human history in connection with earthquakes. In 1811 an earthquake shook the lower Mississippi Valley, and the local sinking of the ground which accompanied it caused such changes in the surface that several new lakes came into existence in the Tennessee portion of the floodplain.

Fluvial Basins. — Streams form basins both by erosion and by deposition. As a result of erosion there are the basins of shallow lakes in cut-off and abandoned meanders (*oxbow lakes*, p. 57) and in abandoned temporary channels excavated during times of flood (*slough lakes*). As a result of deposition there are the depressions formed between natural levees and the outer margins of floodplains, such as Lake Maurepas above New Orleans, and basins formed where tributaries build deltas across the valleys of larger streams. In this way Lake Pepin was formed when a 20-mile stretch of the Mississippi, 60 miles below St. Paul, was dammed by the deposits at the mouth of the tributary Chippewa River.

Basins of Marine Origin. — Along many coasts, waves and longshore currents are able to build up bars offshore, converting the sheltered water back of them into *lagoons* (p. 190). There are long coalescent chains of these lagoons along the Atlantic coast of the United States from New York to Florida. Again, the sea floor contains shallow depressions, and therefore an area newly uplifted from beneath the sea commonly contains such depressions. Some of the Florida lakes are believed to be of this sort, among them Lake Apopka near Kissimmee.

Solution Basins. — Small lakes occur by the hundreds in sinks in extensive limestone regions such as those in Kentucky and Indiana, central Florida, Yucatan, and Yugoslavia (Chap. IV). Ordinarily the sinks that contain water are those whose bottoms are below the water table, or whose outlets are clogged with insoluble clay left after solution of the limestone.

Glacial Basins. — The majority of existing lakes are the direct result of glaciation (Chap. VI). This is well shown by the fact that most of the lakes of North America and Europe are concentrated within areas recently glaciated. Some of these lakes occupy depressions of erosional origin (Fig. 81), resulting from quarrying and abrasion of the bedrock (*cirque lakes* are among the most common). The basins of others are the result of deposition. Among these are the basins of lakes in kettles, lakes ponded back of end moraines, and lakes occupying shallow depressions in ground moraine. Most are small, but some major lake basins are of glacial origin. Many of the large lakes of the Alps (Lucerne and Constance on the north and Maggiore, Lugano, Como, and

Alaskan Aerial Survey, U. S. Navy.

Fig. 81. — Chain of three lakes in basins excavated by glacial erosion in a recently glaciated valley, Baranof Island, Alaska. The falls at the outlet of each lake, working headward, will in time drain the lakes. Deltas and fans built into the heads of the two farthest lakes are gradually filling them up.

Garda on the south) are held in partly by end moraines at the mouths of deep glaciated valleys.

Wind-Formed Basins. — Basins of considerable size are known to be formed by the wind picking up and blowing away fine material such as that which constitutes beds of clay and shale (p. 156). But since these basins are excavated only in arid regions, they rarely contain lakes except temporarily after infrequent heavy falls of rain. In many parts of the world, however, the hollows between active dunes contain water which is prevented from sinking down through the sand by layers of decaying plant matter. Several large lakes of this kind occur among the dunes at the south end of Lake Michigan, and others occur in the Sahara.

Volcanic Basins. — Lava flows in regions where streams have already cut valleys are likely to form dams across valleys, giving rise to lake basins. These barriers of lava are eroded with difficulty because they are of solid rock. Lac d'Aydat in central France is of this type, as are Lake Tahoe in California and several of the lakes surrounding the volcanic cones of Mount Hood in Oregon and Mount St. Helens in Washington.

In many volcanic regions there are lakes in the craters themselves. Notable among them are Lago de Bolsena and others in the great volcanic " campagna " surrounding Rome, Lac Pavin in the volcanic plateau of central France, and the maars of the Eifel district in northwestern Germany. Enlarged craters known as *calderas* (p. 266) contain the largest lakes of this type. The largest in the world, Crater Lake in southwestern Oregon, is more than 5 miles in diameter. Although the lake is 2000 feet deep, it is without tributary streams, being entirely dependent for its maintenance on the fall of rain and snow directly into the basin.

Landslide Basins. — Landslides (p. 33) occasionally pile up across valleys, damming streams and converting them into lakes. Several landslide lakes are known in the region of the Alps and in northeastern California. A new one was formed at the base of the Gros Ventre Range in western Wyoming by a great slide in 1925.

Climatic Control of Lakes

Lakes in Humid Regions. — If a depression is formed in a certain locality, will it contain a lake, and if so, what kind of a lake? In general the answer depends on rainfall and evaporation and hence ultimately on climate. Most of the lakes with which we are familiar in eastern North America and in western Europe have streams or springs flowing into them, and an outlet or spillway determined by the lowest point in the rim of the containing basin (Fig. 81). Since these regions are humid the rate of evaporation is relatively slow, and the constant inflow and outflow not only prevent the lake surface from fluctuating greatly but also keep the water fresh.

Lakes in Arid Regions. — In arid and semiarid regions, where rainfall is slight and evaporation great, lakes rise and fall seasonally, and many dry up and disappear for months at a time. In fact, the desert basins lying between the scattered ranges of Nevada, Utah, Arizona,

New Mexico, and Sonora usually contain water (*playa lakes*, Figs. 82, 83, and p. 78) only for short periods after infrequent rains.   Here, as well as in the Gobi Desert in central Asia, the great deserts of western Australia, the intermontane basins of the Andes, and many other arid regions, evaporation is so rapid and continuous, the mantle so porous, and the water table so far below the surface, that most of the streams, fed by the rains and snows of high mountains, disappear long before they reach their destinations.   Some of them dwindle away, spreading out

C. E. Erdmann.

Figs. 82–83. — Ephemeral playa lake in a desert basin.   Braun's Playa, southern Nevada.

Fig. 82. — The Playa filled with water, forming a shallow playa lake.
Fig. 83. — View two weeks later, showing the dry lake-bed after the water has evaporated.   The wind is whipping up the fine lake sediments into small dust storms.

their detritus in great barren flats, covered with incrustations of salt and alkali, which in wet seasons become shallow lakes and marshes. Streams whose water supply is greater end in permanent lakes. Wherever evaporation prevents the water from overflowing the rims of these interior basins, the lakes turn salt.   Every stream carries dissolved salts (p. 42), usually in quantities too small to be detected by taste.   Slowly but steadily these salts are added to the total already in the water of the lake.   They can not escape, and year by year the proportion of salts to water increases.

The Great Salt Lake in Utah has a salinity of 18 per cent compared with 3.5 per cent for the sea; its water is so dense that a bather can not sink, but floats buoyantly upon the surface. As the bather wades ashore the water evaporates from his body, leaving it incrusted with tiny crystals of glistening salt. Recent shrinkage of the lake through evaporation has left great beds of white salt to mark its former gently sloping shores. The chief salts are sodium chloride (common salt) and sodium sulphate. In some lakes calcium carbonate is deposited in great spongy masses of calcareous tufa (p. 98). By covering large rocks with thick incrustations, this material produces many curious and striking forms.

Extinct Lakes. — Observant travelers in western Utah have had their curiosity aroused by frequent sights of parallel rows of cliffs and great

C. D. Walcott, U. S. Geol. Survey.

Fig. 84. — Terraces of Lake Bonneville, on the western flank of the Oquirrh Range north of Tooele, Utah.

flat-topped terraces forming huge flights of steps up the mountain sides to levels as high as 1000 feet above the valley floors. When examined in detail, these steps prove to be wave-cut cliffs and wave-built terraces, bars, and beaches, as well as deltas high and dry (Fig. 84). These features occur at several levels, and when traced along the mountain flanks the highest level is found to mark the shoreline of a lake that had an area of 20,000 square miles (nearly as great as that of Lake Michigan) and a maximum depth of more than 1000 feet. At one period the water must have been 850 feet deep above the site of the Mormon Temple in Salt Lake City. The outlet was to the north, through Red Rock Pass to the Snake River, and thence through the Columbia to the Pacific. Since there are several abandoned shorelines at different levels, we must conclude that the lake dwindled by stages from

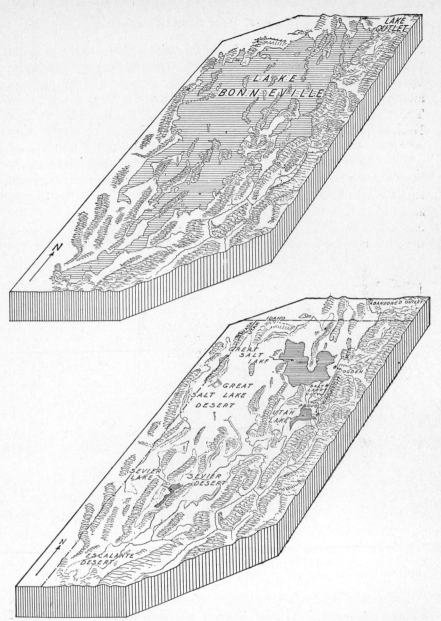

Figs. 85–86. — Extinct Lake Bonneville and its successors in Utah and adjacent parts of Nevada and Idaho.

Fig. 85. — Block 375 miles long and 175 miles wide, showing the extent of the former Lake Bonneville at its maximum, and the outlet through which it temporarily overflowed. Isolated mountain ranges formed islands and peninsulas in the lake.

Fig. 86. — The same region at present. The former lake floor is mainly desert, but three water bodies still remain in the lowest parts of the basin. Several sets of discontinuous terraces marking old abandoned water levels are shown flanking the ranges.

its former gigantic size to that of the Great Salt Lake, which represents
the deepest pool in the bottom of the basin of its predecessor. Similarly,
Pyramid Lake and its neighbors in Nevada are the residual pools of
another huge water body, which rivaled in size the present Lake Erie.
The Utah lake has been named *Bonneville* (Figs. 85, 86), and the
Nevada lake *Lahontan*. The highest terraces of Lake Bonneville were
overridden by valley glaciers descending from the Wasatch Mountains,
whereas lower terraces formed during a later stage of the lake partly
bury deposits made by the same group of glaciers. These facts indicate
that the lake had its origin in the Ice Age. At that time the climate
seems to have been somewhat more humid than now, because since the
disappearance of the ice the lakes have been gradually drying up. Salt
deposits, now high and dry, bear witness to the evaporation that has
been going on since the Ice Age came to an end.

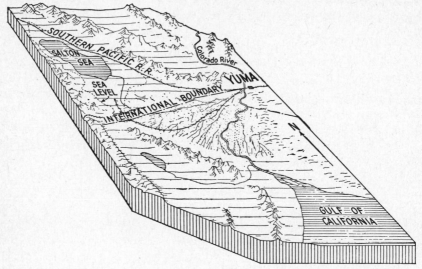

Fig. 87. — The Salton basin at present. Block 200 miles long, showing the head of
the Gulf of California, and the Salton basin separated from it by the combined delta and
fan of the Colorado River. Sea level in the Salton basin is shown by dashed line.

The Salton Sea. — The main line of the Southern Pacific Railroad
running eastward from Los Angeles has the curious distinction of
traversing for more than 60 miles a region below the level of the sea.
The region is the Salton basin. It is a depression without outlet, and
its bottom is 273 feet below sea level. In its center is a shallow salt
lake known as the Salton Sea (Fig. 87). In the recent geologic past
the floor of this basin sank, and would now be filled with sea water but
for the fact that the Colorado River, heavy with silt, discharging into the

Gulf of California near what is now the southern end of the Imperial Valley, had built up a combined delta and fan so large that they formed an effective dam at the head of the Gulf. Like all deltas and fans this one was trenched by shifting distributary channels of the river, which discharged water sometimes into the Gulf and occasionally into the isolated basin, filling it with water. When dry, the basin was kept virtually a desert under the prevailing arid climate. The last natural discharge into the basin occurred perhaps 300 to 1000 years ago. By 1900 the trapped water had dwindled to a small salt lake. At this time the fertility of the alluvial soil was realized, the basin area was settled, and an irrigation canal was dug from the Colorado River to the bottom of the basin. Since the floor of the basin is well below the baselevel of the river, the gradient of the canal was greater than the gradient of the river between its mouth and the head of the canal. The flow of water into the canal was inadequately controlled by headworks designed to be protective. In 1905 the Colorado rose in flood, overtopped the headworks, poured into the canal, and, following the steeper gradient, cut a great trench in some places 80 feet deep, swelled the Salton Sea to many times its former size and depth, and flooded the railroad right-of-way for 40 miles. During 18 months the floodwater resisted all efforts at permanent control, but it was finally mastered. The railroad tracks were shifted from 200 feet to 150 feet below sea level as a pre-caution against possible later floods. The Salton Sea began to dwindle as soon as the abnormal supply of water was cut off, but now the waste water from irrigation keeps the level nearly constant.

Life History of Lakes

Although lakes are constantly coming into being through the agency of basin-forming processes, other lakes are as constantly being destroyed. The broad playa lake in an arid basin is the most ephemeral of all. The water is already evaporating rapidly as it flows into the playa. But the basin itself is not destroyed, and with the next cloudburst the lake reappears as before. In moist regions, on the other hand, evaporation takes place much more slowly, and at the same time the inflow of water into lake basins is greater. Therefore lakes in humid regions ordinarily do not dry up. Nevertheless, other forces are at work which, although they operate much more slowly, destroy the basins themselves. " Rivers are the mortal enemies of lakes." This striking epigram is especially well illustrated by Lake Geneva and the river Rhone.

Lake Geneva and the Rhone. — Lake Geneva occupies a deep valley in the Alps and is at present 40 miles long. It was originally 7 miles longer, but each year the turbid Rhone, entering the lake from the east, brings down quantities of sediment from the glaciers at its source and dumps this material into the quiet water, forming a delta that fills the upper end of the lake from side to side. The water is nearly a thousand feet deep and the delta is correspondingly thick, but each year its bank-like front creeps farther west, and in time it will destroy the lake. While this is going on, the water that spills from the surface of the lake at its lower end is eroding its channel and lowering the lake outlet. As it passes under the many bridges of the city of Geneva, the water is blue and clear. Nearly all the sediment from the upper Rhone has been either added to the delta or dropped upon the bottom during the slow passage of currents down the lake, so that the lake acts as a great settling-basin, depriving the lower Rhone of tools with which to cut. Although downcutting of the outlet is thereby retarded, it can not be stopped. If these processes continue, the outlet will be cut lower and the water level will correspondingly drop, until the lake will be destroyed by this process if it has not already been filled up by the encroaching delta.

Lake Erie and Yellowstone Lake. — Downcutting of the rim of a large lake basin is more forcibly illustrated by Niagara Falls at the outlet of Lake Erie. The water at the brink of the falls is lowering its channel in a bed of dolomite (Figs. 23, 24). At the same time the falls is retreating upstream at a rate which averages 3.4 feet per year (p. 50). Retreat of the falls is accompanied by decrease in height, because the bed of dolomite dips downward as it is traced upstream. Therefore if the falls should continue to migrate up the river to a point opposite Buffalo, Lake Erie would be largely drained. A lake may acquire a wholly new outlet through being tapped by a stream. An example seen by thousands of people every year is Yellowstone Lake near the center of Yellowstone Park. In former times this lake was larger than at present and is believed to have had its outlet at a point on its southwest rim, draining through the Snake River to the Pacific. The present Yellowstone River, flowing north, was then a small stream engaged in lengthening its valley rapidly headward on a steep slope. The head of this young valley eventually reached the lake, tapped and partially drained it, and diverted its waters into their present course through the Missouri to the Atlantic.

Extinct Lake Florissant. — In the South Park of Colorado, in the district west of Pike's Peak, a stream is flowing through a valley whose sides are made of layers of tightly packed volcanic ash. These layers were deposited in a narrow lake, and they came from an active volcano not far distant. The delicate ash, sifting down through the lake water, carefully protected and perfectly preserved the remains of plants and animals that lived in and around the lake. The basin gradually filled with ash and lava and was then converted into a stream valley. From the layers of ash exposed by fluvial erosion there have been taken more than 1000 species of insects, 250 species of plants (including numerous trees), and many fishes and birds, all representatives of the life of the time during which the lake existed. The filled-up lake, known as Lake Florissant, has become a storehouse of great scientific value.

The examples given serve to show that lakes are destroyed sooner or later by sedimentation in their basins, or drainage at their outlets, or

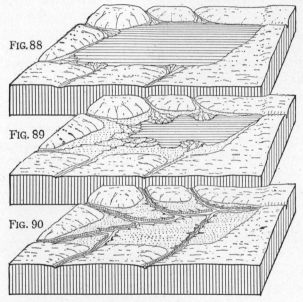

Figs. 88–90. — Stages in the history of a typical lake. Block about 5 miles long.

Fig. 88. — Stream system dammed by gentle upwarp across the upper right-hand corner of the block, forming a shallow lake with outlet across the upwarp. The streams begin to build deltas into the lake, and the shoreline is somewhat wave-eroded.

Fig. 89. — The growing deltas enlarge and coalesce, gradually filling the basin.

Fig. 90. — Downcutting of the outlet eventually drains the lake and allows the streams to trench the delta deposits, leaving them as terraces.

both. The basin-filling sediments include not only stream detritus but also wind-blown material, the accumulated bones and shells of lake-dwelling animals, and the remains of aquatic plants (pp. 116, 220).

Life History of a Typical Lake. — In considering the sequence of events in the complete history of a typical lake, we may assume a broad shallow basin brought into existence by a gentle bending of the crust in a region of low relief and humid climate, resulting in the damming of a consequent stream and some of its tributaries (Fig. 88). The water flowing into the basin rises to the level of the lowest point in the broad dam, over which it pours, forming an outlet for the lake.

The gravel, sand, and silt carried into the basin by streams are deposited in the form of deltas (Fig. 88) built outward from the stream mouths, while the particles of clay, remaining longer in suspension, slowly settle out over the entire basin. Only a little of the very finest material remains long enough to be carried through the outlet at the lower end of the basin. Erosion of the outlet channel by escaping water therefore takes place very slowly. The lake being wide enough to generate waves of effective size, the shoreline is wave eroded, and a narrow beach (p. 183) develops. Wave-generated currents seize material from the deltas and shift it along the shore, thereby smoothing somewhat the outlines of the deltas.

As the deltas grow larger, the area of the lake is decreased by the deposition of foreset and topset beds (Figs. 44–46) and its depth is decreased by the bottomsets. As the lake grows smaller and shallower, the current of water flowing through it becomes gradually stronger and more like that of a stream, and for this reason the volume and coarseness of sediment that can remain in suspension long enough to reach the outlet slowly but steadily increase. With more cutting-tools, the escaping water begins to erode the outlet channel, lowering it and correspondingly lowering the level of the lake. This shallows the lake still further, increases the strength of the currents, speeds erosion at the outlet, and so accelerates the process. The resulting deposit on the lake floor shows a persistent increase in coarseness from bottom to top. Meanwhile the deltas have grown so large and have coalesced so extensively that the upper end of the basin has been converted into a floodplain across which the inflowing streams wander with sluggish flow (Fig. 89).

At some time during this process, the rate of downcutting of the outlet channel overtakes the rate of delta building. As the lake level is lowered, the delta-forming streams are forced to cut downward into their own deposits, excavating trenches in the deltas. The inflowing streams cut downward as fast as the outlet channel is lowered, and the tops of the deltas are left high and dry above the ever-deepening channels that trench them. By continued erosion of its outlet, the lake is gradually converted into a stream system, and the history of the lake is over. Remnants of the lake deposits, however, are left as broad terraces flanking the streams, recording the lake-episode that gave rise to them (Fig. 90). But in time even the last remnants of these deposits are stripped away as the streams cut laterally into them, and the fluvial cycle, interrupted by the crustal movement that formed the lake basin, once more holds sway.

This sequence of events is ideal, but every lake illustrates some part or some variation of it. Terraces recording extinct lakes occur in many parts of the world, and it is probable that there have existed in the past a vastly greater number of lakes, all traces of which have since been destroyed.

Indirect Functions of Lakes

Large lakes are effective in modifying local climates by increasing atmospheric humidity and by cooling the air in summer and warming it in winter. Lakes of all sizes are very important as regulators of stream flow, acting as storage reservoirs and minimizing floods in lower regions to which they are tributary. This fact has been recognized by the Egyptian government in its project to increase artificially the size of Lake Tana in Abyssinia, one of the important sources of the Nile, in order to increase its effectiveness as a regulator of water supply in the valley of the lower Nile, an area of great economic importance. Similarly, suggestions have been made in the United States that a series of artificial lakes be constructed in the Mississippi drainage basin in an attempt to control near their sources such floods as caused the disaster of 1927. Again, all lakes act as settling basins for stream detritus, delaying temporarily the erosion of the lands. Most of the streams tributary to Lake Erie are well loaded with mud, but the clarity of the water that spills out of the lake over Niagara Falls bears testimony to the amount of material that is dropped upon the lake bottom.

SWAMPS

Swamps are areas of saturated ground. The majority of swamps represent a stage intermediate between lakes or ponds and dry land. Most lakes in humid regions will in time become swamps, and many shallow basins alternately contain swamps and lakes according to the season. Swamps commonly occur in three types of regions, but these regions by no means exhaust the possibilities. (1) Nearly level coastal plains that are former sea floors slightly uplifted. Such swamps are distinguished from tidal marshes and are almost continuous along the South Atlantic and Gulf coasts of the United States, chief among them being the Dismal Swamp in Virginia and North Carolina, and the Everglades in southern Florida. It may be that some of these swamps occupy the sites of former lagoons, uplifted together with the offshore bars by which they were shut off from the sea (p. 190). (2) Floodplains and deltas with their basins formed by old channels and by natural

levees. Such areas include a great deal of swamp land. (3) Broad
glaciated areas such as the greater part of the Great Lakes region of
the United States, northeastern Canada, Ireland, and the Baltic plain
of northern Germany. These regions are dotted with swamps, most
of them small. Some of the swamps occupy poorly drained initial
depressions in ground moraine (p. 145). Others are the basins of former
lakes filled up with vegetation.

In an entirely different category are *tidal marshes*, which occur only
along coasts, in shallow bays and lagoons that are alternately submerged
and laid bare by the tides. The vegetation consists chiefly of certain
grasses which grow only under such conditions. For this reason the
composition of tidal-marsh deposits differs markedly from that of freshwater swamp material.

Formation of Peat. — In humid regions the shores of small lakes and
the protected coves of large lakes support an abundance of aquatic

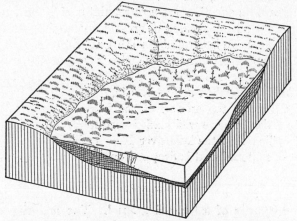

Fig. 91. — Destruction of a small lake by filling with peat. The accumulating layer of
peat (crosshatched) is fringed by aquatic vegetation, consisting of water weeds and pond
lilies. These plants are being encroached upon by semi-aquatic plants, mosses, and bushes.

vegetation such as pond lilies, water weeds, and rushes. As these
plants die, their substance decays in the water, largely as the result of
the activities of bacteria. During the metabolism of the bacteria,
waste products, antiseptic in their action, are excreted; hence when this
waste matter reaches a certain concentration in the lake water the bacteria can no longer exist, further microbial decomposition is prevented,
and the partially decomposed matter is preserved. This matter is
brownish or blackish, has a high carbon content, and is known as *peat*.

As peat is built up near the shore, newer generations of aquatic plants
advance toward the center of the lake, and other types of vegetation,

such as mosses, encroach over the peaty area that was formerly water. In this way the lake, surrounded by concentric belts of different kinds of plants, gradually decreases in size until it is obliterated, and a swamp or bog floored with a thick accumulation of peat takes its place (Fig. 91).

Economic Aspects of Peat. — In many countries, especially in Europe, peat is cut from the bogs, dried, and used as a domestic fuel. In America, peat has hitherto been little used because of an abundance of coal and wood. Nevertheless the peat resources in swamp lands within the United States are enormous, and constitute a valuable potential source of fuel for the future.

Peat is of special interest to the geologist in that it represents the first stage in the transformation of vegetable matter into coal (Chap. XVIII). A complete gradation can be traced from peat through lignite, bituminous ("soft") coal, and anthracite ("hard") coal. If the peat bogs of today were left untouched, many of them would in the course of time be covered with sediment, the remaining necessary changes would take place, and the result would be the formation of coal interbedded with other sedimentary rocks.

Quaking Bogs. — In the lakes and swamps of cool-temperate and cold climates there flourishes a plant known as *sphagnum moss*. Sphagnum grows abundantly in the northern United States, Canada, and northern Europe, giving these northern swamps an aspect different from the swamps of the south. It readily grows outward at the surfaces of small lakes, forming floating mats that conceal clear water and black liquid muck beneath. When one walks on the mossy surface, the whole mass shakes and quivers; hence these bogs are called *quaking bogs*. Not infrequently men and animals have fallen through these unstable mats and have perished in the quagmires below. Because the antiseptic nature of the bogs, deadly to bacteria, largely prevents the decomposition of organic matter, the bodies of animals entombed many thousands of years ago are dug up in remarkable states of preservation. In New York state alone the remains of more than 200 elephants that became mired during or after the Ice Age have been dug up from peat swamps.

Economic Value of Swamp Lands. — Swamp land, after it has been artificially drained, has a high agricultural value because swamp soils are very fertile. Swamp lands in the United States have a combined area greater than the area of New England, and with proper draining much of this land could be reclaimed for farming. For centuries, drainage canals and ditches have been used in Flanders and Holland; and now in many parts of the United States large areas of wet land are being prepared in this way for agricultural use. Thus artificial means are being used to accomplish what would have been achieved in time by unaided erosion and deposition — more perfectly graded drainage of the lands.

READING REFERENCES

1. Les Lacs; by Léon Collet. 320 pages. Paris, 1925.
The most up-to-date work on lakes.
2. The Lakes of Southeastern Wisconsin; by N. M. Fenneman. 187 pages. Wisconsin Geological Survey, Bulletin 8, 2d edition, 1910.
Description of glacial lakes.
3. Lake Bonneville; by G. K. Gilbert. 438 pages. U. S. Geological Survey, Monograph 1, 1890.
A complete and highly interesting treatise on the geologic record of a great extinct lake.
4. The Scientific Study of Scenery; by J. E. Marr. 361 pages. Chapters 11 and 12. 6th edition. London, 1920.
A short popular discussion based largely on European lakes.
5. Lakes of North America; by I. C. Russell. 125 pages. Boston, 1895.
A comprehensive popular account.

CHAPTER VI

GLACIERS AND GLACIATION

Geologic Rôle of Glaciers. — To anyone who has observed with a critical eye the Alps, the Sierra Nevada, or the higher ranges of the Rocky Mountains, it is at once obvious that their pinnacled peaks and trough-like valleys are unlike those sculptured by streams in lower mountain ranges. The trained observer at once would recognize these alpine forms as the work of glaciers, even if the glaciers themselves had disappeared. A study of the character and behavior of these striking and impressive sculptors of the land explains not only how and why they operate as they do, but also how we know that ice sheets have recently extended over large parts of North America, Europe, and South America, altering the landscape, redistributing the soil in a wholesale manner, and exercising a powerful effect upon the sea. An inquiry into the geologic effects of glaciers also enables us to learn many curious things about the climates of past time. To begin with, how do glaciers originate?

DEVELOPMENT OF GLACIERS

Distribution of Snow. — Snowfall is controlled entirely by climate. In the tropics it falls only on the highest mountains and plateaus. In the middle latitudes it falls on lowlands as well, but disappears in summer. Over many parts of the cold polar regions it covers wide areas and remains from year to year. *Snowfields*, areas of perennial snow, in which summer wastage fails to remove winter snowfall, are therefore found only in high latitudes and at high altitudes. The lower limit of perennial snow in any region is the *snowline*. Obviously the snowline rises from low levels in parts of the polar regions to very high elevations indeed in the mountains near the equator. In Greenland it is about 2000 feet, in southern Alaska about 5000 feet, in the Rocky Mountains of Wyoming about 11,000 feet, and in the Andes at the equator about 18,000 feet. The snowline varies also according to precipitation and exposure to the Sun; if the drier side of a mountain range happens to be the side exposed to the Sun, the snowline is much higher there than on the moister, shaded side.

Change of Snow into Ice. — Successive snowfalls gradually increase the depth of the snowfield, and at the same time the accumulating

snow gradually changes in character.   Under the influence of moisture
and the gentle pressure exercised by new falls above, each feathery
snowflake is slowly consolidated into a little ball of ice, and the resulting
mass (the *névé* of the Alpine mountaineers) assumes the granular texture that we find in the last lingering remnants of winter snowdrifts.
If snow continues to accumulate above and to add its weight to the
mass, the névé gradually becomes solidified, part of the air between the
granules is squeezed out, and the result is compact ice.   The ice nevertheless betrays its snowflake origin by the fact that it is distinctly stratified, each layer representing a single snowfall.   The planes between
some of the layers are sprinkled with films of blown dust, making the
stratification even more distinct.

Initiation of Flow. — When the snowfield, normally consisting of
compacted ice overlain successively by névé and fresh snow, attains a
critical thickness that depends partly on the steepness of the slope on
which it is resting and partly on temperature, it begins to creep gently
downhill, flowing outward and downward.   The part of the ice that
takes on motion is *glacier ice*, and the moving mass is a *glacier*, which
will continue to transfer ice to lower levels as long as the snowfield
above continues to receive an adequate supply of snow.

There is no sharp dividing line between snowfield and flowing ice.
In one sense even the ice in the snowfield is in motion, since every
particle of fallen snow that does not melt or evaporate at the point
where it falls is imperceptibly but surely transferred downward and
outward into what is definitely the glacier.   Since most snowfields
occupy broad basins near the crests of mountain ranges, and since the
glaciers that flow from them follow narrow valleys down the mountain
flanks, the ice flowing outward from broad snowfields is crowded into
narrow glaciers.   The result is that imperceptible movement in the
snowfield becomes perceptible movement in the glacier.

Rate of Flow. — The first study of glacier flow was made by the Swiss
Professor Hugi in 1827, when he built an observation hut on the Aar
Glacier in the northern Alps.   By 1841 the hut had been carried 4700
feet down the valley, indicating a rate of flow of nearly 1 foot per day.
In 1858 Professor Forbes, after studying the movement of the Glacier
des Bossons on Mont Blanc, made a sensational prediction.   In 1820
three guides had been buried beneath a snow avalanche near the source
of this glacier.   The bodies, he stated, would be delivered up at its
lower end about 1860.   In 1861 the first remains appeared, having been
carried more than 4 miles from the site of the avalanche at a rate averaging between 1 and 2 feet per day.

The figures given above are higher than the average for glaciers in

the Alps.   On the other hand, some of the Alaskan glaciers are known to
have flowed at times as rapidly as 40 feet per day, and in Greenland
rates of more than 60 feet per day have been observed.   The rate of
flow is influenced by several factors.   As a rule it is high in large glaciers,
but more particularly in glaciers that are small in proportion to the
snowfields that feed them.   It is favored by steep gradients, by steeply
sloping upper surfaces of the ice itself, and by temperatures near rather
than far below the melting-point.   As a result of the temperature factor,
some glaciers flow three times as rapidly in summer as in winter.

Differential Flow. — Not long after Hugi began the work of timing
glaciers in the Alps, some of his followers proved that the rate of flow
in a glacier differs from place to place.   Stakes were driven into a
glacier, making straight rows from side to side.   After a time these
rows became convex down the valley, showing that the ice in the center
was moving faster than the ice at the sides.   Furthermore, stakes which
had been driven deeply into the ice began to lean forward, proving that
the ice near the surface was moving faster than that lower down.   This
differential flow is analogous to that in a stream, and the principal
underlying cause is the same in both cases: the upper, centrally located
part of the flowing mass is least retarded by friction.

Physical Character of Glacier Ice. — Since glacier ice flows downward
and outward it was long believed that this movement was similar to that
of a viscous fluid like asphalt.   Each particle of ice in a glacier, however,
is a crystalline solid.   We have visible proof that glacier ice maintains
a firm grip on rock fragments frozen into it, that it persistently develops
cracks (represented by the numerous *crevasses* found in nearly all glaciers),
that parts of it tend to shear forward over other parts along well-defined planes, and that it flows down a main valley, towering above
the tributary valleys whose mouths it crosses without flowing up them
to an appreciable extent.   On the other hand, we can see that the courses
of most glaciers are sinuous, and that the flowing ice partially accom-
modates itself to the bends and curves.   These facts indicate that
although ice is a solid it is weak and easily deformed.

Mechanism of Flow. — We have already seen that the cause of movement in glaciers is the piling up of successive snowfalls, giving sufficient
superincumbent weight to the snowfield to make its basal part flow
outward.   Once the critical weight is attained, then for as long as snowfall continues to exceed local wastage, the glacier must continue to
move.   The actual mechanism of flow is another matter.   We know
that any solid can be made to flow by the application of sufficient force;
for example, a lead bar can be made into a thin plate by squeezing it in
a vise.   Ice near its melting-point is a weak solid and flows in the same

way. The processes involved are complex and have only an indirect geologic significance; therefore they are not discussed here.

Stagnation. — Whereas most existing glaciers maintain their downward and outward motion until their ice is wasted away, this is not universally true. The Malaspina Glacier, a broad ice mass on the Alaskan coast, is entirely inactive. Parts of it are covered with thick rock débris on which trees grow undisturbed. Other ice masses in Alaska, northern Greenland, and Antarctica, obviously remnants of former glaciers, today lie stagnant, their ice gradually wasting away without further movement. The cause of this behavior is uncertain, although it seems likely that it results from climatic change involving decrease in snowfall.

Wastage. — Sooner or later every mass of ice or snow is converted into water or water vapor. Three processes by which glacier ice is wasted away are *melting, evaporation,* and *calving.* Calving is the breaking-off of ice masses to form bergs, and occurs on a large scale only in high latitudes in those glaciers whose lower ends reach the sea. It is widespread in the polar regions, and the resulting bergs float long distances before they melt away. Evaporation[1] of glacier ice is a universal process, affecting the whole surface from snowfield to lower end. We have no means of determining the relative importance of evaporation and melting, but there are grounds for the belief that certain former glaciers disappeared almost entirely by evaporation (p. 147). Melting is common in all glaciers except those of the Antarctic continent, where calving and evaporation seem to be dominant. Melting gives rise to drainage in the form of streams and lakes adjacent to and beyond the ice, and this drainage leaves characteristic imprints in the land surface. Where the records of streams and lakes are absent from wide glaciated areas above sea level, evaporation may have been the chief wasting process.

The extent to which a glacier moves downward and outward depends on (1) supply of snow at its head and (2) wastage. A preponderance of supply causes the end or foot of the glacier to advance; a preponderance of wastage causes it to recede. In the latter case the motion of the *ice* continues to be forward; it is only the *front* of the glacier that moves backward. A great deficiency in supply may cause the glacier to lose its motion over a wide area and pass into a stagnant condition. The balance involved is so delicate that equilibrium is seldom attained; the front of an actively moving glacier is nearly always either advancing or

---

[1] As used here, this term includes also *sublimation,* the conversion of solid into vapor without passing through the liquid state. It is not practical to separate the two processes as applied to glacier ice.

receding (Figs. 92, 93). In general, all the glaciers in one region tend to advance for a period of years and then to recede more or less in unison. Attempts are being made to chart these changes accurately in order to learn whether they are related to changes in climate. For example, the Nisqually Glacier on Mount Rainier in Washington, with a present length of between 4 and 5 miles, was observed to retreat through an average distance of 68 feet per year during the 11-year period from 1918 to 1929. Evidence has been found that the glaciers of the Alps reached their greatest modern advance about 1855. The subsequent recession of the lower Grindelwald Glacier uncovered a marble quarry, the stone from which had been used in houses of the seventeenth century in Berne. The source of the stone had been unknown until the receding glacier laid bare the quarry. Therefore there must have been oscillations of the ice front before the advance of the mid-nineteenth century.

In September, 1899, severe earthquakes affected the region of Yakutat Bay in Alaska, where there are

Figs. 92–93. — Two views of the Rhone Glacier in the Swiss Alps. A comparison of Fig. 92 (taken in 1870) with Fig. 93 (taken in 1905) shows the wastage of the ice within a 35-year period.

many glaciers in a nearly stagnant condition. By 1906 most of the glaciers were advancing rapidly, but later they returned to their former sluggish movement. The sudden advance appears to have been the result of enormous quantities of additional snow avalanched by the earthquakes from the surrounding cliffs into the snowfields that fed the glaciers.

Types of Glaciers

Valley Glaciers. — The glaciers of the Alps originate in snowfields high up on the mountain sides and flow away down valleys that had been cut by streams before the glaciers were formed. The glaciers (Figs. 92, 93, 98), held in by the valley walls and conforming to the valley trends, are *valley glaciers*. There are about 2000 of them in the Alps. Most of them are less than 2 miles in length; a few are from 3 to 5 miles long, and one, the Great Aletsch, is nearly 10 miles long. Valley glaciers lie high in the other great ranges of Europe — the Pyrenees, the Carpathians, and the more lofty of the ranges of Norway. To the east they are found in the Caucasus and in the Himalaya, Karakoram, Pamir, and other high ranges of Asia. The Fedtschenko Glacier (Fig. 108) in the Pamir region is more than 44 miles long, the longest valley glacier in the world. The high mountain valleys of the Andes and of New Zealand carry many large glaciers, and along the Alaskan coast thousands of valley glaciers, favored by great snowfall and low temperature, reach down to or near the level of the sea. Southward through British Columbia, Washington, and Oregon, the snowline rises and glaciers become steadily less numerous. Within the United States they are found chiefly on the high volcanic peaks of the Cascade Range, of which the most important are Mount Baker and Mount Rainier in Washington, Mount Hood in Oregon, and Mount Shasta in northern California.

In the Alps there are in addition to the long valley glaciers many fields of snow, névé, and ice, lacking perceptible motion, and too small in size to give rise to actual glaciers. These small fields persist in regions that are not quite cold enough or moist enough to nourish full-sized valley glaciers. This is true of even the highest ranges of the Rocky Mountains in Montana, Wyoming, and Colorado.

Piedmont Glaciers. — Some of the Alaskan valley glaciers emerge from the mountain ranges and spread out upon a narrow coastal plain, coalescing to form a continuous thick sheet of ice. The spreading-out process is illustrated on a small scale in Fig. 92. The greatest of these *piedmont glaciers* are Malaspina Glacier and Bering Glacier. The former covers an area of 1500 square miles. Its stagnant condition (possibly resulting from its large size in proportion to the small valley glaciers that feed it), and its mantle of rock and soil topped with forest growth are mentioned in a preceding paragraph. Piedmont glaciers today are confined to high latitudes, and even there they are rare. Formerly, however, they were common in northern Europe, as far south as the British Isles, but climatic changes have caused them to disappear entirely.

Ice Sheets. — Most of Greenland is covered by a continuous mantle of ice known as an *ice sheet*. This great glacial blanket has an area of more than 700,000 square miles and is thick enough (5500 feet near the center) to cover high mountains and plateaus, burying them completely. Its form is double, consisting of two broad low domes or mounds (Fig. 94), a large one in the north and a smaller one in the south. These domes are centers from which the ice slowly radiates toward the coast, sending narrow tongues down the valleys of the coastal belt. The broad monotonous surface is barren of life, and the only visible movement upon it is furnished by the strong winds that continually sweep it, some of them bringing the snow by which the ice is maintained.

The Antarctic continent is covered by a similar but much more extensive ice sheet, with an area of probably more than 5,000,000 square miles. Its interior has been partly explored by Shackleton, Amundsen, Scott, Byrd, and Wilkins. These two great ice sheets differ from valley glaciers not only in size and form,

Fig. 94. — The Greenlandic ice sheet, showing twin centers of ice radiation and narrow ice-tongues forming a fringe near the coast.

but also in the fact that they are not confined by valley walls but rise above valleys and mountains alike, so that over great regions no peaks project above their surfaces. This striking difference has an important bearing on the erosion accomplished by the two kinds of glaciers, as appears later in the discussion.

The ice sheets of Greenland and Antarctica, together with much smaller ones in Iceland, are the only existing glaciers of their kind. In former times, however, ice sheets of comparable size formed over northern North America, Europe, and Patagonia, and spread outward, covering vast regions. Although the last remnants of the ice itself disappeared many thousands of years ago, the erosion accomplished by the ice and the characteristic deposits it left on the lands make it possible to reconstruct with fair accuracy the extent, behavior, and appearance of these great glaciers. In order to understand the significance of these deposits and erosional features, we must examine the work accomplished by the glacier ice of today.

Geologic Work of Valley Glaciers

In 1834, Louis Agassiz, a Swiss naturalist, noticed that the boulders (Fig. 118) and other deposits lying at low elevations in the ice-free valleys of the Alps were identical in shape and arrangement with the deposits he had seen being built up by living glaciers in the high ice-filled valleys. At that moment he realized that the glaciers of the Alps, high and comparatively small then as now, had at some former time spread outward and downward, filling most of the valleys of Switzerland with ice. In publishing this revolutionary idea he paved the way for our modern knowledge of the work accomplished by valley glaciers, since we can now compare the valleys vacated by these former glaciers with valleys never occupied by ice, and attribute the differences to the changes wrought by the glaciers themselves. These changes involve both erosion and deposition, and to their combined effects we apply the term *glaciation*.

Processes of Glaciation. — Glaciation consists of the destructive processes of abrasion, quarrying, frost weathering, the transportation of waste, and the constructive process of deposition. Discussion of deposition follows the discussion of the glaciated valley by which it is mainly controlled.

Clear ice moving continuously over a rock surface would not be capable of abrading the rock, but the presence of rock material frozen into the under surface of the ice makes it enormously destructive. No glacier as a whole is free from rock débris. Loose material in its path is gripped by the ice freezing around it, rock fragments torn from the bedrock are added to the load, and waste avalanched from cliffs and pinnacles projecting above the glacier surface provides further contributions. Boulders and smaller fragments that remain high within the ice or on top of it are carried forward and eventually deposited essentially in the form in which they were acquired by the glacier. Fragments carried near the bottom and sides of the ice, however, are subject to wear against the subglacial bedrock surface. This wear, combined with the fact that the ice occasionally loses its grip and allows its pebbles and boulders to change their position somewhat, results in the beveling of the fragments to form pronounced facets separated by rounded edges and without regular arrangement. No agency other than glacier ice makes facets like these[1]; therefore they are a positive indication of glaciation.

Abrasion and Quarrying. — Active erosion by the ice takes place chiefly by abrasion and by quarrying. *Abrasion* involves scouring, gouging, and scratching by the rock-shod basal ice. It occurs chiefly on nearly horizontal surfaces, and on surfaces that oppose the movement of the ice (*stoss* surfaces). Bosses of bedrock smoothed and polished by this means are *roches moutonnées* (Figs. 11, 95, 103). *Quarrying* involves the pulling-away of blocks of rock from cliffs and projections that are

G. A. Young.

Fig. 95. — *Roche moutonné,* Middle Fork of Kern River Valley, California. The ice (a former valley glacier) moved from left to right. Note the difference between the abraded (stoss) side on the left and the quarried side on the right.

unsupported on the side toward which the ice is moving (Figs. 95, 102). It is of comparatively slight importance in rocks free from joints, but takes place readily in rocks with vertical or highly inclined joints or planes of stratification.

Frost weathering is a static factor which in some cases plays an important auxiliary rôle. Meltwater percolates into joints and cracks, freezes, expands, and spalls out blocks some of which are of considerable size (Fig. 7). This process goes on not only beneath glaciers in regions warm enough to permit subglacial melting, but on exposed bedrock surfaces above the general level of the ice. Alpine peaks owe not a little of their jagged form to this process.

[1] In certain respects they resemble the facets of ventifacts (p. 160).

Transportation of rock waste by glaciers is more continuous than transportation by streams, chiefly because rocks avalanched on to the ice ride easily along on the surface, whereas particles of stream detritus constantly sink toward the bottom and require to be lifted up again by minor eddies. Glaciers deposit very little débris *en route*. Most of the load is carried to the end of the glacier and there dropped. While in the ice, it is concentrated in two zones, one on the surface and at the sides of the ice (accumulated chiefly by avalanching from the valley sides), and one at the base of the ice (consisting of material picked up from the valley bottom). Between the two zones the great bulk of the ice is pure and nearly free from débris except near its outer margin, where it becomes concentrated by wastage of the ice.

The Cirque. — Nearly all valleys that are or have been occupied by valley glaciers have strikingly steep, blunt heads, differing markedly

A. P. Church.

Fig. 96. — Crest of Uinta Range, Utah, scalloped by cirques that have eaten into the range from both flanks. The cirques are no longer being enlarged.

from the delicate creases at the heads of non-glaciated stream valleys (Figs. 96, 97, 113). These blunt valley heads, whose inclosing walls are nearly vertical, are known as *cirques*, and are characteristically the result of glaciation by valley glaciers. They develop through the gradual excavation of hollows and niches that are occupied from year to year by snowbanks at the heads of mountain valleys. Meltwater formed on summer days permeates the loose surface material and enters the bedrock at and near the edges of the snowbanks. Frost weathering occurs as the temperature at night drops below freezing. The bedrock at the surface is broken up, the débris is comminuted, and the finest products are carried away by the percolation of meltwater formed during daytime thaws.   At the same time, settling and compacting of the snow, together with a sliding movement brought about in part by avalanching, cause slow quarrying of the rock surface beneath the ice.   The net result through a long period of time is gradually to countersink each snowbank into the surface, forming a concave depression.   This process, compound because it involves static frost-weathering, active though slow removal by percolating water of the products of weathering, and actual quarrying, is termed *nivation*.   The nivated hollow gradually increases in size, from year to year it holds increasing quantities of snow and ice, with a grow-ing proportion of ice to snow, and with steadily increasing quarrying and abrasion it becomes a full-fledged cirque.   It seems probable that the

Humphreys Airplane Co.

Fig. 97. — Cirques, no longer being excavated, cut into the Colorado Front Range southwest of Denver; looking south.   The cirque and glaciated valley (Chicago Creek) in the middle foreground contain two small lakes (Chicago Lakes) occupying basins scoured out of the bedrock.   A tributary cirque lies to the right.   In the left middleground are another lake and more cirques tributary to a different valley.   At the crest of the cirque that contains a snowbank is Mount Evans, one of the highest peaks of the Colorado Rockies.

sharp break between the steep headwall of the cirque and its flat floor is the result of increase of erosive power at the point at which névé is transformed into glacier ice.

Because great accumulations of snow hide from view their characteris-tic features, cirques are more apparent at the heads of small glaciers than of large ones, and at the sources of vanished glaciers than of living ones.

The Glaciated Valley. — Glaciers do not excavate new valleys; they remodel old ones.   The amount of remodeling depends chiefly on the length of time that the glaciers have been at work.   The ice tongues

R. Finsterwalder.

Fig. 98. — The Notgemeinschaft Glacier (*left*), one of the longest valley glaciers in the world, and the "Tanimas 2" Glacier, Northwest Pamir region, central Asia.

F. E. Matthes, U. S. Geol. Survey.

Fig. 99. — Valley abandoned by a valley glacier after strong glaciation. Note the characteristic U-shape, smoothed sides, and absence of interlocking spurs. Deadman Canyon, Sierra Nevada, California.

that descend from the snowfields near the crest of a mountain range follow the valleys that had been excavated by streams before glaciation began. Glacier ice, being much less mobile than water, does not conform so readily to the bends and curves imparted to the valleys by the former streams. For this reason it grinds persistently against the spurs that project alternately into the valleys, steadily snubbing their ends and gradually beveling them into sharp facets. These facets grow larger as the spurs grow shorter, until at length the spurs are worn away entirely, leaving wide and nearly straight smooth-sided U-shaped troughs through

J. T. Boysen.

Fig. 100. — Yosemite Valley with a tributary, Bridalveil Creek. Widening and deepening of the Yosemite by valley glaciers have converted it into an open trough and have left the tributary valley hanging high above the floor of the main. Bridalveil Creek has been forced thereby to cascade into the Yosemite, in a falls which originated at the time the glacier wasted away.

which the glacier can flow with the minimum of effort (Figs. 98, 99, 101, 113).

The grinding-away of the spurs also affects the tributary valleys between them. The mouths of these valleys are steadily cut back at a rate faster than their own streams can cut them down. The result is that the tributary valleys can no longer enter the main valleys at grade, but are left hanging above them, so that after the ice has disappeared their streams flow out to the edges of cliffs down which they must cascade in order to join the mains. These *hanging tributary valleys* (Fig. 100) are characteristic of regions sculptured by valley glaciers. If the cut-away parts of their profiles are restored by projecting them into the main val-

ley (Fig. 101) they are usually found to meet at a point above the floor
of the latter.   This proves that the main valley has been not only widened by the ice but deepened as well.   The Yosemite Valley in California, originally cut by a stream, was later deepened 1500 feet at one point
by glaciers that occupied it for a considerable time.

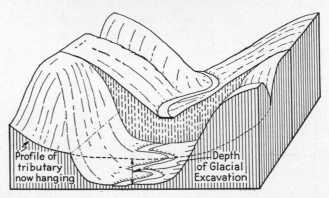

Fig. 101. — Block showing alteration of a stream valley by a valley glacier.   Rear half
of block shows stream valley before glaciation.   Front half shows valley deepened and
widened by glaciation, with tributaries left hanging above the main stream.   (Compare
Figs. 100 and 110–113.)

The gradients of many of the main valleys themselves are greatly altered by glaciation.   Their former smooth, concave stream-profiles are
cut up into short treads alternating with steep risers, the whole forming a
gigantic flight of stairs.   Furthermore some of the treads slope back-

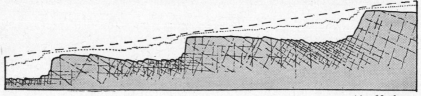

After Matthes.

Fig. 102. — Longitudinal section of part of a glaciated valley showing smoothed surfaces
of glacial abrasion alternating with steep faces caused by glacial quarrying, imparting to
the valley a steplike profile.   The steps are shown to be controlled by the unequal distribution of joints and other planes of weakness throughout the bedrock.   Dashed line
indicates valley profile prior to glaciation; dotted line indicates profile during an early
stage of glaciation.

ward, giving each step a "down-at-the-heel" appearance (Fig. 102).   As
a rule the outer parts of the treads are cut from resistant rock comparatively free from joints and fissures, whereas the "down-at-the-heel"
parts, at the bases of the risers, are cut into thoroughly jointed and fissured and therefore weaker rock (Fig. 102).   This appears to indicate

that the flight of stairs is made by glacial quarrying in the jointed areas
and glacial abrasion in the places where joints are scarcer.   Abrasion by
rock-shod ice is very evident in the latter places, for the humps and
bosses of bedrock are smoothed and polished, forming *roches moutonnées*.   Furthermore, the polished surfaces are marred by long grooves or
scratches (*glacial striae*, Fig. 103) made by sharp rock fragments frozen
into the base of the moving ice.   The trend of these striae records the
direction in which the ice was flowing.

A. W. Rogers.

Fig. 103. — Glaciated bedrock surface, striated, polished, and partly covered with a
veneer of till (foreground).   The glaciation represented is very ancient, and the till has
been cemented into a hard tillite.   Near Kimberley, South Africa.

A valley, then, can be recognized as having been occupied by a valley
glacier if it heads in a cirque, if it is free from sharp bends and interlocking spurs, if the shortened spurs have beveled triangular facets, if it is
smoothed and U-shaped and has a step-like gradient, if its tributaries
hang above its floor, and if *roches moutonnées* are visible along its bottom and sides.   In middle latitudes these features disappear as the valley is traced downward, and the lower limit of glaciation is thereby readily determined.   In very high latitudes, however, even the valleys along
the coasts are glaciated throughout their length, giving rise to *fjords*,
such as characterize the coasts of British Columbia and Alaska, Labrador
and Greenland, Norway, Chile, and parts of New Zealand (Fig. 104).
Soundings show that some fjords are 4000 to 6000 feet deep, but this

great depth is probably due more to regional depression of the coast than to excessive glacial excavation.

Deposits Made by Valley Glaciers. — The rock waste deposited by glaciers and by their meltwater constitutes the *drift*.   Débris deposited directly by the ice, without being reworked by meltwater, lies in jumbled dumps irregularly laid and without any arrangement according to size of particles.   Nearly all the rock fragments are rough and broken, but a few — on the average fewer than 5 per cent — are smoothed and polished

New Zealand Government Publicity Photo.

Fig. 104. — Fjord, Milford Sound, South Island, New Zealand.   The valley sides have the greatly steepened profiles characteristic of the work of valley glaciers.

and neatly faceted by the slow grinding action of the glacier.   Such material is known as *till* (Figs. 103, 117), and considerable accumulations of till with a topographic expression of their own are referred to as *moraine*.   There are two general types of moraine, differing in origin and surface form, *ground moraine* and *end moraine*.

Ground Moraine. — The ground moraine left by a valley glacier is usually composed of loose rubbly till lying in irregular heaps over the valley floor as a result of unequal deposition by ice unevenly charged with débris.   Along the sides of the valley the ground moraine commonly lies in long ridges of rock fragments avalanched from the cliffs into the narrow spaces between the former glacier and its confining valley walls.

These ridges, sometimes called *lateral moraine,* are seen forming at the sides of many living valley glaciers.   Where two tributary valley glaciers join, their adjacent lateral moraines are brought together as a single band of débris near the middle of the large glacier formed by the two tributaries (Fig. 107).   These bands of *medial moraine* are prominent features of existing valley glaciers but are rarely seen in the ground moraine left after the ice has disappeared, because they are spread out and scattered by the wasting of the ice.

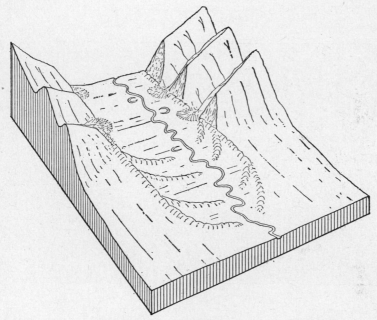

Fig. 105. — Recessional end moraines recording stages in the retreat of the end of a valley glacier.

End Moraine. — A ridge of till banked up along the front of a glacier is an *end moraine.*   Deposits of this type are formed only by actively moving ice in either of two ways: (1) The forefoot of an advancing glacier sometimes pushes loose débris ahead of it, snowplow-fashion.   This material, urged forward like a slowly breaking wave, is left as a ridge at the position of maximum advance of the ice, regardless of whether the ice front lingers in that position or immediately recedes.   (2) If melting-back of the ice front exactly counterbalances forward movement of the ice, all the rock waste carried by the ice to its front must be dumped at that front, accumulating as a ridge without actual advance of the front itself.   Many end moraines may have been built by a combination of both processes.

The end moraines of valley glaciers range from a few feet to scores and exceptionally hundreds of feet in height (Figs. 105, 106). Ordinarily their breadth is slight. The width of fully formed and undissected end moraines is controlled by the width of the containing valley. In plan the end moraine is almost invariably convex down-valley, recording more rapid movement of the center than of the sides of the ice. The degree of convexity reflects the rate of movement of the ice, and the volume of the deposit as a whole is a measure of the distance through which the material has been pushed, or of the duration of halt of the ice front, or both.

A. P. Church.

Fig. 106. — Broad shallow glaciated valley containing two lakes dammed by small end moraines. The ridge in the center distance is indented by three broad cirques. White Rocks Canyon, Uinta Mountains, Utah.

Some end moraines lie along the lips of cirques, showing that although the ice had motion it was unable to extend itself down the valley below. The volumes of such moraines are closely comparable with the volumes of the cirques back of them, little of the material excavated from the cirques having been carried down the valleys. On the other hand, the end moraines of long valley glaciers contain but a small proportion of the waste removed from cirque and upper valley, much of it having been strewn along the valley floor as ground moraine, and much having been seized by meltwater and carried off down the valley. This is entirely expectable in view of the great expanse of ice exposed to wastage, and the rapid rate of wastage at the lower elevations to which the glacier has descended. In many steep, narrow, trough-like valleys, indeed, end moraines do not form at all, because the rock waste is sluiced away by water as rapidly as it forms. The fact that an end moraine of a vanished valley glacier is incomplete, however, does not indicate that it was not once fully formed, as a vigorous stream readily breaches it and eventually destroys it.

Water-laid Deposits of Valley Glaciers. — In the middle of a summer day, when melting is at a maximum, a climber traversing the lower part of a valley glacier is always within sight of little streams of meltwater pouring along through miniature channels in the surface of the ice, and

Alaskan Aerial Survey, U. S. Navy.

Fig. 107. — Lower end of Crillon Glacier, Lituya Bay, Alaska. Note transverse crevasses, surface débris (mostly contributed by the nearest tributary glacier on the left), lines of glacier flowage, sharply faceted valley spurs, and an alluvial fan of glaciofluvial sand and gravel being built up by a braiding stream emerging from the right margin of the ice. There is no end moraine since the glacier ends in an arm of the sea (shown in the foreground) and wastes away chiefly by calving.

he hears coming from deep within the glacier mass the muffled roar of much larger streams and cascades. Once clear of the ice from which they usually emerge through tunnels, these streams are seen to be heavily loaded with detritus — boulders, sand, silt, and clay, all contributed by the glacier from which they sprang. The silt, made of finely ground particles of fresh rock (*rock flour*), gives the water a whitish, milky appearance. This load begins to be deposited at once. The boulders are rolled a little distance and dropped, then the coarser pebbles, followed by finer gravel, sand, and silt. The whole deposit, *glaciofluvial* because built up by ice-born streams, is likely to begin as a series of alluvial fans (Fig. 107) and to extend for many miles down the valley. It is some-

W. Rickmer Rickmers.

Fig. 108. — Valley train of sand and gravel being built up by heavily loaded, braided streams emerging from the margin of a valley glacier and flowing toward the observer. Note the rock débris ("dirt") covering the surface of the glacier, and the cirques, arêtes, and horns along the mountain crests. Fedtschenko Glacier, northwest Pamir Region, Central Asia.

Alaskan Aerial Survey, U. S. Navy.

Fig. 109. — Valley train built of glacial silt, with the braided stream that is building it. North Fork of Eastern Arm of Berners Bay, Alaska.

times referred to as a *valley train* (Figs. 108, 109). The clay particles remain in suspension and may even reach the sea before settling out.

Because the outflowing streams are continually filling up their channels with deposits, they overflow, shift their channels, and form a braided network. In so doing they repeatedly work over the deposits, searching out the finer particles to carry farther, and leaving the coarser behind. The result is a conspicuous sorting and stratification such as is characteristic of any stream deposit. Although nearly all the pebbles have been rounded by stream transportation, the preservation of facets on some of them suggests their glacial origin.

In some valleys the outflowing water is dammed by end moraines farther down the valleys or by irregularities in the bedrock surfaces that form the valley floors. In such places the water pouring from the ice builds deltas outward into the lakes, gradually filling them with even more perfectly stratified deposits whose pebbles, like those of glaciofluvial origin, retain some of the facets ground into their surfaces by the ice.

The Cycle of Glaciation by Valley Glaciers

Our knowledge of the Earth, not only as it is today but as it has been throughout its history, points to the fact that glaciations are local and temporary affairs, brought about by changes of climate resulting in lower temperatures whose duration, as geologic time is reckoned, is comparatively short. Let us assume a mountainous region with abundant precipitation, drained by streams and affected by a climate growing steadily colder (Fig. 110).

Stage of Growth. — As the winter snows gradually persist throughout the summer, small snowfields are formed in protected niches. Nivation at once begins, and cirques slowly develop (Fig. 111). The snowfields increase in size and imperceptibly give rise to glaciers, which push down the stream valleys, widening and deepening them. The small tributary valleys, either free from moving ice or containing small feeble glaciers, are thereby left hanging above their mains, and at the same time the ends of lateral spurs are beveled off, so that the main valleys are gradually straightened. Some of the rock waste is piled along the sides and lower ends of the glaciers, and some is carried away by streams of meltwater.

While the valleys are being widened and deepened and their waste is accumulating at lower levels, the mountain crests are being sharpened by frost-weathering along joints, and the cirques immediately below them are growing larger. The continued headward growth of cirques on opposite sides of a mountain range eventually reduces the interven-

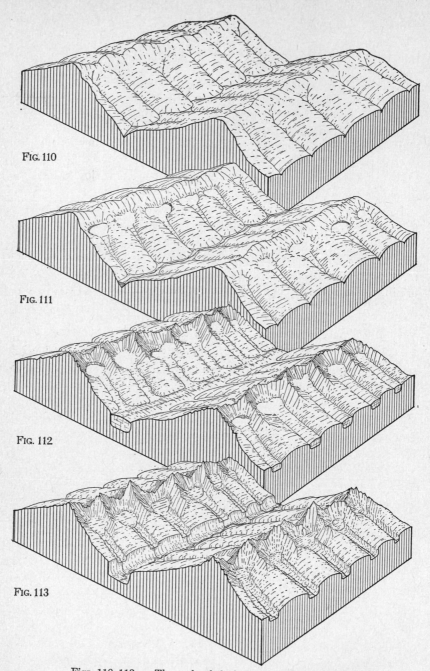

FIG. 110

FIG. 111

FIG. 112

FIG. 113

Figs. 110–113. — The cycle of glaciation by valley glaciers.

Fig. 110. — Segment of a mountainous region being eroded by streams.

Fig. 111. — Evolution of cirques as small glaciers develop with changing climate.

Fig. 112. — Coalescence of the small glaciers to form large ice tongues in the main valleys, enlargement of the cirques, and sharpening of the uplands by frost-weathering.

Fig. 113. — Appearance of the mass after its abandonment by the glaciers.   (140)

ing divide to a narrow razor-edged ridge (an *arête*) kept sharp by constant frost-weathering. Similar arêtes form along the divides between adjacent cirques on the same side of the range, so that the latter is gradually sculptured into a main arête sending off smaller arêtes as lateral spurs (Figs. 112, 114).

Two cirques growing toward each other from opposite sides of an arête ultimately gnaw through it, forming a great sharp-edged gap or *col*

Alaskan Aerial Survey, U. S. Navy.

Fig. 114. — Twin Glaciers, Alaska, from an altitude of 6000 feet. The glaciers flow outward from an extensive snowfield that lies in a low basin nearly shut in by ridges and peaks. The valleys have spurs which although faceted have not been entirely ground away. Both glaciers end in an arm of the sea and their ends waste chiefly by calving as the bergs float slowly seaward. Loop-shaped lines of flowage are very distinct in both glaciers, showing clearly that their centers move faster than their sides. In the background is the mountain range that catches the snowfall necessary to the maintenance of the ice. The range has progressed far through the cycle of glaciation as shown by the prominent cirques, arêtes, cols, and horns. Note the two cirques, arêtes, and horn in the middle foreground.

(Fig. 113). Many high mountain "passes" are merely large cols. In some the arêtes have been worn down by abrasion during periods when snowfall increased and glaciers filled the cols, converting them into smoothed troughs. Headward sapping of three or more cirques inward against a common upland high-point results in the sculpture of the high-point into a pyramid or *horn* with several facets, each facet representing the headwall of one of the cirques that helped to form it (Figs. 113, 114). Outstanding examples in the Alps are the Matterhorn (Fig. 115) and the Jungfrau; smaller horns dominate many of the glacially dissected ranges of western North America. This succession of arêtes, cols, and horns gives a jagged, serrate appearance to the crest of the range (Fig. 113).

Stage of Wastage. — Now let the climate grow warmer by imperceptible degrees. Decrease in snow supply slows up the rate of glacier motion, allowing wastage to gain the upper hand. The position of farthest advance of the ice front in each valley is marked by a festoon-like end moraine with a valley train beyond it. The ice fronts, abandoning these end moraines, shrink backward up the valleys. Temporary halts or slight readvances of these ice fronts result in the building of other end moraines (*recessional end moraines*), giving a festooned appearance

Fig. 115. — The Matterhorn (14,780 feet), a typical horn in the southern Alps. This unreduced pyramid has four facets, formed and kept steep by sapping in four cirques on the Italian-Swiss divide.

to the valley floors (Fig. 105). The streams of meltwater form temporary lakes back of some of these ridges, and spilling over, cut trenches through them. Year by year the glaciers dwindle, finally becoming mere cakes of ice in the cirques. As the glaciers shrink, and rain replaces snow, streams resume possession of the valleys. At once the glaciated form of valley, spur, and divide begins to be altered, and eventually, after a long lapse of time, all traces of ice occupancy are obliterated.

GEOLOGIC WORK OF ICE SHEETS

The New England-Adirondack region and the highlands of Scotland and Ireland are mountainous, and except for some of the highest peaks, have been recently more than once glaciated, yet their landscape differs strikingly from that described in the foregoing account. The crests of the ranges (Fig. 116) are not serrate; there are neither arêtes, cols, nor

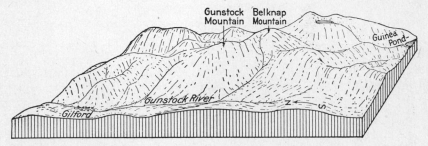

Fig. 116. — Belknap Mountains near Lake Winnepesaukee, New Hampshire, showing profiles smoothed by ice sheets. Area of block 5 by 4 miles. Maximum relief 1800 feet. Vertical exaggeration 2×.

horns. Cirques are very rare, and the few that are visible are poorly developed. On the contrary, even the divides are smoothed and rounded, and striated *roches moutonnées* are plentiful on the ridges as well as in the valleys. Obviously their glaciation did not involve cirque-sapping and frost-weathering, but consisted chiefly of abrasion. We must conclude therefore that these regions were affected not by mere tongues of ice in their valleys, but by huge ice sheets that overtopped valley and range alike, as do the ice sheets of Greenland and Antarctica today.

Erosion by Ice Sheets. — When little or none of the land surface projects above the ice, quarrying and abrasion are the only processes that can operate. As the ice sheet slowly moved from north to south over such a region as New England it smoothed down the north-facing slopes by abrasion and slightly steepened some of the south-facing slopes by quarrying. Throughout a huge area in Canada north of the Great Lakes, the weathered mantle was stripped away, and the ice bit deep into the fresh bedrock beneath, so that today it is naked or insufficiently covered with scanty vegetation. Most of the thousands of lakes in this vast region lie in shallow basins scooped out of the rock by the ice.

Transportation by Ice Sheets. — Because of their great size, the ice sheets that formerly covered the northern part of North America transported rock waste in vastly greater amounts than do valley glaciers. Most of the material of the drift has not been moved more than a few miles, although some of it has traveled many hundreds of miles. This is known through the finding of rocks far distant from their place of origin. Slabs of native copper from the great copper lodes of the Keweenaw Peninsula of Michigan have been found as far south as Missouri, and boulders of an unusual conglomerate containing reddish pebbles of jasper, found throughout Ohio, have been traced to outcrops of bedrock on the north shore of Georgian Bay in Canada. In eastern Finland, boulders of ice-transported copper ore were traced backward in the direction of ice flow. This resulted in the discovery in 1910 of Finland's most

U. S. Geol. Survey.

Fig. 117. — Exposure of densely packed till, showing its unassorted character and the smoothed and faceted surfaces of the pebbles and boulders it contains. Bangor, Pa.

important copper mine. Several isolated diamonds of good quality have been found in glacial deposits in Wisconsin, Michigan, Ohio, and Indiana. Their position in the deposits indicated clearly that they had been transported and deposited by the ice, but their source is as yet unknown. It is presumed to be somewhere in central Canada.

Deposition by Ice Sheets. — Like valley glaciers, ice sheets leave characteristic deposits in the form of both till (Fig. 117) and water-laid detritus. The till, however, covers uplands and lowlands alike. In New England and in the Scottish Highlands, where the bedrock is resistant and hard to erode, the till has an average thickness of less than 5 feet, and being a mere veneer over the bedrock surface, forms little ground moraine. In Ohio, Indiana, Illinois, and Iowa, however, where the rocks are weaker, the till is thick enough over large areas to have obliterated the hills and valleys of the surface on which it rests, substituting for them its own ground-moraine topography.

The surfaces of New England, New York, and the Scottish Highlands are strewn with glacial boulders (Fig. 118). In these regions of resistant rocks the former ice sheets found it difficult to grind the fragments of bedrock they acquired into sand and silt. From Ohio to the Rocky Mountains and throughout northern Germany, however, the much softer bedrock was easily ground up by the ice, and therefore in these regions

C. R. Longwell.

Fig. 118. — Angular, ice-transported granite boulder ("erratic") perched on the top of a high ridge of dolerite, Mount Tom, near Northampton, Massachusetts. The nearest outcrops of granite lie many miles away.

boulders are rare, those found being strays (" erratics ") from regions of hard rocks far to the north.

Ground Moraine; Drumlins. — The ground moraine left by an ice sheet has a gently irregular surface, probably caused by irregular deposition from the ice. The gentle elevations and depressions are called *swells-and-swales.* Areas of ground moraine in some regions, notably Great Britain, Ireland, western New York, central Wisconsin, and southern New England, are dotted with scores of smooth whalebacked hills with oval bases, very much like the inverted bowls of teaspoons. These hills, ranging in length from a few hundred feet to more than a mile, and in height from 25 to about 200 feet, lie pointing in the direction of movement of the former ice sheet. Most of them are made of solid, compact, clayey till. These are *drumlins* (Figs. 119, 120). The origin of these curious hills has long been a problem, and is not yet fully under-

stood.   Their streamline form would have offered a minimum of resistance to ice moving over them.   Some similar hills (notably in New York
and New England) called *rock drumlins* are merely smoothed hills of

R. F. Flint, Conn. Geol. Survey.

Fig. 119. — Small drumlin, Bloomfield, Connecticut.

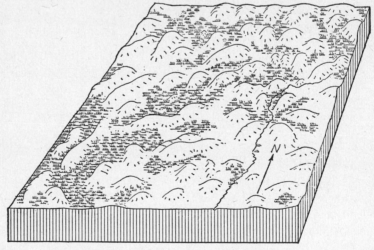

Fig. 120. — Mass of drumlins near Fond du Lac, Wisconsin.   The area shown is 4.5
× 4 miles.   Vertical scale exaggerated.

bedrock plastered over with clayey till.   Obviously they are mainly the
result of glacial erosion, but whether the (till) drumlins also are erosional,
or built up by the local deposition of till, or both, is still a mystery.

End Moraine. — End moraines are built up at the outer margins of ice
sheets just as by valley glaciers; they differ only in size and extent.   End

moraines rarely form along the entire margin of an ice sheet because the important factors of topography, atmospheric moisture, and movement of the ice vary greatly from region to region. Some of the ridges left at the margin of the ice sheet that recently covered part of North America are 100 to 150 feet high and 1 to 5 miles wide (Fig. 121). Their slopes are gentle, and except for their broadly ridged character they have almost the same swell-and-swale topography that characterizes the ground moraine back of them. Their continuity is broken by gaps through which meltwater formerly flowed. End moraines of this kind cross the broad region south of Lake Erie and Lake Michigan in great festoons,

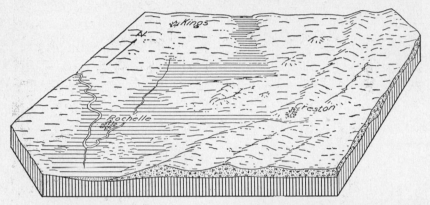

Fig. 121. — End moraine and outwash plain of a former ice sheet near Rochelle, Illinois, represented by ridging and thickening of the till. The ice moved from right to left; its edge failed to reach the sites of Rochelle and Kings. An outwash plain (ruled area) of gravel, sand, and silt was built up by meltwater discharging from the ice. Length of front of block = 8 miles. The moraine ridges are 100 to 150 feet high.

each of which marks a pause in the recession of the edge of the ice sheet that formerly covered the region.

Water-laid Deposits. — The meltwater issuing from ice sheets builds up stratified deposits of gravel, sand, and silt (Fig. 122) just as does the meltwater originating in valley glaciers. If concentrated along valleys, it forms valley trains, but if spread out over a wide area, it forms broad *outwash plains* (Fig. 121), beginning near the ice front as a row of alluvial fans.

Under normal circumstances outwash plains grow headward as fast as the ice edge along which they originate recedes. By continuation of the process the ground moraine becomes covered with a network of outwash deposits after the ice has completely disappeared. Some very large areas of ground moraine left by former ice sheets are, however, entirely free from outwash. This has led to the belief that, instead of melting and giving rise to streams of water, the ice sheets in those places wasted away chiefly by evaporation and so deposited their loads only in the form of till.

In some places where the land slopes up away from the front of the wasting ice the meltwater is dammed to form lakes, which are gradually filled with glacial detritus. A great series of lakes, now extinct, were formed in this way throughout western New York between Albany and Buffalo, and a similar series was formed under the same conditions in Yorkshire in England. The record of these former lakes still exists in the form of old shorelines, beaches, lake deposits, and outlet-channels.

C. R. Longwell.

Fig. 122. — Stratified glacial deposits, New Haven, Connecticut.

Active and Stagnant Ice Compared. — The former ice sheets did not universally continue their forward motion throughout their existence. Some of them lost their motion over large areas, as a result possibly of changes in climate or of rough topography over which they stood, and became stagnant, with no more activity than a block of ice in a refrigerator. The former ice sheets over New England, New York, northern Indiana and southern Michigan, parts of northern Wisconsin and northern Minnesota, parts of the Pacific Northwest, and parts of England, Scotland, Ireland, northern Germany, Poland, and Finland wasted away partially under stagnant conditions, and in so doing gave rise to deposits that could form only by the wastage of stagnant ice. In these regions recessional end moraines are rare, since end moraines can form only through the combination of forward movement of the ice and wasting-away of the ice front. Stratified drift is more abundant than till, because the ice lacked movement and because melting occurred throughout considerable areas at the same time instead of being confined chiefly to the outer margin. Streams of meltwater flowing off through crevasses and through

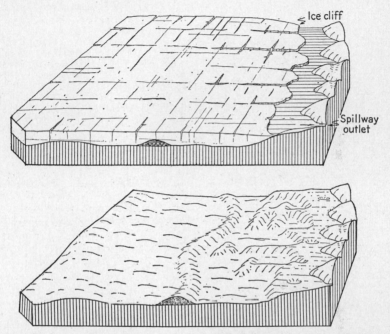

Figs. 123–124. — Formation of stratified deposits from a mass of stagnant ice.

Fig. 123. — Ice seamed with crevasses and penetrated by a tunnel. The ice dams up a lake along its margin.

Fig. 124. — After the disappearance of the ice the deposits in the tunnel are left as an esker, the deposits in the lake are left as a terrace with kettles, and the deposits in the crevasses are left as crevasse fillings. Essentially the same forms would be left if the lake had been replaced by a stream.

tunnels in the bases of these areas of stagnant ice built up long, narrow strings or trains of sand and gravel, which were left, after the ice wasted away, as irregular ridges of stratified drift (Figs. 123, 124, 125). Some of these *eskers,* common in all the areas mentioned above, are many miles in length. Not all eskers have been formed in this way, but many eskers are characteristic of stagnant ice. In some areas the stagnant ice was so thoroughly seamed with a network of cracks and crevasses that as it wasted it separated into thousands of separate remnants between which meltwater flowed in streams or stood ponded in long, nar-

Finnish Air Force.

Fig. 125. — Esker, crevasse fillings, and kettles, Tolvajärvi, Finland.   The whole mass visible above the lake is built of sand and gravel, deposited beneath and between great masses of stagnant ice from a wasting ice sheet.

U. S. Geol. Survey.

Fig. 126. — Large kettle recently made by the melting-out of an isolated mass of stagnant ice.   Note the stratified drift deposited around it.   Below Hidden Glacier, Yakutat Bay, Alaska.   Compare Fig. 127.

row lakes.   Rock débris from the ice was deposited in these streams and lakes and, like the eskers, was left by the wasting-away of the ice in the form of narrow ridges or hummocks (*crevasse fillings*), separated by deep holes (*kettles*), many of which contain ponds or swamps (Fig. 126). Most of the natural ponds of New England, Michigan, and Wisconsin, and nearly all of the ten thousand lakes of Minnesota lie in kettles, large or small (Fig. 127).   The crevasse fillings represent the cracks, and the

R. F. Flint, Conn. Geol. Survey.

Fig. 127. — Kettle made many thousand years ago, Attawaugan, Connecticut. Compare Fig. 126.

kettles the blocks of ice that lay between them.   In some places the crevasse fillings are broad and flat-topped, and the kettles between them very small.   But even though broad, the sides of the crevasse fillings bear the irregular imprint of the wasting masses of ice against which they were deposited, and so have ice-contact faces, for they are merely casts of remnants of the wasting ice sheets.

EXTENT AND SIGNIFICANCE OF FORMER ICE SHEETS

The widespread occurrence of glaciated bedrock surfaces, till, and stratified drift over northern Eurasia, North America, and southern South America shows us that these regions were formerly covered by ice sheets. So clear is the evidence that it is difficult to realize that the idea of widespread glaciation was not thought of until 1837, and that more than 30 years elapsed before the " glacial theory " was generally accepted. Up to that time it had been believed that the drift had been deposited during the Deluge of Noah's time.

Thousands of measurements of glacial striae made in all parts of northern North America and carefully plotted on a map of the continent have shown beyond doubt that the former North American ice sheets originated, not at the North Pole, but in three well-defined centers from which the ice radiated outward in all directions, north as well as south. These centers lay over Labrador, the region west of Hudson Bay, and the Rocky Mountains of Canada, respectively, and in them the ice was probably thousands of feet in thickness. In the Adirondack region the top of the latest ice sheet reached only 3800 feet above the sea, for above this level on the sides of the Adirondack Mountains there are no signs of glaciation. The principal ice sheet of Europe centered in Scandinavia, and spread southward to Scotland, Holland, Germany, Poland, and Russia.

While these great ice sheets were spreading over the lands, many mountain ranges including the Alps and parts of the Rockies supported large valley glaciers, some of which still exist, although greatly diminished in size. Altogether about one-fifth of the land area of the world was covered by ice during the last glacial period.

Careful studies of the glacial deposits in North America and Europe have revealed several layers of till and stratified drift, separated from each other by thin deposits obviously made under warm climates free from the influence of ice. In view of this clear evidence we are forced to conclude that there were no less than four successive incursions of ice separated by times during which the glaciers almost completely or wholly disappeared.

Influence of Ice Sheets on Drainage. — Regions recently abandoned by great ice sheets are usually characterized by sluggish streams in valleys that appear to have carried formerly much greater volumes of water than at present.

Sluggish streams are characteristic for one of two reasons. In Wisconsin, for example, the ice sheets decreased the relief of the land over which they spread by partially and irregularly filling the preëxisting valleys. This lowered the gradients of the streams that formed as the ice wasted, and deprived them of much of the cutting power they would otherwise have had. In much of Illinois, Indiana, and Iowa, on the other hand, the ice sheets completely buried the bedrock surface beneath their own (ground moraine) deposits, and so left this region, when they wasted away, as a rolling plain of till with very low relief. The local rainfall was forced to run off in streams consequent (p. 44) on this plain, and the streams were therefore both low in gradient and wandering in pattern, as they sought the lowest courses in the poor choice offered them.

The Illinois River and the Minnesota River wander through valleys that are much too large for them, and that obviously were cut before the present rivers found and occupied them. At the head of each valley is the bed of a former large glacial lake, one in the vicinity of Chicago and the other covering a vast area in Minnesota, North Dakota, and Manitoba. It is clear that these two valleys formed the spillway-outlets for the two lakes, and were therefore the conduits of huge volumes of water which excavated the valleys on a large scale and subsided only when the ice that fed the lakes wasted away.

Cause of Glaciation. — What caused the formation of these great ice sheets? This question has puzzled investigators ever since the fact of widespread glaciation became firmly established. Although there is as yet no entirely satisfactory explanation, it is becoming clear that the ice sheets owe their origin not to a single cause but to a combination of causes, among which are probably variations in the amount of solar energy received by the Earth, variations in the configuration of the continents, variations in the paths of important marine currents and of certain wind belts, and possibly, variations in the amount of carbon dioxide and volcanic dust in the atmosphere.

Effect of Glaciation on the Level of the Sea. — Whatever the cause of glaciation, we have no doubt as to the effect on the sea brought about by the formation of ice sheets on the continents. Ice sheets are built of atmospheric moisture precipitated in the form of snow. All of this moisture is derived ultimately by evaporation from the sea. It follows that the greater the amount of moisture temporarily locked up on land in the form of snow and ice, the less water there is left in the sea. Although the area of the sea outranks that of the land by a ratio of about 3 to 1, nevertheless it is estimated that the complete wastage of the polar ice sheets existing today would return enough water to the sea to raise its level about 80 feet and so drown enormous areas of land now dry and habitable. But the ice sheets formed during the last glaciation covered about twice as great an area as do those of today. In consequence, the level of the sea at that time must have been considerably lower than it is now. Recent estimates range from 150 to 300 feet.[1] It is evident therefore that glaciation has not only an important direct effect in sculpturing the land, but an equally important indirect effect in shifting the

[1] One estimate, bearing on the coral-reef problem, is cited on p. 196.

line of attack of the sea upon the land (Chap. VIII) and thus in influencing erosion by two different processes.

Recurrence of Glacial Periods. — The comparatively fresh and slightly weathered character of the drift indicates that the latest glacier cover over North America and Europe wasted away only a short time ago, and that the four successive incursions of ice discussed in a preceding paragraph have taken place probably well within the last million years. These deposits, however, are comparatively very recent, for occasionally there are discovered very much older rocks which prove on examination to be till with characteristic ice-worn pebbles, firmly cemented into hard rock. These very ancient glacial deposits have been found in so many parts of the world and in rocks of so many different ages that we can conclude that glaciation has occurred at many times during the past, separated by long intervals during which there was probably no ice at all on the Earth, even at the poles. We are living now in a condition intermediate between these extremes, and as far as we can predict the future, other heavy glaciations and ice-free times probably will occur. For this reason the behavior of glacier ice and its effect in sculpturing the land is an intensely interesting study, not only because of the impressive glacial features in the landscapes of today, but also because of its bearing on the study of the Earth's past and on our speculations as to its future.

READING REFERENCES

1. Alaskan Glacier Studies; by R. S. Tarr and Lawrence Martin. 448 pages. National Geographic Society, Washington, 1913.

An interesting study, finely illustrated, of present-day glaciers on the coast of Alaska.

2. Characteristics of Existing Glaciers; by W. H. Hobbs. 301 pages. The Macmillan Co., New York, 1911.

An entertaining general discussion of glaciers and ice sheets in various parts of the world.

3. Glaciology; by C. S. Wright and R. F. Priestley. British (Terra Nova) Antarctic Expedition, 1910–1913. Harrison and Sons, London, 1922.

A sound and careful discussion of studies of part of the Antarctic Ice Sheet.

4. The Natural History of Ice and Snow; by A. E. H. Tutton. 319 pages. Kegan Paul, London, 1927.

A popular account of the glaciers of the Alps, illustrated with excellent photographs.

5. Ice Ages Recent and Ancient; by A. P. Coleman. 296 pages. The Macmillan Co., New York, 1926.

A popularly written discussion of the records left by former ice sheets and the causes that may have contributed to ice-sheet formation.

6. The Ice Age in North America; by G. F. Wright. 763 pages. 5th edition. Oberlin, Ohio, 1911.

An account in simple style dealing with the ice sheets that formerly covered parts of North America and prefaced by a discussion of glaciers and ice sheets in various parts of the world.

7. Das Eiszeitalter; by Paul Woldstedt. 410 pages. Ferdinand Enke, Stuttgart, 1929.

The only up-to-date discussion of the Ice Age in any language. Sound and informative.

CHAPTER VII

EROSION AND DEPOSITION BY WIND

Moving currents of air have both indirect and direct geologic effects. They are of prime importance in controlling weather conditions, including rainfall; and these conditions in turn govern not only weathering of the rocks but also erosion by streams. Winds also create waves and currents on the sea; thus they bring about marine erosion of coasts, and also establish a large part of the mechanism by which sediments derived from the lands are distributed on the sea floor (Chap. VIII). If the atmosphere in motion performed only these indirect functions it would be one of the most significant geological agents; but its importance is increased greatly by direct erosion and distribution of rock material.

WIND EROSION

Erosion by wind is of two distinct kinds. Loose particles of the mantle, such as grains of sand and silt, are picked up by moving air and carried from one place to another. This process is *deflation* (from Latin *de + flare*, to blow from). In their motion the wind-driven particles strike against each other, against pebbles and boulders on the ground, and against exposed bedrock; as a result additional particles are worn from the bedrock and from the original loose pieces. This process, analogous to abrasion by running water (p. 41), is *wind abrasion*.

Deflation. — In regions that have large or moderate rainfall the results of deflation are not conspicuous. Grass and other vegetation protect a large part of the mantle, and where no vegetation exists the soil particles and sand grains are held together by moisture much of the time. In dry weather, however, clouds of dust are raised from streets, roads, and plowed fields, and the abundance of fine material transported by a hard dry wind is suggested by the quantity swept into houses. Along seashores the beach sand dries to some extent at low tide, and the wind blows it bit by bit beyond the reach of high tide. Storm waves and unusual tides also carry quantities of the sand to a high level, where it becomes thoroughly dry and is driven farther inland by onshore winds. The shores of large lakes also are favorable localities for wind work; parts of Lake Michigan, for example, are bordered by large areas of shifting sand. But the essential combination of conditions for effective deflation — abundant fine-grained, dry mantle unprotected by vegetation — exists only rarely and locally in lands with humid climates. Not only is the ground frequently dampened by rain, but also the water table is near the surface and the mantle is kept moist by capillary action (Chap. IV). In semiarid and in arid regions vegetation is scanty and the upper part of the mantle is dry most of the time. As fine particles are detached by weathering they are caught up and moved by wind; this action explains in part the abundance of rock outcrops in dry regions of rough topography. Silt and sand carried into lowlands by streams are shifted in large quantities by the wind (Fig. 83). Even when the weather is comparatively quiet, the air, heated by contact with the hot ground, rises in whirls and lifts the dust in tall columns which move slowly across the plains. On a hot summer afternoon dozens of these columns can be seen at the same time in different parts of a wide arid basin. During storms the air is filled with dust to a great height and a sheet of sand is driven along the ground. In the deserts of central Asia and Africa sand storms are a great danger to travelers. Large quantities of dust driven out of the Sahara by exceptional winds fall in the countries of southern Europe, and also in a wide area of the sea as evidenced by dustfalls on the decks of ships in the Mediterranean and hundreds of miles off the west coast of Africa. Great areas in the Libyan Desert of northern Africa are floored with boulders and pebbles that once were scattered through a considerable thickness of finer-grained loose material. When the strong winds blew away the surrounding dust and sand the coarse fragments remained in place, except that they settled down slowly as they were undermined, and so they have accumulated until they mantle the entire surface.

The effects of deflation are conspicuous also in some parts of the Mohave Desert and other arid regions in the southwestern United States. Sand storms are common in the basins (p. 78), and every strong wind sweeps clouds of dust from the bare surfaces of playas (Fig. 83 and p. 80). Remnants of layers that once were continuous over some of the playas now form isolated knolls, the heights of which give a minimum measure of erosion accomplished by the wind within comparatively recent times (Fig. 128). Many gentle slopes above the levels of the playas are floored with " desert pavements " consisting of pebbles fitted so closely together and with their top surfaces so even that the general effect suggests a mosaic. Such surfaces result from slow removal of the fine material, partly by deflation and partly by slope wash, until the pebbles are concentrated to form a continuous layer and thus the fine material beneath is protected from further erosion.

No doubt much of the dust blown from a desert lowland is dropped in

other parts of the same basin or in neighboring basins, and later is returned by storm waters to the playas.   However, the wind carries much
of the finest material across the mountains and drops it outside the region
of interior drainage.   In this way the Gobi Desert of central Asia has
lost vast quantities of fine silt, part of which has accumulated as a thick
cover on the hills and plains of northern China (p. 169).   It is not possible to estimate the rate at which the average surface of an arid region
is lowered by deflation, but the process appears to be extremely slow in
comparison with stream erosion in regions of plentiful rainfall.   Even
in arid lands streams may accomplish considerably more erosion than

Eliot Blackwelder.

Fig. 128. — Danby Playa, Mohave Desert, California.   The low hills are capped with
a layer of gypsum, which protects the underlying silt from the wind.   Presumably the
caps were once continuous and all the material that once filled the spaces between the
buttes has been blown away by the wind.

the wind.   It should be kept in mind, however, that in areas of interior
drainage, such as the Great Basin, running water can do no more than
level the surface in some degree by eroding material from higher altitudes and depositing it in the basins (p. 79).   The only actual lowering
of the general surface through erosion is accomplished by the wind, which
is the one agent that can carry material outside the boundaries of the
region.

Extreme aridity is not essential to effective deflation.   On the Great
Plains east of the Rocky Mountains and in similar semiarid districts,
large quantities of the silt and sand deposited by streams during floods
are blown from the dry floodplains and channels in times of drought
when the streams shrink to small trickles or disappear.   Not all parts
of the uplands are protected by grass, and the wind takes its toll where

dry soil is exposed. Since " dry farming " has been instituted on a large scale the plowed fields have greatly increased the effectiveness of deflation on the Great Plains. Occasionally during winter months the dust carried by a high wind sweeping the dry plains sifts down and discolors the surface of snow far to the east in the northern Mississippi Valley. On such rare occasions the reality of deflation is emphasized and one gets some conception of the great distances to which fine dust is carried. During most of the year, however, the films of dust borne by wind into humid regions settle unnoticed and are washed away by the next rain.

Wind Abrasion. — The abrasive effect of wind-blown sand is illustrated by the artificial sandblast, operated with compressed air, which is used to clean the begrimed surfaces of stone and brick buildings. Along coasts the sand driven by winds abrades so effectively that glass in the window panes of houses has been known to lose its transparency during a single storm. In some arid regions wooden telegraph poles can not be used because they are cut down quickly by wind-blown sand, and in exceptional localities the steel rails of railways have been worn thin by the natural sandblast. The effectiveness of wind-blown sand as a cutting or abrading agent is explained by the hardness and strength of sand grains, most of which are made of quartz. Any grains composed of soft minerals like calcite, or of such minerals as feldspar that are weakened by cleavage planes, are ground or broken to bits by continued wear, and the quartz grains, with some garnet and other less common hard minerals, become concentrated. Thus with continued use the tools of wind abrasion become more effective.

The most essential conditions for wind abrasion on a large scale are extreme aridity with consequent lack of vegetation, persistent strong winds, an abundance of hard sand grains, and bedrock that is fairly soft or weakly cemented. These conditions are combined ideally in the Libyan Desert, in northern Africa west of the Nile Valley, one of the most rainless districts known. For eleven consecutive years the weather station at Dakhla reported no rainfall. Except for a few small scattered oases around springs and wells the country is almost without vegetation. Strong winds blow steadily from the northwest, and since there are no abrupt mountain ridges the force of the wind is not seriously checked. In the northern part of the region there are large outcrops of weakly cemented sandstone which disintegrates easily; the loose sand thus formed is carried to the south, where the bedrock is chiefly limestone and weak sandstone. With such a combination of favorable factors wind abrasion is an important process in wearing away the surface of the land. Its effects are most evident on the limestone, which is soft but firm and compact, and therefore becomes polished and grooved under the persistent action of the sandblast (Fig. 129). Hard objects in the rock, such as fossils or flint nodules, are etched out in strong relief as the surrounding limestone is worn away, and outcrops are carved into rugged fantastic forms. Since abrasion is most effective near the ground, where most of the coarse sand moves, cliffs tend to be undercut, and slender columns are worn at their bases until they topple over. Areas that have unusually weak bedrock and others that are most favorably situated for wind attack are abraded, and the ground-up material is blown away until large undrained depressions are formed. None of these results are produced rapidly, however; at best the process is ex-

A. W. Rogers, Geol. Survey, Union of South Africa.

Fig. 129. — Limestone polished and grooved by wind-blown sand.
Namib, Southwest Africa.

tremely slow, and it is not possible to judge how much is accomplished directly by abrasion and how much by mechanical weathering combined with deflation of the loosened particles. Disintegration and abrasion together produce fine material which is carried away by the wind. So long as Libya keeps its present climate the wind will remain the only important agent of erosion. Running water is a negligible factor, as shown by the total absence of modern stream channels in most of the region.

Ventifacts. — A conspicuous effect of abrasion in arid regions, and in a more limited way along sandy coasts in humid countries, is the polishing and peculiar shaping of pebbles that have lain for a long time on the ground in wind-swept areas. Sand driven by the wind grinds the pebbles smooth and slowly cuts upon many of them slightly curved facets that intersect along sharp edges (Fig. 130). If one side of a pebble fronts for a long time toward the prevailing wind it finally develops into a facet that slopes upward away from the wind at an angle ranging from 30° to 60° from the horizontal (Fig. 130).   If the pebble becomes undermined so that it topples into a different position another facet develops in the same way. Thus the number and the shape of facets vary considerably; but a common form of sand-blasted pebble is elongate, with three nearly equal faces that taper toward the ends.   This form suggests a Brazil nut. Ordinarily the pebbles are made of quartz and of other minerals or rocks of superior hardness, and the facets have a high polish.   Many of these

Fig. 130. — Typical ventifacts (wind-worn pebbles). The large one with three converging corners came from the desert of western Australia; the others — which resemble Brazil nuts — are from Southwest Africa.   About natural size.

remarkable stones have a striking resemblance to artifacts made by men of the Old Stone Age.   Partly for this reason, but chiefly to suggest the origin of the polish and the peculiar form, a wind-worn pebble is called a *ventifact* (*made by wind*).

Ventifacts are valued in geology not for their own sake, but because their presence in large numbers in a region where conditions now are not suitable for their formation indicates a radical change in the physical environment after their development.   For example, an ancient gravel deposit widely distributed in northwestern Scotland contains numerous

ventifacts, although the humid climate and consequent abundant vegetation do not permit any appreciable wind abrasion in that region at
present.

Wind Abrasion in the United States. — No part of the United States
is comparable to Libya as a theatre of wind erosion.   Even the driest
portions of Nevada, Arizona, and eastern California have rainfall enough
for the development of stream channels, and it is clear that running water
is the dominant agent of erosion and deposition in that region.   Wind

C. E. Erdmann.

Fig. 131. — Cloud of sand raised by a moderate wind, head of Black Canyon, Colorado
River, southern Nevada.   Violent winds sweep sand through such narrow defiles with
great force, polishing and grooving the rock walls.

abrasion is conspicuous locally, as on the lower parts of the walls of narrow canyons through which sand-laden wind is forced with unusual violence (Fig. 131).   Polished rock surfaces, usually grooved or fluted, are
developed in this way.   Areas floored with weak sandstone and exposed
to exceptionally hard winds are abraded irregularly to form shallow basins that hold water after rains.   It does not appear, however, that the
total effect of abrasion is large.   If natural sandblasting operated widely
in that region we should find polished and grooved surfaces widely distributed.   Instead, most of the outcrops are rough from weathering,
and many surfaces are dark with *desert varnish*, a peculiar shiny black
coating of manganese oxide which forms very slowly, probably through

the activities of lichens that draw the manganese from the rock and use it in their growth. Effective wind abrasion would prevent this slow accumulation on exposed surfaces, and would remove all weathered rock particles from such surfaces.

Pedestal rocks, which consist of wide caps supported by slender columns, are often cited as products of abrasion in the arid Southwest; but most of them result from differential weathering (p. 35). The winds help only by removing some of the loosened particles.

It is concluded, therefore, that the only wind erosion of general importance in the southwestern United States is performed by deflation of dust and sand (p. 156). Abrasion is a subordinate process, local in its operation.

WIND DEPOSITS

Like running water, wind loses its carrying power for various reasons and drops its load of débris. Some of the resulting deposits are only temporary; they are partially or wholly destroyed by the next strong wind. Other accumulations remain in place until by compaction and cementation they become sedimentary rocks (p. 211). Numerous layers of ancient sandstone are interpreted as wind-laid or *eolian* deposits.

Dunes

Wind-blown débris, usually sand, accumulates to form rounded or irregular hillocks known as *dunes*. Ordinarily the growth of a dune is started by an obstacle, such as a stone, a bush, or an irregularity in the surface of the ground, which breaks the force of the wind; after the resulting heap of sand has grown to appreciable size it acts as its own windbreak and causes further deposition. Where sand is abundant and the winds are exceptionally strong some dunes grow as high as 100 feet or rarely, as in northern Africa, more than 400 feet. If prevailing winds blow inland across a sandy shore a belt of dunes is formed; such a belt, with some exceptionally large dunes, exists along the east coast of Lake Michigan, where the westerly winds are furnished with a large supply of beach sand. In arid regions the lack of vegetation and the dryness of the ground permit the most effective accumulation of sand grains by the wind and therefore the most extensive development of dunes. However, the popular conception that the entire surface of a desert is mantled with shifting sand is erroneous. Arabia is more widely mantled with dune sand than any other large region, and yet the sand covers only one-third of the total area. About one-ninth of the Sahara is covered with drifting sand. Large tracts in all deserts are floored either with bedrock or with boulders and pebbles. Fine-grained material is swept from these areas as fast as it forms; dust is carried far away, and ordinarily the sand accumulates on the lower ground, either on the lee sides of low ridges where the force of the prevailing wind is broken or at the windward bases of high, steep ranges across which the wind can not transport it.

Even in the most arid districts the abundance of sand available for dune formation varies greatly with the character of the exposed bedrock. In southern Nevada some large areas in which the bedrock is chiefly limestone and shale are almost devoid of dunes. The most favorable bedrock is sandstone, which becomes loose sand as it disintegrates. In

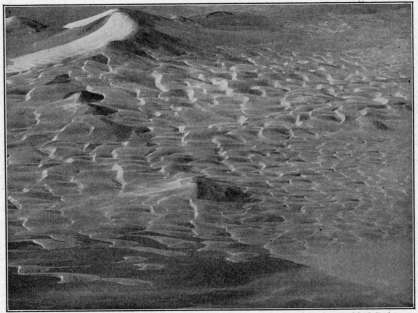

American Geographical Society.

Fig. 132. — A large group of sand dunes seen from the air. The prevailing wind is from right to left; hence the right-hand slopes are gentle, the left-hand slopes steep. Note the crescentic form of the isolated dunes in left foreground. Ancon, Peru. (G. R. Johnson, "Peru from the Air.")

Utah and Arizona some thick formations of sandstone disintegrate so rapidly that the wind can not remove the sand as fast as it is set free, and dunes form among the rock outcrops on high ridges as well as in the more protected lowlands.

Form and Structure of Dunes. — In the growth of a dune the sand is swept up the windward slope, falls over the crest, and rolls down the lee side. The result is a form with an asymmetric profile (Fig. 132); the force of the wind tends to flatten the slope up which it moves, but on the protected side the sand is influenced only by gravity and so lies at the *angle of repose,* which ranges from 20° to 30°, and exceptionally to 40°, depending on the coarseness and angularity of the grains. If the dune is an isolated feature, the wind, provided it blows steadily in the same direction, sweeps by on either flank and builds two long, pointed arms, making a typical *barchan,* which is a dune with crescent-shaped plan (Fig. 132). Even where dunes are closely crowded many of them approximate this form if the wind has a prevailing direction. Shifting winds prevent completion of the typical form or quickly modify it and cause extreme irregularity. Usually the surface of a dune is covered with small parallel ridges an inch or so in height (Fig. 133); these are called

W. C. Mendenhall, U. S. Geol. Survey.

Fig. 133. — Ripple marks on traveling dunes. Colorado Desert, California.

ripple marks from their resemblance to markings made at the bottom of shallow water by the action of small waves or ripples (p. 223).

The successive layers of sand added to a dune are deposited parallel with its surface and so are more steeply inclined on the lee than on the windward side. Thus the form of a dune is reflected in its internal structure. When shifting winds partly destroy the original form the layers are cut across and their edges are covered by new layers deposited at a different angle. Therefore sand-dune deposits are characterized by extremely irregular *cross-bedding* (p. 225).

Migration of Dunes. — So long as the sand on its surface is free to move, a dune is not stationary. The windward slope is not a fixed incline up which the wind moves only newly acquired sand; the slope itself is eroded by the wind, and the sand grains removed from it are dumped over the crest. By this subtraction of material from one side and addition to the other the dune moves forward slowly, provided the wind direction is fairly constant. In this way dunes formed along a shore migrate inland across low country, and the movement halts only when grass or other vegetation gains sufficient foothold in the sand to hold it in place. In France and some other European countries belts of dunes moving from the coast have destroyed farm lands, forests, and villages. Along some parts of the Bay of Biscay and of the Baltic region the menace of dune migration has been ended by skilful planting of trees and shrubs. In the United States also considerable damage has been done by drifting sand, particularly near some of the Great Lakes and along many parts of the coasts, both east and west (Fig. 134).

The largest belt of coastal dune sand is along the Bay of Biscay in western France; it is about 150 miles long and from 2.5 to 6 miles wide.

D. W. Johnson.

Fig. 134. — Shore dunes near Cape Henry, Virginia, migrating inland (to the left) and killing the forest in their path.

From this tract dunes travel inland at varying rates up to more than 100 feet per year, across a low swampy area known as the *Landes*. Numerous villages and considerable areas of farm land have been destroyed. At Lège the church was taken down at the end of the seventeenth century and built 2.5 miles farther inland to save it from the encroaching sand; 100 years later it had to be rebuilt again, because the sand had once more reached it. The average rate at which the dunes traveled during this time was 81 feet per year.

Economic Value of Dunes. — Although dunes generally are destructive and barren, in some arid countries they are the only natural reservoirs of fresh water. The sands absorb the scanty rainfall, the water table rises in a curve roughly parallel with the surface (Fig. 135), and at favorable localities shallow wells furnish enough water to form oases of considerable size; in northern Egypt large groves of palm trees are supported in this way.   In some parts of western Texas, ranches get water from shallow wells put down at the very summits of large dunes.

Fig. 135. — Cross section showing conditions favorable for local water supply in dunes. Northern Egypt.   *A, A, A*, tops of dunes; *B, C*, shallow wells.   (After W. F. Hume.)

Ancient Dunes. — Over a wide area between Albany, New York, and the Adirondack Mountains there are numerous knolls that have the form of typical dunes, although they are completely covered with grass and trees.   Excavations made into many of these knolls reveal that they are made of clean sand deposited with the typical structure of dunes.   It is thought that near the close of the Ice Age, when much of the surface was mantled with deposits washed from the wasting ice and there was little protecting vegetation, the wind swept great quantities of sand from the Adirondack region and formed dunes on the adjacent plain.

In Bermuda many artificial cuts reveal a peculiar limestone that has the cross-bedded structure of dunes.   Evidently this is an old dune deposit similar to that now forming along the Bermuda shores, where the sand consists of coral limestone ground up by wave action.   Dunes are built of this sand, the grains become cemented, and the result is new limestone like that exposed in the cuts.   Under exceptional conditions various other minerals and rocks have furnished débris that has been built into dunes.   An area of 500 square miles in New Mexico is covered with dunes made of snow-white gypsum which was derived from disintegrating beds of gypsum exposed at the surface.   Some of this gypsum sand is still shifting with the winds; but in many of the older dunes the mineral has crystallized until the grains are bound together firmly.

The examples cited above relate to dunes which, though they are no longer active, were formed in fairly recent geologic time.   In the older sedimentary strata we recognize dune structure, now preserved in firmly cemented sandstones, which gives a record of shifting sands in ancient geologic periods.

Loess

What has become of the great quantities of fine material removed from land surfaces by deflation?   Part of the answer is given by a peculiar yellowish, fine-grained sediment that covers vast areas in Asia, Europe, and North and South America.   Typically it has no horizontal stratification, like that in ordinary sedimentary formations, but occurs in a single massive layer, 20, 50, or even more than 100 feet thick.   On the other hand, it is full of slender perpendicular tubes which cause a rough vertical cleavage; for this reason it forms high bluffs along valley sides in spite of the soft, earthy character of the material (Fig. 136).   This sediment, so similar in widely separated continents, is known by the German name *loess*.

Although loess is exceedingly fine grained, examination with a powerful microscope reveals that a large proportion of the material is not decomposed but consists of fresh, sharp-cornered particles of feldspar, quartz, calcite, mica, and numerous other minerals mingled with clay.

U. S. Geol. Survey.

Fig. 136. — Typical bluff of loess with vertical columnar structure. Near Beverly, Missouri.

It is evident, therefore, that much of the material was ground up mechanically, and that the particles thus formed were not affected by chemical weathering before their deposition.   Because of these characteristics loess is interpreted as an accumulation of wind-blown dust.   In support of this conclusion numerous shells of land snails and bones of land animals are found in the deposits.   Moreover, loess is distributed at various heights on very irregular topography; the wind is the only agent that could deposit in this way sediments that are uniformly fine grained. Lack of stratification is to be expected in wind-laid dusts, since the deposit at any one time is thin and after deposition it is worked over with the underlying sediments by rain, frost, worms, and growing plants. The vertical tubes that are so common in loess appear to represent the stems and roots of successive generations of plants that were buried by the accumulating dust.

In central Europe and in the Mississippi Valley the dust forming the loess probably was supplied by the dried floors of temporary lakes and by floodplains of streams that drained from the wasting glaciers during the Ice Age. While these wide sheets of sediment lay unprotected by vegetation the wind carried the finest-grained material and spread it out on the uplands; the abundance of fresh rock flour ground up by the ice movement explains the large percentage of unweathered, angular particles derived from numerous kinds of rocks and minerals.

In northern China an area as large as France is covered with loess with a maximum thickness of several hundred feet. Streams have cut canyons into it, and the quantities of yellow silt continuously eroded from the area are responsible for the names of the Yellow River and the Yellow Sea. Without reasonable doubt this vast deposit of loess represents the age-long accumulation of dust blown across the mountains from the arid interior of Asia, and especially from the Ordos and Gobi deserts. Thus, although dust forming this loess was quite different in its origin from that in Europe and the United States, the material is similar because it also was prepared mechanically; in the deserts of Asia it is the result of disintegration and wind abrasion in an arid climate, and therefore fresh, angular particles make up a good proportion of the deposit. The Chinese loess forms the richest soil of China, and for centuries many of the humbler farmers in the hilly districts have made their homes in artificial caves dug into the steep loess bluffs. In these districts some of the roads used for a long time have become narrow, steep-walled canyons as the dust loosened by travel has been removed steadily by wind and rain wash.

A great belt of rich black soil extending from east to west across Russia is supposed to be a deposit of wind-blown dust. In the southwestern United States some of the widespread clay and silt known as *adobe*, from which sun-dried bricks are made, probably originated as a wind deposit, although in large part it was later worked over and redeposited by water. Some of the Chinese loess also has the stratification and other characteristics of water deposits. It is to be expected that fine sediments dropped by the wind in semiarid and humid countries would be modified to some extent by the action of running water.

Loess and related deposits represent only the most conspicuous accumulations of wind-blown dust; unquestionably, dust carried in the upper air, supplied either by deflation or by eruptions of fine volcanic ash (Chap. XI), settles slowly on the entire land surface and on the sea floor. Probably almost every layer of sedimentary rock contains at least a small amount of eolian dust.   Some thick-bedded shales or mud-stones are interpreted as loess laid down in various periods of geologic history and preserved by favorable circumstances to become part of the sedimentary record.   Most loess deposits, however, because of their elevated positions on the continents and the weak character of the material, are subject to rapid destruction by stream erosion.

READING REFERENCES

1. Geology of Egypt, Vol. 1; by W. F. Hume.   220 pages.   Government Press, Cairo, 1925.

Contains valuable data on wind erosion and dune formation in the Libyan desert.

2. The Movement of Soil Material by the Wind; by E. E. Free.   173 pages. U. S. Department of Agriculture, Bulletin 68, 1911.

An extensive study of deflation.   Gives an exhaustive bibliography of eolian geology to 1911.

3. The Indiana Sand Dunes and Shore Lines of the Lake Michigan Basin; by George B. Cressey.   73 pages.   University of Chicago Press, 1928.

CHAPTER VIII

MARINE EROSION AND DEPOSITION

The gradual crumbling of the land under the ceaseless pounding of the surf is a fact familiar to all who have lived near the shore, especially along coasts composed of weak rocks. The seaward shores of Cape Cod and the islands near it yield to the sea from 1 to 6 feet each year, and at the present rate these lands will disappear entirely at the end of about 4000 years, leaving only submarine banks to mark their former positions. Certain stretches of the Yorkshire coast in England have been worn back a mile since the Norman conquest, and 2 miles since the time of the Romans. In the space of 200 years the considerable town of Egmont, on the Dutch coast, was undermined and entirely destroyed by the persistent work of the waves. The cliffs at Dover on the English Channel are receding at the rate of 15 feet each year, and east of them the Goodwin Sands, now a shallow submarine bank, were formerly an island. The island of Helgoland off the mouth of the Elbe, once very large, was being eaten away so rapidly that it would by this time have disappeared entirely had erosion not been checked, near the end of the nineteenth century, by the construction of a powerful sea wall.

The cases cited above concern coasts formed of weak materials, such as chalk, clays, and sands, but the effect of waves on hard rocks is the same except that erosion takes place more slowly.

A study of the sea's behavior therefore has practical value, for its destruction of the land can be stopped for long periods, measured in human terms, as is demonstrated by the case of Helgoland. Thousands of thickly populated districts, where shore property is valuable, have been artificially protected in this way. There is also, however, a philosophical value to the study of the sea, for if marine processes are busy destroying the land, several questions arise. How far can this destruction be carried? Why do not beaches, bars, and other wave-built features stop erosion? And above all, since the sea-covered areas of the Earth are three times as large as the land areas, and since the Earth is admittedly very old, why have the continents not already been destroyed by marine erosion?

Geologic Rôle of the Sea. — There are answers to all these questions, but we must begin by examining the part played by the sea in the evolution of the face of the Earth. Not only is the sea a direct and energetic agent of erosion, tearing away bit by bit the margins of the lands, and thereby aiding the streams in their work of wearing down the continents, but its floor is the final resting-place of all the rock waste eroded from the lands by the waves and currents, and by streams, subsurface water, glaciers, and the wind. This land-derived sediment is shifted for a while along the sea floor, and coming to rest, is ultimately solidified into the sedimentary rock that forms so important a part of the Earth's crust.

Indirectly, too, the sea exercises a great influence on the development of the Earth's surface. Throughout the hundreds of millions of years of geologic history the general temperature of the Earth has never fallen below the freezing point nor exceeded the boiling point of water. For this stability the nearly uniform rate of radiation of energy by the Sun is chiefly responsible, but the sea also serves as an important stabilizer by storing up excess heat against times of lessened solar radiation. The great currents that carry warm water from the equatorial zone into the higher latitudes and the currents that transfer cold polar water toward the equator also exercise an important influence in distributing heat more evenly upon the Earth's surface and in softening the contrasts between climatic zones. Moreover, in the last analysis, evaporation from the surface of the sea supplies all the moisture borne by the winds to fall upon the lands as rain and snow. Thus the sculpture of the lands by streams, glaciers, and subsurface water is ultimately dependent on the great reservoir of the sea.

Terminology. — It is impossible to discuss adequately the great areas of marine water that cover nearly three-quarters of the globe without defining the terms used. The terms " ocean " and " sea " have no universally accepted usage. In popular speech they are more or less interchangeable, although the greatest bodies of water (the Atlantic, Pacific, Indian, and Arctic bodies) are called *oceans*, whereas ordinarily smaller and shallower bodies such as the Yellow Sea and the Bering Sea are spoken of as *seas*. Even this usage is not distinct, for the North Sea, a relatively small shallow body, is called by some the German Ocean, and other seas of similar size and depth are called *bays* and *gulfs* (as Hudson Bay and Gulf of Siam). Moreover, many large salt lakes are called *seas*, as for instance the Caspian Sea, the Dead Sea, and the Salton Sea.

There is, nevertheless, a technical distinction observed by scientists who use the term *ocean* only for the four vast bodies of water mentioned above, occupying the deep basins that lie between the continents. On the other hand, the same people speak of *deep-sea deposits*, of *going to sea*, and of *sea level* when they have in mind the ocean.

In view of these discrepancies it seems best for the purpose of our discussion to define the *sea* as the entire body of confluent marine water of the globe. This includes all the so-called oceans and all the so-called seas actually connected with the oceans, and leaves out only the separate inland bodies of water which, whether fresh or salt, belong in the category of lakes (Chap. V). *Sea level* is then the surface of the sea, and according to variations of depth we shall have *deep sea* and *shallow sea*, each with its characteristic processes, deposits, and living inhabitants.

Shallow seas that lie far in upon a continent and are nearly land-locked are commonly referred to as *epeiric seas* (Greek *epeiros*, a continent). At present there are but two good examples, the Baltic Sea and Hudson Bay, but in the past, when the lower portions of the continents became widely flooded, epeiric seas were of vast extent and of great importance. In fact, most of the sedimentary rocks of the present lands were formed in seas of this kind.

Deep-Sea Basins; Relation to Continental Masses. — If the waters were withdrawn from the deep-sea basins we should see that the grandest relief features of Earth's rocky crust are not its mountain ranges but the continental masses that stand as vast plateaus 3 miles above the extensive plains of the deep-sea floor (Fig. 2). The naked face of the Moon presents to us a spectacle of this sort, for its *maria* or " seas " would be seas in reality if there were water upon its surface.

Presumably the continental masses stand high because they are made of light granitic rocks, and the deep-sea areas are depressed because they are formed of heavy basaltic rocks. On the Moon, the depressed segments are relatively small; but the deep-sea basins of the Earth are far greater than the continental masses.

Size of the Deep-Sea Basins. — Not only do the deep-sea basins have more than twice the area of the continental masses, but they attain a maximum known depth of more than 6 miles (35,410 feet) and an average depth of 2.5 miles (13,000 feet), whereas the average height of the continents above sea level is only about 0.5 mile. So vast is the volume of the deep-sea basins that, if the continents were planed down and their débris dumped into the basins, leveling the Earth to a smooth sphere, the sea would cover the entire Earth to a depth of nearly 2 miles. Even this depth, however, is slight in comparison with the diameter of the Earth. If, for example, a globe 3 feet in diameter were dipped into water and then withdrawn, the film of moisture adhering to it would represent to true scale a sea half a mile in depth. If, in drying, the globe should warp so slightly as to lessen its diameter at any place by only one-hundredth of an inch, the change would correspond to the depth of one of the deep-sea basins.

From such an illustration emerges a fact of the first importance, namely, that a very slight warping of the Earth's crust as a whole produces very great changes in the volumes of the deep-sea basins. Downwarping of their floors greatly increases their capacity and draws water away from the continental shores. Upwarping of the basin floors notably decreases their capacity and forces the water to rise and creep landward across the lower parts of the continents. The presence of widespread marine deposits high and dry upon the land, together with the presence of terrestrial deposits submerged beneath the sea, suggest that these upwarpings and downwarpings have occurred repeatedly throughout the history of the Earth.

Topography of the Deep-Sea Basins. — The term *basin* suggests a concave depression, but the deep-sea basins are depressions only by comparison with the continental masses, for, since they are very shallow compared with the Earth's radius, their floors are actually convex (Fig.

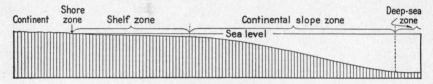

Fig. 137. — The four marine depth zones at the margin of a continental mass (Fig. 2).   Vertical exaggeration 10 ×.

2).   At present the sea more than fills its basins, and spilling over them, it floods the margins of the continental masses, covering the continental shelves (Figs. 2, 137) with shallow water. The shelves are widened partly by continuous erosion of the land by the sea and partly by the deposition of sediment swept into the basins by marine currents. Along stable coasts where these processes have operated with least interruption for long periods of time, the shelves are broad. Thus the shelf beyond the long-quiescent Atlantic coast of North America is 60 to 80 miles wide off the Carolinas. The shelf off the unsteady Pacific Coast, however, is in many places less than 10 miles wide, because throughout recent geologic time this part of the continent and the adjacent sea floor have not stood still long enough to allow a broad shelf to be made.

The deep-sea floor lacks the sculptural detail that characterizes the lands. Broad elevations and depressions there are, but the fine network of valleys that covers the greater part of the continents is lacking. This sharp contrast between the lands and the sea floor is explained by the fact that on the lands erosion is the dominant process, whereas on the

sea floor deposition is dominant.   Deposition tends to fill the minor
depressions and thus to smooth the floor.

Here and there the surface is interrupted by islands and by submerged peaks that are not quite islands.   Most of these, especially those
in the Pacific, are merely great volcanic cones (Chap. XI).   Others
probably are caused by local buckling or fracturing of the Earth's
crust, forming submerged ridges and mountain ranges.   Complemen-
tary to these are the great downwarped or downfractured areas, the
" deeps " of the sea floor (Fig. 2).   Fifty-seven of these " deeps "
are now known, all more than 18,000 feet below sea level.   They are of
two distinct classes: (1) the vast basin-like depressions with irregular
borders that form the central portions of the several major basins; and
(2) narrow troughlike depressions mostly situated near the continental
margins and several of them parallel with coastal mountain ranges.
A good example of the second class is the *Tuscarora Deep*, 28,000 feet in
depth, paralleling the Islands of Japan.   These marginal deeps, or foredeeps, appear to be areas that have been depressed by breaking or
sharp bending of the deep-sea floor in contrast with the uplifted
marginal mountains.

The greatest depth known is in the *Swire Deep*, which lies east of the
Philippine Islands.   About 50 miles east by north of Mindanao, a
depth of 35,410 feet was discovered by the cruiser *Emden* in 1927,
and numerous other soundings in the vicinity show depths of approximately 6 miles.   In the Atlantic, which in general is shallower than the
Pacific, the *Nares Deep*, off Porto Rico, holds the record with 27,972
feet.   These great depressions in the sea floor correspond in area and in
magnitude with the highest elevations on the land.   The greatest deeps
lie more than 6.5 miles below sea level, and the loftiest mountain range,
the Himalaya, stands 5.5 miles above it.

Sea Level. — Although it is customary to use sea level as a common
datum of reference, it should be noted that the surface of the sea is not
a perfect sphere.   Its polar diameter is about 27 miles less than its
equatorial diameter, and in addition there are irregular local departures
from the spherical surface, the most obvious of which is the periodic
distortion imparted to it by the tides.

Tides. — The combined gravitative attraction of the Moon and the
Sun pulls the surface of the Sea into two low but vast bulges, one on each
side of the Earth.   These bulges are the *tides*.   They are fixed with
respect to a line connecting the Earth with the Moon, but since the
Earth in its daily rotation turns from west to east, they seem to move
around the Earth from east to west.   Far out at sea, the surface merely
rises a little and then subsides again as each tidal bulge passes; but

where the bulge impinges against a coast the water is dragged forward, piling up on the shore and then receding (p. 179).

Depth Zones. — It has been stated that the deep-sea basins are over-full, and that the overflow submerges the continental shelves. As a result, there is a sharp distinction between the depth of water over the shelves (whose greatest depth, as it happens, is rarely more than 600 feet) and the depth of water in the basins themselves (which averages 13,000 feet). The shelves slope off into the basins forming *continental slopes*, most of which are so gentle as to require many miles to attain the depth of the deep-sea floors. Accordingly, three important depth zones can be recognized: (1) the *shelf zone*, covering the continental shelves, (2) the *continental-slope zone*, covering the continental slopes, and (3) the *deep-sea zone*, covering the deep-sea floor. At present the combined area of the first two is but a fraction of the area of the third, although a slight upwarping of the deep-sea floors with concurrent downwarping of the continents would enormously increase the shelf zone by forcing the sea to spread far inland over the lowest lands. A fourth zone must be included to make the classification complete: a *shore zone*, which embraces the area between the levels of high and low tide, and which therefore loses its water twice every day. These four zones (Fig. 137) have an important geologic significance, because the processes in operation upon them, the deposits being formed within them, and the forms of life that inhabit them differ strikingly from zone to zone (pp. 197, 209).

Composition of Sea Water. — Dissolved mineral substances constitute 3.5 per cent of the weight of sea water. Chemical analyses from all parts of the sea and from various depths show that the composition of the water is remarkably uniform, and that probably more than 99 per cent of the dissolved mineral matter is represented by only 6 salts,[1] as follows:

	Per cent
Sodium chloride, $NaCl$ (common salt)	77.8
Magnesium chloride, $MgCl_2$	10.9
Magnesium sulphate, $MgSO_4$	4.7
Calcium sulphate, $CaSO_4$	3.6
Potassium sulphate, K_2SO_4	2.5
Calcium carbonate, $CaCO_3$	0.3
Minor constituents	0.2
	100.0

The minor constituents occur in almost infinitesimal amounts, but even these are of geologic importance. Silica (SiO_2) is taken out of the sea by certain organisms and used in building their shells, which accu-

[1] The dissolved mineral matter does not actually exist in the form of these salts; in the table above the components are merely grouped as salts for convenience.

mulate in places as rock-forming sediments. Economically important iron formations have been precipitated from sea water, as have most of the valuable phosphate deposits of Idaho, Florida, and elsewhere.

Although common salt constitutes more than 75 per cent of the mineral matter dissolved in the sea, and although there is little more than a trace of calcium carbonate, yet the streams of the land pour into the sea far more calcium carbonate than common salt. The discrepancy is due to the fact that the carbonate is removed about as fast as it is delivered to the sea, partly by chemical precipitation and partly by the activities of shell-building organisms. On the other hand most of the salt dumped into the sea since the beginning of its history probably has remained in solution.

The total quantity of the dissolved salts is astonishing, amounting to 32,000 million million tons. If precipitated and crystallized into a bed of solid salts, it would form a layer nearly 150 feet thick over the entire surface of the Earth.

Movements of Sea Water

The chief geologic work of the sea is the erosion of the lands and the deposition of the resulting rock waste on the sea floor. This work is accomplished almost entirely through movement of the water, and the various kinds of movement must therefore be considered. The chief motions of sea water take the form of *waves* and *currents*. Of the two. waves are much the more effective as agents of erosion.

Waves. — Waves of the sea are generated by the wind blowing in irregular gusts and pressing unevenly upon the surface of the water, which is thereby thrown into undulations. Once formed, these undulations are maintained and increased by the pressure against their windward sides, and so are driven forward in endless succession.

It is only the *wave form* — not the water itself — that travels forward. An analogous case is the rippling of wind across a field of grain, making the stalks bow as each wind-wave passes, but allowing each to return to its former position. Indeed, if the water actually rushed forward with the velocity of storm waves, the sea would hardly be navigable. The path of movement of any one particle of water is almost a circle, for it rises and rides forward with the crest of the wave only to slide back into the next trough, nearly to its original position,[1] a fact that can be observed by watching a bit of cork or driftwood as the waves pass under it.

The height (of crests above troughs) and length (from crest to crest)

[1] Wind-friction prevents it from returning to exactly its original position, so that it is slightly advanced by each wave. In this manner, *wind-formed currents* are generated.

of the waves increase with the velocity of the wind, with its duration in a given direction, and with the length of " fetch " across open water. For this reason small bodies of water and protected embayments of the coast are never affected by great waves.

Wave motion decreases so rapidly with increasing depth of water that even great storm waves can not disturb the bottom at depths greater than a few hundred feet. Observations indicate that sea floors off exposed coasts are generally affected by waves to a depth of 200 to 300 feet, and that exceptional waves move fine sediments outward to the edges of the continental shelves at depths of about 600 feet.

When a wave passes into shallow water, an important change takes place in its form and behavior. The wave becomes higher and shorter and its front side steeper and more deeply concave until the crest arches forward, loses its support, and collapses in a rush of water, forming a *breaker* (Fig. 138). The water in the breaker, unlike that of the unbroken wave, actually moves forward. The height of the wave determines the depth at which it will break, and therefore small waves break in the very shallow water close inshore, whereas great storm waves usually break farther out, where the water is from 10 to 20 feet deep.

Currents. — There are several kinds of marine currents, only the chief of which need be considered here. *Surface currents* are produced

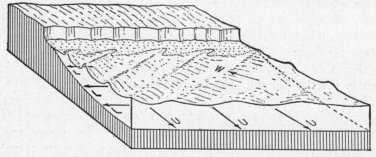

Fig. 138. — Relation of undertow (*U*) and longshore currents (*L*) to direction of waves (*W*), when waves strike the shore obliquely. In the background are a wave-cut cliff and beach.

by the friction of the wind when it blows persistently in one direction for a time. Two types of current, *undertow* and *longshore currents*, are generated by waves. Undertow is set up by the seaward escape of water piled up on the shore by the breaking of waves (Fig. 138). Longshore currents are set up by waves that strike the shore obliquely, and thus have a component of motion along the shore (Fig. 138). Since nearly all waves are oblique to the shore, longshore currents are very common. Sweeping rock fragments along, they are responsible for the formation of beaches, spits, and bars.   The fine sand of Daytona Beach, Florida, comes not from Florida, but from alongshore farther north, where the rivers of Georgia and the Carolinas bring it down to the sea out of the southern Appalachians.

Figs. 139–140. — Tides in the Bay of Fundy, Port Williams, Nova Scotia.
Fig. 139. — High tide.
Fig. 140. — Low tide.   Note the same bridge and ship in both views.

Tidal Currents. — Strong currents are set up along many coasts by the tides (p. 175).   The height of tide is determined largely by the configuration of the coast. On open, exposed coasts it is not more than 6 or 8 feet, and in nearly land-locked embayments such as the Gulf of Mexico it is only 1 or 2 feet. In estuaries that open out toward the advancing tide, however, the water piles up as it is crowded forward into the ever-narrowing bays. This " funneling action " brings about exceptional conditions, such as those in the Bay of Fundy, where the tide rises normally 30 to 40 feet and exceptionally as much as 50 feet (Figs. 139, 140).

These immense tidal bodies of water, ceaselessly moving in and out of bays and estuaries and along coasts, set up strong currents which scour the bottom and transport quantities of sediment. The rise and fall of the tides also aids indirectly in the attack of the waves on the land, by increasing their vertical range.

Ocean Currents. — In addition to the currents generated near the shore there are much broader, less readily perceptible movements that constantly affect the sea far from land. Some are so faint as to be mere drifts. A number of factors combine to keep them in operation. One is the greater amount of solar heat received by the sea at the equator than near the poles. This sets up a slow poleward flow of surface water. Another factor is contributed by the trade winds, which, blowing steadily westward, give a westward direction to the drift of the surface water in each hemisphere. Where they strike continental shelves, these slow currents are deflected poleward along the continental slopes, and are thereby given a circular eddying motion.

The ocean currents reach the sea floor only in very shallow parts of the continental shelves and rarely pass over it with sufficient velocity to move sediment. As agents of erosion therefore they are only very locally significant. On the other hand, they exert a strong indirect effect by greatly modifying the climates of the lands they pass to windward. The equatorial currents carry warmth to the polar sea, and polar currents bring low temperatures and icebergs into middle latitudes.

The Work of Waves and Currents

Erosion. — The chief factors inherent in marine erosion are mechanical, and are caused by the attack of waves upon the land. They are *hydraulic action, abrasion,* and *transportation.* (Compare processes of stream erosion, p. 40.)

Hydraulic Action. — The force of impact of large waves due to the sheer weight of tons upon tons of surging water is enormous. Measurements made with a dynamometer on the coast of Scotland show the average force of waves to be 611 pounds per square foot during the summer, and 2086 pounds (with extremes up to 6083 pounds) in winter. The damage done by storms to harbors and breakwaters bears further testimony to the force of sea waves. At Wick, Scotland, during a great storm in 1872, a solid mass of stone and concrete weighing 1350 tons was torn from its place at the end of a breakwater and dropped unbroken inside the pier. When great waves strike against a cliff or sea wall they not uncommonly dash up to heights of 100 feet or more. During a storm on the exposed coast of Oregon in 1902, water from the waves at Tilla-mook Rock lighthouse was thrown vertically more than 200 feet, and during the winters of both [1912 and 1913 the impact of the waves broke panes of plate glass in the lantern of the same lighthouse at a height of 132 feet above the sea. It is not surprising, therefore, that the faces of cliffs are shattered by the impact of storm waves.

Hydraulically compressed air is an additional factor important in eroding cliffs made of fissured and jointed rocks. The air in the fissures, violently compressed by the impact of the waves, acts as a wedge, springing out large pieces of rock.

Abrasion. — Abrasion is much more important than hydraulic action in the erosion of coasts by the sea. The waves are well equipped for abrasion since they are continuously supplied with rock particles of various sizes by streams and with the débris they themselves wrest from the shore. Sand and pebbles are rubbed together and ground against the shore by every breaking wave, but the erosive process is enormously hastened by the great waves of occasional storms, which fling large pebbles and even boulders against the land, and then return to the at-tack with new weapons in the form of fragments of the eroded shore it-self. By this process the sea slowly but steadily advances upon the land as the opposing cliffs stubbornly yield ground.

In the process of abrasion the eroded rock fragments, shifted back-ward and forward by the waves, are themselves ground up and reduced to increasing fineness. Angular when first torn from the land, they gradually become rounded.

Transportation and Deposition. — If wave erosion is to continue, the ground-up rock débris must be removed, in order that fresh rock surfaces may be exposed to attack; otherwise the fine material would act as a buffer, protecting the shore from further erosion. This removal is ac-complished by backwash, undertow, tidal currents, and longshore currents.

Because of the circular motion of the water in an unbroken wave, a grain of sediment on the bottom tends to be lifted and carried slightly forward as each wave crest passes, but is carried down and back to its original position by the trough of the wave, so that no actual transportation is accomplished by the wave itself.   But when the particle of sediment is lifted free of the bottom, even the gentlest current can deflect its fall; in this way gentle currents, aided by the repeated lift of the waves, can sweep along sediments that they alone would be powerless to move.

When waves reach shallow water and begin to drag heavily on the bottom, their movement ceases to be one strictly of oscillation, for then the water tends to roll ahead and drag the bottom sediment forward with it. Since the waves drag bottom only when approaching the shore, they tend to transport the sediment landward.   This tendency is opposed by the undertow which tends to shift the sediment down the seaward slope. These seaward forces act continuously and are able, therefore, to overcome the stronger but intermittent surges of the waves.   Although the sediment is dragged back and forth with each passing wave, the net movement of the fine material is seaward.   On the other hand the undertow may be unable to transport coarse material which the breaking waves drag forward, and when this is true the coarse sediment migrates landward even though the fine material is being shifted seaward.   It is recorded, for example, that stone ballast discharged from ships off the British coast in water 60 feet deep was thrown up on the beach during a subsequent storm.   This factor keeps the coarse sediment concentrated at the shore, where it forms *beach shingle*.

When sediment is so abundant that the waves can carry forward more than undertow and longshore currents can remove, even fine sand is shifted shoreward and piled up in beaches.   The beach deposits are but temporary accumulations, however, for shoreward transportation necessarily deepens the water offshore, reduces the amount transported shoreward, and permits undertow and longshore currents to remove the beach sand again bit by bit.

Throughout the attack of the sea upon the land, therefore, all the rock waste handled by the waves and currents is in a state of irregular transit seaward.   To be sure, there are temporary halts and temporary reversals of direction, but the ultimate result is the removal of all the material derived from the land, and its deposition in places too deep to be affected by the motion of the water.

Development of the Shore Profile.[1] — Having examined the processes of erosion by waves and currents, we can now study the effects of erosion on the profile of the shore.   As the waves eat into the land they form a

[1] Technically, the *shoreline* is the line along which the sea intersects the land, the *shore* is the narrow zone lying between the low-tide shoreline and the high-tide shoreline, and the *coast* is a strip of indefinite width extending landward from the shore.

wave-cut cliff (Fig. 141) which retreats under their attack.   Actual cutting is confined to the narrow zone between the wave crests at high tide and the wave troughs at low tide.   The rock above this zone is gradually undercut, however, and falls down in occasional slides to the foot of the cliff.   Here is built a *beach*, composed of wave-handled débris worn from the cliff and therefore sandy or pebbly according to the kind of rock into which the cliff is cut.   Sometimes the beach is partly cut away, sometimes it is greatly added to, but always it consists of rock waste in intermittent transit from the cliff to the deeper water offshore.

American Geographical Society.

Fig. 141. — Wave-cut cliff at Lagarto Head on the coast of Peru.   An early stage of the cycle of marine erosion, in which not even a beach has yet formed.   The sea is cutting into an upland maturely dissected by streams.   (G. R. Johnson, "Peru from the Air.")

If the rock forming the cliff is cut by vertical fissures, the waves commonly widen them and quarry out blocks, leaving great masses of rock standing isolated as *stacks* (Fig. 142).   If the joints are more irregular and intersect before reaching the summit of the cliff, *sea caves* and *arches* are formed at the base of the cliff.   As the cliff slowly retreats, followed by the beach, it leaves behind it a rock platform over which the water is shallow.   This is the *wave-cut bench* (Figs. 142, 143).   Its submerged surface is lowered by abrasion as waves and undertow sweep débris back and forth across it, and it is widened landward as fast as the cliff retreats. The bench is usually covered with a veneer of rock waste in seaward transit across it, and at its outer edge this waste is dumped in deeper water, forming a *wave-built terrace* (Fig. 143), which widens as it is gradually built seaward.

These three elements of the shore profile — the retreating cliff, the wave-cut bench being widened landward by erosion, and the wave-built terrace being widened seaward by deposition, continue to develop as long as waves come ashore and as long as the level of the sea remains constant.

G. W. Stose, U. S. Geol. Survey.

Fig. 142. — Elevated wave-cut bench surmounted by stacks, north of Port Harford, California. The coast has risen in relation to sea level since the formation of the bench, which is now being attacked and undermined by the waves.

The double curve ultimately formed by the combined profiles of the bench and the wave-built terrace is the *profile of equilibrium,* representing a delicate adjustment between erosion on the one hand and deposition on the other. It corresponds to the profile of grade in a stream (p. 48). Notably curved at first, it gradually flattens out like the graded stream profile as erosion and deposition continue.

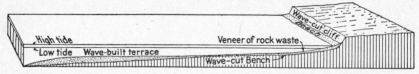

Fig. 143. — Typical shore profile showing (1) the wave-cut cliff with the beach at its base, (2) the wave-cut bench veneered with rock waste, and (3) the wave-built terrace made of accumulated débris.

EVOLUTION OF THE SHORELINE

An examination of the shorelines of all the continents shows that most of them are of two distinct kinds. Some, like those of New England and most of western Europe including the British Isles, are bold, rocky, and highly irregular, with alternating bays and promontories (Fig. 144). Others, like those along the southern Atlantic coast of the United States and the Gulf coast of the United States and Mexico, are low, devoid of hard rocks, and fringed with long, low, sandy islands back of which are shallow lagoons.

These two kinds of shorelines are wholly unlike and tell very different stories as to their past history. The bold irregular shorelines border land areas that have been depressed by downwarping of the Earth's crust or by actual rise of sea level, so that the mouths of the stream valleys have become flooded, forming estuaries, and the higher interstream areas

Compagnie Aérienne Française.

Fig. 144. — Shoreline of submergence in the stage of youth. St. Briac, Brittany. The finer débris eroded from the headlands has been swept into the bays, forming bayhead beaches. Two islands have been tied by bars to the mainland.

have remained above water, forming long promontories or headlands. The mouths of the valleys are then said to be *drowned*. On the contrary, the low, weak-rock shorelines border areas of former sea floor (of the shelf zone) raised slightly above the water by upwarping of the crust or lowering of sea level. The drowned shoreline we may call the *shoreline of submergence*, and the latter the *shoreline of emergence*.[1] Once formed, each is exposed to attack by the sea, and shaped by waves and currents, each goes through a cycle of marine erosion involving youth, maturity, and old age, just as do land masses under the control of

[1] Certain shorelines, it is true, show the effects of neither submergence nor emergence, as for example those formed by deltas and by the pouring out of lava upon stationary volcanic islands. Such features, however, form but a small proportion of the shorelines of the world.

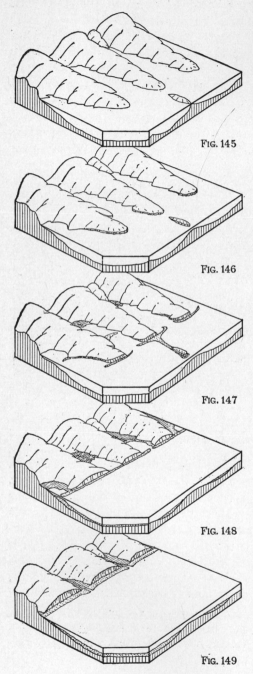

FIG. 145

FIG. 146

FIG. 147

FIG. 148

FIG. 149

streams, glaciers, and subsurface water. The succession of forms sculptured from shorelines of submergence, however, are so strikingly different from those sculptured from shorelines of emergence, that each must be followed separately.

Shoreline of Submergence. — A coast newly submerged has a shoreline of extreme irregularity, since submergence brings the sea against a land surface dissected by streams, allowing it to drown the valleys and form deep bays between sloping headlands (Figs. 144, 145). Off the headlands are islands, the tops of isolated hills on the drowned land surface.

Stage of Youth. — The waves are forced to concentrate their attack on headlands and islands, for as we have already seen, they can

Figs. 145–149. — Development of an ideal shoreline of submergence.

Fig. 145. — Newly submerged coast marked by deep bays, headlands, and islands.

Fig. 146. — Stage of early youth, showing cliffed headlands.

Fig. 147. — Stage of middle youth, showing beaches, spits, and a tied island.

Fig. 148. — Stage of late youth, showing truncated headlands connected by bars, forming a much simplified shoreline. The shortened bays are being filled with fluvial detritus and vegetation.

Fig. 149. — Stage of maturity, showing the headlands and bays destroyed and the shoreline simplified to the greatest possible extent.

not effectively reach the sheltered bays (Fig. 146). Wave-attack cuts cliffs into the seaward shores of the islands and exposed headlands, and quickly indents those parts of the headlands where the rock is weakest, forming little coves between small promontories of harder rock and scattered stacks. As the headlands are cliffed, the débris first eroded sinks out of sight into the deep water that washes them. Gradually, however, the headlands are cut back until the débris supplied by their erosion is built up into the zone of wave action, where it forms beaches fringing the cliffs. Longshore currents generated by oblique waves sweep past the cliffed headlands and carry part of the beach material into the deeper water of the bays where, losing velocity, they dump it, building out sub-

I. C. Russell, U. S. Geol. Survey.

Fig. 150. — Recurved spit, Duck Point, Grand Traverse Bay, Lake Michigan. The spit has been built out from a point of land on the left, just out of view.

marine embankments, much as artificial fills for railroads and highways are made across valleys by dumping at the ends of the fills. Incoming waves dragging bottom upon the seaward sides of the embankments build them above sea level, thereby converting them into *spits*. Currents crossing the free ends of spits commonly turn them shoreward, making them into *recurved* spits (Fig. 150). Spits not seriously impeded by transverse currents continue to be built across the bays, closing or nearly closing them, and forming *bay bars* (Fig. 151). The erosion of smaller headlands farther up the bays results in the deposition of lesser bars nearer the bay heads. Other bars are built in the sheltered water between islands and the mainland. These bars are termed *tombolos*, and the islands they link to the mainland are *tied islands* (Figs. 144, 147).

While beaches, spits, bars, and tombolos are being built with the débris of the crumbling headlands, deltas are being built out by the larger streams into the heads of some of the bays, which are fringed with tidal marshes in protected stretches where aquatic vegetation can grow undisturbed.

As the islands are cut away, the headlands cut back, and the bays correspondingly shortened, the shoreline becomes much simplified (Fig. 148). The truncated headlands are now connected by nearly continuous bars and the bay-heads are filled with sediment washed in by the streams. This simplification of the shoreline is the work of the stage of *youth*.

Stage of Maturity. — When the headlands have been completely cut away and the bay-head fillings removed, the shoreline is *mature* (Fig. 149). The waves can now attack the entire shoreline, except that stretches

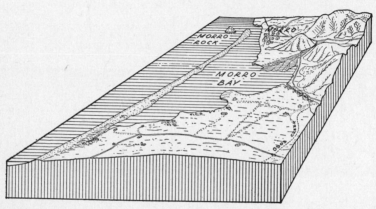

Fig. 151. — Bay bar nearly landlocking Morro Bay, California, thereby greatly simplifying an irregular shoreline. The bay is being gradually filled by delta growth and by vegetation.

composed of weak rocks will continue to form indentations, while those composed of stronger rocks will form promontories. Along the whole shore are cliffs as high as the height of the land above the sea. The submerged wave-cut bench is as broad as the original headlands were long, a wave-built terrace extends seaward beyond it, and the combined profile of the two features has become a profile of equilibrium, across which waste from the cliffs is slowly but surely shifted, adding to the terrace and completing the filling of the drowned valleys with sediment. A long period ensues marked only by retreat of the cliffs and widening of the bench and terrace. As the latter widen, the force of the waves reaching the shore becomes correspondingly feebler.

Stage of Old Age. — Old age is attained only when the sea has cut so far inland that the waves spend most of their force in friction upon the shallow bottom as they roll across it, and so make but a feeble attack upon the shore. After this stage is reached, further retreat proceeds very slowly, but the wave-cut bench gradually widens.

Shoreline of Emergence.

— The history of a typical shoreline of emergence begins very differently. When a sea floor emerges by gentle uplift and becomes land it forms a nearly flat coastal plain composed of sea-floor sediments (Fig. 152).

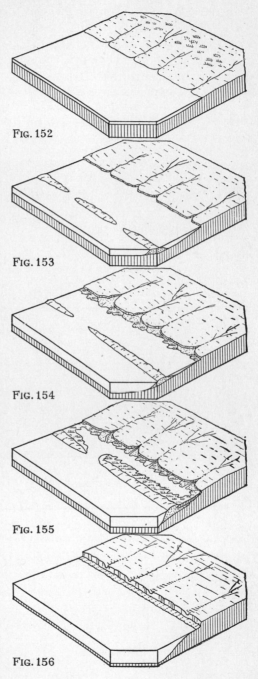

FIG. 152

Stage of Youth. — The water is so shallow for a considerable distance seaward that the waves drag heavily upon the bottom, picking up loose sand and pebbles, which they carry forward to the line of breakers. Here the sediment is dropped by the spent waves and gradually builds up a narrow submarine ridge parallel with the shoreline and just within the line of breakers. Storm waves eventually build the deposit above sea level, forming a long, low, sandy, wave-built island known as an *off-*

FIG. 153

FIG. 154

FIG. 155

Figs. 152–156. — Development of an ideal shoreline of emergence.

Fig. 152. — Newly emerged coastal plain with shallow water offshore.

Fig. 153. — Stage of early youth, showing formation of offshore bar and lagoon.

Fig. 154. — Stage of middle youth, showing shoreward migration of the offshore bar and beginning of filling of the lagoon.

Fig. 155. — Stage of late youth, showing continued migration of the offshore bar and conversion of much of the lagoon into tidal marsh.

Fig. 156. — Stage of maturity, showing removal of the offshore bar and tidal marsh, permitting the waves to attack the mainland directly.

FIG. 156

shore bar (Fig. 153).   The narrow body of shallow water lying between the offshore bar and the shoreline is a *lagoon*.[1]   Ordinarily the sweep of the tide in and out of the lagoon keeps gaps in the offshore bar open to the sea.   The Gulf and South Atlantic coasts of the United States, having rather recently emerged from the sea, consist of a continuous coastal plain and nearly continuous offshore bars and lagoons developed on a huge scale.

The width of the lagoon depends on the seaward slope of the bottom and the size of the storm waves.   It is commonly a mile or more and

U. S. Army Air Corps.

Fig. 157. — Offshore bar with tidal gap, near Cape Charles, Virginia, seen from the air. A longshore current generated by the slightly oblique waves (upper left) is recurving the end of the bar on one side of the gap, while mild currents moving out from the lagoon (left) are building small embankments on the opposite side of the gap.   The sinuous channel behind the bar is an estuary in the tidal marsh which is gradually filling the lagoon. Most of the bar shown in this view is submerged, and is seen through shallow water.

may be several miles.   At Cape Hatteras the offshore bar is about 20 miles from the mainland, but along the east coast of Florida it is near shore, and the lagoon in consequence is very narrow.   The city of Galveston is built on an offshore bar, and its disastrous flood of 1900 occurred when high seas, driven by a hurricane, rose 15 feet above their normal level.

[1] Large lagoons are also called *sounds* but not all sounds are lagoons.   A sound is merely a wide strait.

The sea floor outside the bar is gradually excavated by the waves, and the eroded material is added to the bar. As the depth increases the waves are less impeded by the bottom and are finally able to break with force against the bar itself, eroding its seaward face. Part of the resulting débris is carried out to sea, and part is thrown during storms over the bar into the edge of the lagoon. By this process of erosion of its seaward face and deposition on its lagoonward face, the bar is gradually shifted shoreward (Fig. 154).

Meanwhile the lagoon, rarely more than 20 feet deep at the start, is slowly filled with sediment washed into it from the land, as well as with the débris thrown over the bar. Where the water is shallow enough, vegetation thrives and adds its quota to the accumulating sediment, locally forming extensive *tidal marshes* (p. 116). As the bar is driven shoreward the lagoon becomes a tidal marsh (Figs. 155, 157). Eventually both bar and lagoon filling are completely cut away as the breaking waves deepen the bottom offshore and continue their attack upon the land. The removal of the offshore bar ends the stage of youth (Fig. 156).

Stages of Maturity and Old Age. — Following the disappearance of the offshore bar the sea launches its drive against the shore with unchecked vigor. A continuous wave-cut cliff is rapidly formed, and the shoreline develops minor irregularities controlled by the distribution of weak and resistant rocks. The progress of the remainder of the cycle is identical with that of the stages of maturity and old age in the shoreline of submergence. The most noticeable result is the production of an ever-widening wave-cut bench.

Application of the Cycle to Existing Shorelines. — We can study today actual examples of youthful shorelines (such as that of New England) and mature shorelines (such as that of parts of the English Channel), but we know of no shorelines at present in old age, because extensive crustal movements and changes of sea level have taken place so recently that sufficient time has not yet elapsed to allow a cycle to progress beyond maturity. The stage of old age in which a large island or part of a continent is reduced by marine erosion to a broad wave-cut bench fringed by a broad wave-built terrace, is therefore largely a matter of inference. The reason is that the crust apparently never stands still long enough to permit this process to complete itself. The continents seem throughout their history to have been elevated much more often than depressed, and since a very slight uplift suffices to bring a great deal of land out of water, shifting the zone of wave attack and forcing the process of destruction to begin over again, we must regard the marine cycle of erosion as a thing that practically fails of completion.

On the other hand a broad wave-cut bench, after uplift and erosion by

streams, so closely resembles the peneplane resulting from the completed
fluvial cycle (p. 71), that it is commonly very difficult to distinguish
between them.

Value of the Cycle Concept as a Working Tool. — Since the marine
cycle, unlike the fluvial cycle, is seldom if ever completed, some may
question the value of formulating the marine processes into a cycle at all.
The answer, however, is clear. The linking together of the successive
shore processes into a continuous chain of cause and effect, which we
call the cycle, is based not merely on theory but on actual examples
from many parts of the world of every step in the process from the initial
stage through maturity. Furthermore, the concept of the cycle is not
an end in itself but a means to an end. Unless we know exactly what
stage in a long process is represented by a particular shoreline, we can
neither reconstruct its past nor foretell its future. If, therefore, we try
to reconstruct the history of the Earth, it is essential that we know exactly where we stand at present, so that with the ideal cycle clearly in
mind, we can use it as a key to unlock the events of the past.

For example, knowing the characteristics of each cycle, we can trace
the history of the central Atlantic coast of the United States from New
Jersey to Carolina. Its shoreline is marked by the drowned valleys characteristic of a shoreline of submergence, but has also the offshore bars
developed upon a shoreline of emergence. It is evident that an extensive
submergence has been followed by a later but smaller emergence, leaving
the valleys drowned but at the same time reducing the depth of the water
so much that extensive offshore bars are developing. At first the bars
have gaps opposite the submerged valleys, but gradually the gaps are
filled as the débris is shifted coastwise by longshore currents, forming
subsidiary spits during the process. Without a knowledge of the cycle,
this double history would not be clear.

Shorelines with Complex Histories. — In the example just cited, the
earlier marine cycle was interrupted while still in its youth, and a new
cycle of a different kind was instituted in its place. Yet the forms sculptured during the earlier episode still remain to tell the story. Conversely, the forms developed during the time the last great ice sheets
covered the lands and drew down the level of the sea throughout the
world (p. 153) must have been submerged by the rise of the sea as the
ice wasted away, and so lost to view.

Again, in many regions wave-cut benches formed during periods of stationary sea level are warped up above the sea to form marine terraces
paralleling the shore (Fig. 142). Such terraces are strikingly developed
along the southwest coast of Newfoundland. At Port au Port one of
them evenly bevels the edges of steeply tilted strata and attains a width

of more than 2 miles and a height of 55 feet above sea level.   Shells of marine animals occur in the clay that mantles another terrace lying just 100 feet above sea level along the western end of Cape St. George, New-foundland.   Farther north in both Newfoundland and Labrador there are remnants of older marine terraces at several elevations up to about 500 feet above the present level of the sea, and along the coast of California marine terraces occur up to 1600 feet above sea level.

The landward margins of many of these uplifted marine terraces are bordered by wave-cut cliffs and other shore features such as stacks and sea caves.   Beach deposits also mark the positions of some old shorelines, and where uplift has been intermittent, a series of beaches lie one above another.   The dead, blanched forms of uplifted coral reefs also bear testimony to uplifts of certain tropical shores.

The shoreline of the Atlantic coast from Cape Hatteras to the Maritime Provinces of Canada gives strong evidence of a northward depression of the coast, obviously fairly recent because the shoreline is in a very youthful stage of the cycle.   Between Florida and Cape Hatteras there is no indication of submergence, but northward from Cape Hatteras the stream valleys become more and more deeply embayed.   The Roanoke, James, Potomac, Delaware, Hudson, and Connecticut rivers are drowned throughout their lower courses, and the degree of embayment increases northward.   Even Long Island Sound appears to be merely a stream valley depressed enough to be submerged throughout its length.   Furthermore the water upon the continental shelf deepens progressively northward from Florida to the Banks of Newfoundland, thus bearing out the evidence of tilting yielded by the character of the shoreline.

It is possible, therefore, to reconstruct at least a part of the geologic history of a land mass by studying its shore features, their place in the ideal cycle, and the crustal movements they record.   The value of applying knowledge of the cycle in this way is well illustrated by the coral-reef question, which has interested geologists for many decades, not only for its own sake, but because it has an important bearing on the later history of the Earth.

THE CORAL-REEF PROBLEM

Formation of Coral Reefs. — In the shallow water around many tropical and subtropical islands coral reefs play an important geologic rôle. These limy reefs are estimated to have a combined area of half a million square miles, and the calcareous débris resulting from their erosion by waves is spread over a much greater area of the sea floor.

Corals (polyps) are small, rather primitive marine animals that secrete an external limy skeleton about the base of the body.   They reproduce by budding in plant-like fashion, so that colonies of many thousands of individuals, each living in its own tiny protecting chamber like a cliff-dweller in a city of stone, combine to build an elaborate limy structure of considerable size.

As the colonies expand and build upward the older polyps die, and gradually the dead base is buried by the growth of other animals and by the débris broken by storm waves from the living parts above.   This accumulating deposit is eventually cemented into a white spongy lime-stone upon whose upper surface the living corals flourish (Fig. 158). This structure is a *coral reef*.   It rises until its surface just reaches sea

Saville Kent.

Fig. 158. — Growing corals, visible at low tide, on the Great Barrier Reef of Australia. View looking across the lagoon toward the mainland 20 miles away.

level, where it is laid bare only at the lowest tides for short periods, for corals can stand exposure to the air for only a few hours at a time.   Over the reef the waves swirl and break, and at its outer edges where oxygen, calcium carbonate, and food material are most abundant, corals thrive best.

Coral reefs are sharply limited in their distribution by the depth and temperature of the water, because reef-forming corals thrive only where the water is clear, shallow, and warm.   They can not endure a temper-ature below 68° F., and they live normally where the water is less than 150 feet deep.

Types of Reefs. — According to their position and form, coral reefs have been grouped into three general classes: *fringing reefs, barrier reefs,* and *atolls.*

Fringing reefs (Fig. 159) lie close against the shore, forming platforms laid bare only at very low tide. As the corals can not grow above sea level the growth of the platforms is chiefly seaward. Opposite the mouths of streams the reefs are not developed because the corals can not live in freshened and muddy water.

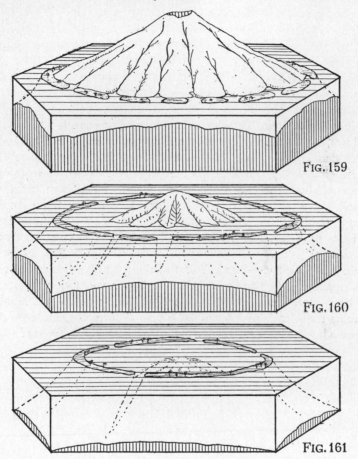

Figs. 159–161. — Fringing reefs, barrier reefs, and atolls, and their development according to the subsidence theory. (Partly after W. M. Davis.)

Fig. 159. — Fringing reef growing around the margin of a volcanic island.

Fig. 160. — The subsiding island after partial submergence and dissection by fluvial erosion. The upgrowing reef parts from the island, forming a barrier reef with intervening lagoon.

Fig. 161. — The subsiding island after complete submergence, converting the still-upgrowing barrier reef into an atoll.

Barrier reefs (Fig. 160) lie at some distance from the shore and are separated from it by shallow lagoons. Breaks in the reefs are kept open

by the tide, so that the deeper lagoons make excellent harbors.   Many of
the high volcanic islands of the Pacific as well as the islands of the Caribbean region are girdled by such encircling reefs.   The west coast of the
island of New Caledonia has a barrier reef 400 miles long, and the eastern
coast of Australia has one 1200 miles long.   The latter lies 20 to 30 miles
from shore, and its great lagoon has a depth of water of 100 to 200 feet.

Atolls (Fig. 161) are ring-shaped reefs enclosing circular lagoons instead
of islands.   Generally there are breaks in the reefs, which afford access
to the lagoons.

Origin of the Reefs. — The origin of fringing reefs is very simple.
Since corals prefer warm shallow water they tend to attach themselves
near the shore and grow at first in scattered colonies that later coalesce as
they increase in size.   Thus a continuous coral growth is built up to low-
tide level, after which it can only grow outward as a fringing platform.
It is evident, furthermore, that barrier reefs and atolls are merely modified fringing reefs, and that they represent two successive stages of
change.   It is the cause of the change that has constituted an important
problem since the middle of the nineteenth century, when coral reefs
began to be studied.   To account for the change many interesting theories have been advanced, of which two have been subject to recent
controversy.

Subsidence Theory. — The subsidence theory, first advanced by Charles
Darwin, elaborated by Dana, and recently rejuvenated by Davis, holds
that barrier reefs and atolls are merely fringing reefs built higher and
higher as the islands about which they were formed gradually subsided
below sea level.   This conception is illustrated in Figs. 159–161.   A fringing reef is built around a volcanic island, which begins to sink.   Since corals thrive best on the seaward margin of the reef, it is only on that margin that the corals can grow fast enough to counteract the sinking of the
island and keep themselves in shallow water.   Continued sinking drowns
the inner part of the reef, forming a lagoon protected by the growing
outer fringe, and causing the original fringing reef to become a barrier
reef (Fig. 160).   As subsidence and erosion continue, the volcanic island
finally disappears below sea level, and the reef becomes an atoll (Fig. 161).
A necessary implication of this theory is that great marine areas now
dotted with barrier reefs and atolls have undergone recent subsidence,
in places amounting to thousands of feet.

The Glacial-Control Theory. — The glacial-control theory, advanced
by Daly, holds that, before the last glacial epoch, fringing reefs were the
only kind of reefs in existence, having been formed around the margins
of still-standing islands.   The removal of sea water to form the great
continental ice sheets universally lowered the sea level by as much as

200 feet (p. 153).   This movement combined with the glacial chilling of the sea, exterminated many growing corals and greatly weakened many more.   Islands that had formerly been protected by growing reefs against wave attack were now subjected to marine erosion, which cut wide benches around the larger islands and those made of resistant rocks, and completely cut away many islands which were small or made of weak rocks.   As the ice wasted away and the sea grew warmer and rose, the corals returned to the wave-cut benches, building at their margins new *barrier* reefs and atolls.   On this theory, barrier reefs and atolls are specialized forms resulting from widespread glaciation, and the floors of the lagoons are benches cut by waves during a lowered sea level and later veneered with coral débris.

Conclusion. — Islands surrounded by barrier reefs very generally have shorelines of submergence.   This proves submergence of the islands, though whether it implies an actual subsidence of the land (supporting the subsidence theory), or purely a rise of sea level (supporting the glacial-control theory) is a matter still being discussed.

There is, however, other evidence from which the problem can be attacked.   Islands maturely dissected by streams and then slowly submerged while protected from the waves by growing reefs (the condition involved in the subsidence theory) have shorelines of submergence whose headlands have had no opportunity to be cliffed by the waves.   On the other hand, islands, especially the smaller ones, whose margins have been eroded to form wave-cut terraces at a time when coral growth had ceased (the condition involved in the glacial-control theory) must necessarily also have wave-cut cliffs which should preserve their wave-cut character even after the rising sea level partly submerged them.   When this argument is applied to the reefed islands of the world, it appears that whereas many of the islands near the margins of the tropical coral reef zone have cliffed headlands, those in the main coral reef regions ordinarily do not.   The conclusion follows that glacial control has played a part in the outer areas of the tropics where reduced temperatures would first inhibit the growth of the corals, but that in the great coral-reef areas in the Pacific, subsidence appears to be the chief cause of the formation of barrier reefs and atolls.

DISTRIBUTION OF MARINE SEDIMENTS

Depth of water is a factor supremely important to marine deposition, for it determines the effectiveness of waves and currents in distributing detritus worn from the lands, and at the same time, by controlling the sunlight and heat that penetrate to the sea floor, it regulates the habitats of rock-forming sea animals and plants.

No two marine regions are exactly alike in the nature and distribution of the sediments accumulating upon them, but certain general principles are applicable to all. The rock waste derived from the land is in more or less constant transit seaward, until bit by bit it comes to rest upon parts of the bottom too deep to be reached by waves and currents, and there it remains as long as those parts of the sea become no shallower. While this transfer and deposition of rock waste are in progress, limestone is being built up in other places which are warm, shallow, and free from much land-derived sediment (Chap. IX).

Shore Zone. — Deposition in the shore zone is only temporary, because this zone advances inland as the shoreline recedes throughout the cycle. The sediment is dominantly coarse. Along shorelines of submergence it builds beaches, spits, bay bars, and similar features; along shorelines of emergence it builds offshore bars and lagoon deposits.

Shelf Zone. — The floor of the shelf zone (p. 176) extending from the low-water shoreline to a depth of roughly 600 feet is remarkably even, for it is mantled by sediment derived from the land and shifted by the waves and currents into the deeper places, smoothing out the inequalities of its surface. Its average width is about 75 miles, and its seaward slope averages less than 10 feet to the mile, so that it would appear to the eye as a monotonous plain.

The shelf zone is a region of change and activity. Waves and currents keep the water in motion, salinity and muddiness vary from place to place, and the temperature changes with the seasons and varies with latitude. For these reasons the sediments vary greatly from place to place. Along the bold and exposed coast of California the near-shore sediments include gravel and coarse sand, off the mouth of the Mississippi the deposits are finer sand and mud derived from far in the interior, and bordering the low and nearly streamless limestone coast of southern Florida are limy deposits of very fine texture.

Soundings show that modern gravels are generally confined to depths of less than 30 feet and are deposited very near the shore, though exceptionally gravel is carried to depths of 150 feet and to distances up to 10 miles from shore. Ordinarily sand does not extend beyond a depth of 250 or 300 feet, and the outer parts of the continental shelves are therefore covered by muds alone or by fine limy deposits.

Limestone is formed characteristically in the shelf zone, but only where the water is warm, clear, and nearly free from land-derived sediment. Most limestone is precipitated directly from solution in sea water, but the extent to which organisms are responsible for this process is not yet clear (p. 218).

Continental-Slope Zone. — The great slopes leading from the edges of the continental shelves down to the deep-sea floor cover an area nearly twice as great as that of the shelves themselves. Because of their depth, they are virtually free from bottom currents, and therefore none but the finest land-derived sediments can be deposited upon them. In addition there are found on them the oozes characteristic of the deep-sea zone.

Deep-Sea Zone. — The huge area of the deep-sea floor is covered by extraordinarily fine, soft deposits known as *oozes*. Thousands of samples of these oozes have been brought up from the depths by ingenious scoops let down on wires miles in length from vessels specially equipped for marine exploration. The thickness of these slimy deposits is unknown, since the scoops are unable to penetrate them far, but probably it is great.

The oozes are of several kinds and are derived from various sources. *Red clay* is the most widespread variety. Apparently it consists of fine wind-blown dust (derived both from erosion of the land and from volcanic eruptions), pumice (p. 264) that has floated for a time before sinking, meteoritic dust that has fallen directly into the sea, and also the insoluble residues of the shells of organisms that have sunk to the deep-sea floor. Most of this material is so thoroughly altered by chemical decay that its original source is obscure. Its red color is the result of oxidation.

Organic Oozes. — In addition to the red clay there are *organic oozes* formed largely of minute shells and shell fragments dropped by organisms that live near the surface of the deep sea. One, the most widespread, is that known as *foraminiferal ooze* (Fig. 162). It is formed largely of the microscopic limy shells of single-celled animals known as Foraminifera, which float in myriads near the surface in the warmer parts of the sea. In the process of reproduction the parent emerges from its shell and subdivides into many daughter cells, each of which in turn secretes a new shell and repeats the life history of its parent. As reproduction is rapid, the abandoned shells drift down like a perpetual snowfall into the depths.

Foraminiferal ooze does not occur at depths of more than 16,000 feet, because the limy shells, slowly dissolving as they drift downward, are completely consumed by solution before they can reach greater depths. Limy ooze is found at lesser depths, indeed, only because the shells drift downward more rapidly than those on the bottom can be dissolved.

Radiolarian ooze is formed by the Radiolaria, another group of floating microscopic animals, which, unlike the Foraminifera, fashion their delicate and ornate shells from silica. *Diatom ooze* is formed by the accumulation of the remains of microscopic plants, the diatoms, which also secrete minute shells of silica.

The deep-sea floor is therefore a huge area in which the finest of all sediments are quietly and continuously accumulating, and whose dreary monotony is broken only here and there by submarine volcanic eruptions, by occasional earthquakes, and, in high latitudes, by the dumping of rocks floated seaward on icebergs calved from glaciers.

Yale Peabody Museum.

Fig. 162. — Foraminiferal ooze from the floor of the Caribbean, 100 miles west of Martinique, at a depth of 2900 feet. *Albatross* expedition, 1884. Magnified 9 times.

Permanence of the Deep-Sea Basins. — The oozes brought up from the great depths tell a story that has an important bearing on the history of the Earth. The sands, muds, and limy deposits of the shelf zone are gradually converted into sedimentary rocks. These rocks are identical with many of the sandstones, mudstones, shales, and limestones found widespread in all the continents. It is therefore certain (and for other reasons as well) that these rocks of the continents were formed in shallow seas, many of them epeiric, at various times when warpings of the crust forced the seas to overspread wide areas of low land. In spite of this fact, no continent has ever yielded a sedimentary rock proved to be a solidified deep-sea ooze.[1] As far as this evidence may be relied on, we conclude that, for as long a time as is recorded by the rocks, the present continental masses have existed as distinct units, and the present deep-sea basins have probably existed for an equally long time. The major relief features of the globe appear therefore to be very ancient and more or less permanent structures.

Deposits of the Shelf Zone as Sedimentary Rocks. — In examining the sandstones, mudstones, shales, and limestones that constitute so important a part of the rocks of the continents (Chap. IX), we can see in their relationships to each other the record of repeated marine flooding of low lands, many of the floods forming epeiric seas. The composition of these rocks reveals the character and proximity of the former coasts and the depth of water offshore, and the relationships of the shelf-zone rocks to shore-zone deposits formed at the same time enable us to locate the actual positions of former shorelines whose expression on the surface of the land has been obliterated long since.

READING REFERENCES

1. Shore Processes and Shoreline Development; by D. W. Johnson. 584 pages. John Wiley & Sons, New York, 1919.

An exhaustive discussion of the evolution of land forms along coasts.

2. The New England-Acadian Shoreline; by D. W. Johnson. 608 pages. John Wiley & Sons, New York, 1925.

A detailed explanation of the evolution of the North Atlantic coast between New York and the St. Lawrence.

3. The Depths of the Ocean; by Sir John Murray and J. Hjort. 821 pages. The Macmillan Co., 1912.

An extensive account of the methods of oceanographic investigation and of currents, temperature, and depths, as well as a description of marine life and sea-floor deposits.

4. An Introduction to Oceanography; by J. Johnstone. 368 pages. University Press of Liverpool, 2d edition, 1928.

A readable work in textbook form.

5. Oceanography. Its Scope, Problems, and Economic Importance; by Henry B. Bigelow. 263 pages. Houghton Mifflin Co., 1931.

An interesting popular account, clearly summarizing the problems involved in the science of the sea.

6. The Coral Reef Problem; by W. M. Davis. 596 pages. American Geographical Society, New York. Special Publication No. 9, 1928.

The only complete and up-to-date discussion of the coral-reef problem.

[1] Solidified oozes are, however, present as rocks on the *islands* of Barbados and some of the Dutch East Indies.

CHAPTER IX

SEDIMENTARY ROCKS

GENERAL FEATURES

As we have already seen, rocks are grouped into three major classes: sedimentary, igneous, and metamorphic, according to their mode of origin. Of these three classes the sedimentary rocks are distinguished by the fact that their substance has been deposited by a transporting medium — water, wind, or glacier ice — and later has hardened into rock. In popular language the term " sediment " usually denotes the fine-grained material that has settled out of a liquid, but in the broader usage of geology coarse material is also included, for, to cite an extreme illustration, boulders many feet in diameter enter into the construction of some of the most striking of the " sedimentary " rocks.

Three-quarters of the land surface of the globe is underlain by sedimentary rocks. Because of the enormous extent to which they make up the outermost part of the Earth's crust, then, they are highly important, and they determine by their variant resistance to erosion and by their structure the aspect of many of our landscapes. Economically also they are of great interest, as they contain the mineral fuels — coal, oil, and gas — and some of our most valuable metalliferous mineral resources, notably the sedimentary iron ores.

The most conspicuous feature of the sedimentary rocks as seen in exposures in the field is their layered structure (Fig. 163). Each layer is called a *bed* or *stratum* (plural, *strata*), the two terms being used interchangeably. In thickness the beds range from less than an inch to many feet; the thinner beds, those ranging from a fraction of an inch down to microscopic thickness, are called *laminae* (from the Latin *lamina*, a thin plate of wood, metal, etc.; a leaf). Each bed as a rule is separated from the bed below it and the bed above it by a distinct plane or approximately plane surface, which is termed the *bedding plane* or *stratification plane*. The persistence of individual beds, the uniformity of thickness, and the sharpness of the separation of consecutive beds depend on the environment in which the beds were deposited. The most regular stratification occurs in the sediments that were laid down in the sea or in lakes.

Stratification is made evident to the eye by differences of color of adja-

202

cent beds, by differences of composition, and by differences of texture; frequently by all three together.   In places other features, such as joint planes, especially where the joints are closely spaced, and the cleavage of slates, simulate bedding.   As bedding is of fundamental significance in interpreting the structure of a region, it is important to be able to distinguish bedding from all other apparently similar features.

As originally laid down, the sedimentary rocks, especially the marine strata, were horizontal or nearly so.   Consequently when we find strata inclined at high angles and in places standing vertically we are compelled

C. R. Longwell.

Fig. 163. — Stratified sandstone and shale.   Near Morgantown, West Virginia.

to conclude that the strata have been subjected to mighty forces which were able to turn them from their initial horizontality; in short, that they have been subjected to a crustal disturbance or revolution.   This conclusion, now a commonplace in geology, carries with it so many astounding implications that it required hundreds of years to become generally accepted.

Sedimentary rocks have been forming ever since the first rains fell on our planet.   Since then some 500,000 feet of strata (100 miles!) have been laid down.   It is not probable, however, that a thickness so great has been deposited in any one place, although it is not possible to make exact determinations for all localities.   The deepest oil-well boring stopped in sedimentary rocks at a depth of 10,000 feet; sensitive geophysical instruments used for prospecting show that in places they extend to depths of 20,000 feet; and geologic inference indicates that in the roots of some of our greater mountain chains they may extend to depths of 20 or 30 miles, partly because of their great thickness and partly because of downfolding.

ORIGIN AND KINDS OF SEDIMENTS

It has been shown in previous chapters how each of the erosive processes tends to wear down the land area of the globe. The products of this ceaseless attack are twofold: one, mechanical — the rock detritus; and the other, chemical — the substances taken into solution, such as calcium carbonate. Eventually the detritus is dropped by the transporting agency, be it water, wind, or ice, and it accumulates as a sedimentary deposit; and the dissolved matter, by less obvious, more complex processes is separated from solution. Consequently there are two broad classes of sediments: (1) detrital sediments, and (2) sediments separated from solution.

The detrital sediments are roughly classified, chiefly according to the size of the constituent particles, into *gravel, sand, silt,* and *clay.*

Gravel is a coarse sediment consisting mainly of fragments of a diameter of 2 mm. or more; commonly more or less sand is admixed. Fragments ranging in diameter from 2 to 64 mm. are known as *pebbles;* those from 64 to 256 mm. as *cobbles;* and those larger than 256 mm. (10 inches) as *boulders.*

The pebbles and coarser detritus in the gravel are more or less water worn. At their sources they were irregular, angular pieces of rock bounded by joints or fracture surfaces, but as the result of abrasion by streams or waves they have lost their edges and corners and have become more and more rounded. Perfectly homogeneous rock fragments become spheroidal or spherical; fragments having planes of weakness, such as cleavage or foliation, become flat discs. Angular and subangular fragments indicate, therefore, that they have not traveled far from where the parent rocks occur in place. Gravels composed of angular fragments such as are common in alluvial-fan deposits are sometimes termed *alluvial breccias.*

During their transit downstream the pebbles of the softer and less coherent rocks are the first to be reduced by abrasion to the size of sand. Consequently durable materials, like quartz or rocks composed of quartz, and coherent, tough rocks predominate in gravels that are composed of well-rounded pebbles. On the other hand, gravels whose pebbles have not traveled far include less durable minerals and rocks such as feldspar, schist, and limestone. Limestone is, in fact, rare in gravels, because it is destroyed not only by abrasion but also by being readily dissolved.

In the gravels of arid regions limestone fragments are common, but this is an exception that proves the rule.

Sand is a detrital sediment composed of grains smaller than gravel, but exceeding $\frac{1}{16}$ mm. in diameter — about the thickness of this page or about the lower limit at which the individual grains can be distinguished by the unaided eye. Most sand is like granulated sugar in grain size. Like pebbles, the sand grains are more or less rounded. The larger ones become rounded first; but the difficulty of rounding the smaller grains, because of the buffer action of the water surrounding each grain, is well shown by the fact that all the grains at the mouth of the Mississippi River, despite their long transport, are angular, being below the size at which rounding by water is effective. In general, river sands are more angular than lake or marine sands. Wind-blown sands are the most conspicuously rounded, and in the so-called millet-seed sands, common in deserts, the grains have become perfect spheres whose mat surfaces resemble ground glass, owing to natural sand-blast action.

Quartz is the commonest constituent in sand, because of its chemical indestructibility and its hardness; and unless otherwise specified " sand " means quartz sand. However, rock fragments and many minerals other than quartz, such as feldspar, occur in sands; and the beaches of coral islands are in places formed of " coral sand " made wholly of calcium carbonate.

Silt and *clay* are sediments composed of the very finest-grained products of erosion. *Silt* is so fine-grained that, unlike sand, it will cohere when wet. *Clay* consists of particles that are still finer than those of silt size — less than 0.004 mm. in diameter. Hand in hand with this decrease in grain size goes a change in the minerals that make up the clay. There is a reduction in the amount of quartz and an increase in the amount of finely flaky minerals in the clay. During transportation the flaky minerals, because of their easy cleavability, become comminuted to the tinest flakelets. They are in fact so minute that most of them can not be certainly identified even with the most powerful microscope; consequently, recourse has been had in recent years to the more potent method of X-ray analysis, and the constitution of clays is now being established.

To its content of flaky minerals and the specific properties of the interstitial water, which acts as a lubricant, clay owes its most characteristic and supremely important technologic property — its plasticity, by virtue of which it can be molded when wet into any desired shape, and will retain this shape on drying.

Clays, as the products of the deposition of the finest detritus, have a wide range of composition. The most characteristic components, the flaky minerals already mentioned, are hydrous silicates of aluminum, white mica, and chlorite. These minerals are chiefly products of chemical weathering. In glacial clays and silts deposited in lakes and seas receiving the meltwater from glaciers, unweathered particles of rocks and minerals predominate, however, since glaciers produce by their powerful abrasive action immense quantities of rock flour.

There remains yet to account for the fate of the matter taken into solution during the erosion of the lands. As we have seen, every square mile of the 40,000,000 square miles of the Earth's surface draining to the sea contributes yearly to it 70 tons of dissolved matter, mainly calcium carbonate and silica, but also other constituents. In part this material is withdrawn by various means; in part it accumulates, increasing the salinity of the sea. At many times in the geologic past, arms of the sea have evaporated sufficiently to cause the dissolved salts to be thrown down as salt beds, but vast as these are, humanly considered, they are mere bagatelles to the enormous deposits of calcium carbonate that have been formed by precipitation either by inorganic action or by the vital activities of plants and animals. The silica of the sea is kept down to a vanishingly small amount because of its steady withdrawal by silica-secreting organisms — radiolaria, sponges, and diatoms (p. 199).

Tuff and volcanic breccia — rocks made of *pyroclastic* material (Chap. XI) in contradistinction to the ordinary *clastic* material produced by the fragmentation of older rocks through weathering and erosion — have formed many thick-layered deposits. The finer pyroclastic materials, the so-called volcanic ash, form the most widely continuous deposits known. A single mighty eruption, such as that of Tamboro in 1815, can spread a continuous deposit over an area of 1,000,000 square miles. Tuffs and volcanic breccias are sometimes regarded as igneous rocks, because they are produced by igneous activity; on the other hand the fragments of which they are made accumulate according to the laws of sedimentation, and hence can be regarded as sediments. If considered to be sediments, they are an exception to the rule that the sediments are products of the destruction of older rocks.

Wind-blown sand and dust, glacial detritus, such as till, and carbonaceous materials such as peat are other sediments of special types; they are of much interest and importance, both practical and scientific, but in bulk they fall far behind those already mentioned.

PLACES OF DEPOSITION OF THE SEDIMENTS

In Chapter III it is explained how streams transport their load of detritus. The spreading of marine sediments by the waves and currents is discussed in Chapter VIII. The conditions under which the sediments finally come to rest must now claim our attention. Two major realms of deposition are generally recognized: the *continental* and the *marine*. The deposits laid down on the dry land of the continents as well as those laid down in streams and lakes are all grouped together as continental sediments to contrast them with those laid down in the sea. This distinction is partly rooted in the history of the science: the marine sedimentary rocks are enormously more abundant as components of the Earth's crust and are commonly more valuable as documents in deciphering the history of the Earth than are the continental rocks. At first, in fact, it was tacitly assumed that all sedimentary rocks are of marine origin; and the recognition of the non-marine, the continental rocks, came much later. Another way of classifying the sediments is based on the environments in which they were laid down: (1) subaqueous, formed below the surface of a permanent water body (lake or sea); and (2) terrestrial, comprising fluvial, glacial, and eolian deposits.

Regions of Continental Deposits. — Although vast areas of the land surface are being actively eroded, 10,000,000 square miles of the continents are now covered with accumulating sediments or with sedimentary deposits formed in the recent geologic past. These regions of deposition fall into four types in which the conditions of accumulation are strikingly different. These are (1) piedmont plains, (2) arid basins, (3) humid basins, and (4) great deltas.

Piedmont alluvial deposits are formed where streams emerge abruptly from a lofty mountain range upon the piedmont belt — the slopes and plains at the foot of the mountains. Here the streams rapidly lose velocity as they enter the flatter piedmont belt, and consequently they drop part or all of their detrital load. During times of flood they are heavily laden with sediment, and after leaving the mountains they overflow their channels and cover the adjacent country with layers of gravel, sand, and clay. In so doing, they overflow into the lowest places, filling them with sediment; and by repetition of this process through a long period of time they build up deposits of great thickness to form alluvial plains in front of the mountains. Such alluvial plains are the results of the coalescence of many alluvial fans, whose origin is described in Chapter III. Striking examples are the deposits that underlie the High Plains east of the Rocky Mountains, the Pampas east of the Andes, and the Indo-Gangetic Plain along the south front of the Himalaya Mountains in India.

Because they are formed on the flanks of the mountains and well above sea level, these sediments will ultimately be destroyed as the cycle of erosion progresses to completion, unless they become protected from erosion by deep sinking of the floors on which they rest. Should they thus become depressed below the zone of erosion, they can survive into a later cycle of erosion.

Desert deposits occupy great areas in the arid basins. More than one-quarter of all the land surface of the world is embraced in interior basins whose drainage is centripetal, without outlet to the sea. Here the waste of the highlands constantly tends to move toward the deeper parts of the basins and accumulate in stratified deposits. At rare times of heavy rainfall the temporary streams spread widely over the lower slopes, shifting sand and gravel toward the centers of the basins, while the finer material is swept on into temporary lakes (playa lakes) that occupy the deeper depressions. Permanent lakes like Great Salt Lake or the Caspian Sea tend to be filled by the sediments carried into them by the larger and more permanent streams. Moreover, in times of drought, sand is shifted by the wind. Except wind-blown dust, none of the sediment can escape and thus, through the continued action of rain wash and streams, the desert basins tend to fill with deposits. If a basin sinks while it is being filled, the sedimentary deposits that can therefore accumulate in it may ultimately reach a thickness of several thousand feet. Deposits laid down in arid basins commonly contain layers of salt and gypsum as well as thick beds of dune sands. Most of them are poor in fossils and have light colors, such as dun, buff, or pink. Some of them are red.

Deposits in humid basins also attain large volumes. Where structural basins form rapidly in regions of abundant rainfall, large lakes are produced; but if the basins deepen slowly by sinking, the sediments that are accumulating in them can keep them filled and thus hold the basins in the condition of swampy lowlands. The second possibility is favored if the basins are bordered by highlands that are being rapidly eroded, for then the streams entering the basins are heavily laden with sediment. A good example of this kind occurs along the upper Paraguay River in South America, where an area 400 miles long and as much as 150 miles wide is a labyrinth of lakes, swamps, and channels in a low grassy plain. During the annual rainy season the whole area is flooded, but during the rest of the year only one-fourth of it is covered. The river enters the lowland heavily laden with sediment brought by its tributaries from the Andes on the west and from the Brazilian highland on the north; it leaves the basin fairly clear, having spread most of its sediment over the lowland. The sediment becomes mingled with organic matter from the abundant vegetation that flourishes in such places. This swampy state, with resulting accumulation of river sediment, can persist for a long time if subsidence of the basin keeps pace with infilling. Deposits of this mode of origin have formed extensively in the geologic past;

and they appear to have been laid down under conditions very much like those under which some of the coal-bearing rocks were formed (p. 116). The abundant organic matter gives such sediments somber or dark colors.

Deposits formed in this manner are likely to escape destruction by later erosion because they lie only slightly above sea level.

A *delta* is a deposit of sediment built out by a stream either into the sea or into a lake. An idealized vertical section (Fig. 44) shows that the delta is partly above and partly below water level. The landward portion becomes widely covered by fresh water when the stream is in flood and carrying its greatest load of sediment. At such times sand and silt are deposited far and wide by the floodwaters in horizontal layers over the landward top of the delta. The sediment that reaches the shore is shifted by the waves and currents toward the deeper water, thereby building out the shallow subaqueous surface near shore like a vast embankment with a nearly horizontal surface, which gives way to a steeper slope at the line of most rapid building. The topset beds are partly fluvial, but the foreset and bottomset beds are marine or lacustrine.

When the level of the sea and the floor of the delta remain stationary (Fig. 44), a marine delta grows chiefly seaward by the growth of its foreset beds, and the fluvial sediments, notwithstanding their large areal extent, are thin and hence make only a small part of the volume of the delta. When a delta is subsiding, however, more of the sediment can be laid down on its upper surface, and if upbuilding of the delta keeps pace with subsidence, the material thus laid down maintains the surface of the delta above sea level. If the landward portion of the delta is large, the volume of the floodplain deposits represented by the topset beds may thus vastly exceed that of the marine portion of the delta.

The deltas of great rivers, such as those of the Mississippi and the Nile, are built of fine detritus deposited in shallow seas on the wave-swept continental shelves, and here the difference in the inclination of foreset and bottomset beds is imperceptible and the distinction between these two parts of the delta is not marked.

Regions of Marine Deposits: *Shore Zone.* — The present shore zone, or zone between high and low tide, is roughly 60,000 square miles in area. On ordinary shores it is generally less than 2 miles wide, but in great deltas like that of the Mississippi the tidal marsh is locally 25 miles or more wide and shore sediments accumulate rapidly on some parts of it. The most remarkable extension of the existing shore zone occurs in the Runn of Cutch, a low flat of 6000 square miles' area on the southeast side of the delta of the Indus River. It is so flat and so nearly at sea level that it is flooded with marine water during the season of the year when the monsoon winds blow inland, and is laid bare or is covered by overflow from the Indus when the winds blow offshore. Some of the older mud-cracked marine rocks may have formed under comparable conditions. In general, however, shore deposits can not attain great thickness, for, if the land is being built out into the sea, they become buried under terrestrial deposits, and if the sea is encroaching on the land, they must yield to purely marine sediments and be covered by them. Under either alternative they have a poor chance to be permanently preserved, as on slight uplift they become exposed to stream erosion, and if sea level remains stationary the waves gradually encroach on the shore zone and remove them. They are likely to be preserved only in subsiding large deltas.

An interesting feature of modern tidal-flat deposits is that they are delicately laminated. The laminae record the ebb and the flow of the tide, the shortest rhythm in nature recorded in the sediments.

Shelf Zone. — The greater part of the land waste finally comes to rest on the sea floor. Most of this land-derived sediment accumulates in the shelf zone, which comprises the continental shelves together with such epeiric seas as the Baltic Sea; but the finest muds are in part transported even beyond the edge of the continental shelf and are found as far as 200 miles from land. Coarse materials accumulate in shallow water near the shore whence they are supplied, for there alone the currents are strong enough to transport gravel and coarse sand. Fine sands extend in places to depths of 200 or 300 feet or more, and beyond them the land-derived muds spread as a continuous blanket not only to the edge of the continental shelf but part way down the continental slope, where they grade imperceptibly into the oozes of the deep-sea floor. It is improbable, however, that much land-derived mud reaches the abyssal region. Although in general there is a seaward gradation from coarse to fine sediment, not all the muds are deposited in deep water, nor is there everywhere a shoreward phase of sandy sediment between the land and the place where mud deposition begins. In many protected embayments, as the Baltic Sea or Chesapeake Bay, muds, even of the finest sort, are now being deposited along the shoreline itself.

Calcareous deposits of the shelf zone form chiefly in clear shallow water, in which clastic sediments are scarce or absent and in which lime-secreting organisms grow luxuriantly. At the present time, calcareous deposits are forming chiefly about tropical coral islands and on submarine banks covered by warm, shallow water, such as the bank bordering Florida on the south and the Bahama Islands on the west. It has sometimes been wrongly inferred that marine sediments grade seaward, *i.e.*, in the direction of increasing depth, from gravel or sand through mud to limy ooze; therefore it must be emphasized that the limestones now exposed on the continents represent deposits that were formed in shallow, not deep water.

The deposits of red clay and organic oozes that cover the deep-sea floor (Chap. VIII) are of enormous areal extent, but inasmuch as such deposits are essentially lost to the continents and only rarely have been elevated into lands (p. 201) their geologic interest is limited.

CONVERSION OF SEDIMENTS INTO ROCKS

Sediments at the time they are laid down are in general loose, incoherent, and highly porous. They become converted into rocks by compaction, by the welding together of the contiguous grains, by the deposition of cement in the pore spaces, and by physical and chemical changes in the constituents. Not all these processes necessarily affect every sediment. The result is to render the material firmer, harder, more coherent — it has become *consolidated*, or *lithified*. The complex of processes by which sediments are transformed into rocks is termed *diagenesis*.

Compaction is most effective in the clay sediments. As the sediments accumulate in increasing thickness, the upper beds press more and more heavily on those under them. In clays this sedimentary loading causes the grains to become crowded together and the water in the pores to be squeezed out. The clay becomes a shale. Recent studies have shown that a freshly deposited clay has a porosity of 50 per cent or more. By the time the clay has been buried 1000 feet it has become compacted to 80 per cent of its original volume; to 60 per cent at 3000 feet; and to 55 per cent at 5000 feet. Although remarkable compaction effects of this kind were long ago pointed out by Sorby, their important bearing on such practical matters as the occurrence of petroleum in the rocks has only lately become apparent (p. 442).

Although compaction is of minor effect in sands, producing little or no reduction of volume, it may cause them to become consolidated by welding, by bringing the individual grains into such close contact that the molecular attractive forces will cause them to cohere.

Another process potent in converting sediments into rocks is due to the habit of the colloidal constituents — the mineral jellies (the hydrates of silica, alumina, and iron) to undergo spontaneous changes soon after coagulation, whereby they lose water and harden. Silica jelly (or " gel ") when freshly precipitated is a soft, gelatinous mass; on aging, as the chemists say, it hardens into opal, and the opal may later crystallize into chalcedony.   Changes of this kind, though affecting only the mineral jellies distributed in small amount through the mass of a sediment, can cause a marked increase in coherence and hardness.

Cementation is the deposition of mineral matter in the spaces between the grains of sediment.   The most common cements are calcite, silica in the form of quartz or chalcedony, and iron oxide.   These cements may be deposited hand in hand with the crystallization of the interstitial colloids, or they may be brought in later by percolating solutions, either from the adjacent body of sediment or from afar.

The conversion of a sediment into rock as a result of the compaction effects, the welding together of adjacent grains, and the hardening caused by the aging of the colloidal constituents may go on practically contemporaneously with accumulation; or it may be postponed, and in some sediments it may never occur.   In general, the older sediments have become more thoroughly consolidated than the younger.   Formations of geologically recent origin consist as a rule of loose or incoherent materials;   the more ancient formations consist of hard rocks.   A most remarkable exception to this general rule is afforded by the Paleozoic sediments of Russia and adjacent parts of Finland.   In Karelia, Finland, is a clay of Cambrian age, which is commercially used in preference to the clays of Recent age.   After treatment with water to wash out the salts entrapped from the Cambrian sea, it molds well.   In short, the Cambrian clay sediment has remained unchanged since it was deposited on the floor of the Cambrian sea half a billion years ago and has kept its plasticity after this tremendous lapse of time.   In Russia the Carboniferous limestone is so loose and crumbly that it resembles the chalk of western Europe, which is tens of millions of years younger, and the coal near Moscow, though older than the coals of the world's principal producing districts, has not advanced beyond the stage of lignite, the stage so typical of the immensely younger " brown coals " of Germany.   The freedom of these ancient sediments from diagenetic changes is doubtless due to the fact that they were never buried under a heavy load of superincumbent strata and that they have remained undisturbed because they are in a region of great geologic tranquillity.

KINDS OF SEDIMENTARY ROCK

The different kinds of sedimentary rock are manifestly determined chiefly by the nature of the sediments from which they were formed. The chief sediments and the sedimentary rocks derived from them are as follows:

Sediments	Consolidated Equivalents: Sedimentary Rocks
Gravel......................	Conglomerate and breccia
Sand.......................	Sandstone
Silt........................	Siltstone
Clay (mud).................	Shale and mudstone
Calcareous mud and sand.....	Limestone

The several kinds of rock shown above are not invariably sharply defined from one another as wholly distinct types. Just as muds grade through silt and sand into gravel, and pure calcareous deposits grade into silts or clays, so the various rocks formed from them necessarily grade into one another. In describing these impure or mixed varieties of rock, those that were formed from muddy or clayey sediments are termed *argillaceous* (from the Greek *argillos*, clay). Similarly, sandy rocks are termed *arenaceous* (from the Latin *arena*, sand), and limy rocks are described as *calcareous* (from the Latin *calx*, lime). These three adjectives are used to characterize both the sediments and the rocks derived from them.

The chief types of sedimentary rock are described in Appendix B, but some of their significant features deserve more detailed explanation.

Conglomerate and Breccia. — The fragments cemented to form a conglomerate, or a breccia, range from pebbles a fraction of an inch to boulders many feet in diameter. They may be closely crowded together with little matrix or mingled with any proportion of matrix. If the pebbles are sparsely scattered through the matrix, the rock is termed a *conglomeratic sandstone*, or *pebbled sandstone*. In other words, Nature has produced transitional varieties of rock that bridge by imperceptible gradations the gap between conglomerate and sandstone.

The fragments in a conglomerate may consist of rock of one kind or of many kinds, depending on the environment in which it was formed. A marine basal conglomerate formed by the landward incursion of the sea over a granite area would consist largely of granite pebbles, but a fluvial gravel might contain pebbles of all the rocks that occur within its drainage area. If the fluvial gravel consisted chiefly of quartz, we would at once be led to infer that the topographic and climatic conditions at the time the streams were flowing were such as to cause the destruction of all rocks and minerals less stable than quartz. Conglomerates are extraordinarily useful as aids in reconstructing the geologic past.

A conglomerate or breccia of special type is formed when the layers of accumulating sediments, hardening as fast as they form, are broken up and the dislocated fragments are rolled about and then recemented. This happens when exceptional storm waves violently stir up the bottom; when layers exposed to the atmosphere on tidal flats or floodplains are broken up by mud cracks; when streams in flood undercut the sides of their channels; or when disturbances of the crust rupture the beds on the sea floor. The conglomerates thus formed represent merely a brief interruption in the orderly deposition of the series of strata in which they occur, and they are therefore termed *intraformational conglomerates*. The fragments in such conglomerates necessarily consist of the same materials as those of the inclosing beds. As a rule, the individual fragments in the intraformational conglomerate are imperfectly rounded; if they are sharply angular, the rock is *intraformational breccia*.

Sandstone. — Sandstones are composed of cemented sand grains, which consist most commonly of quartz. There are, however, transitional varieties that grade into the various other sedimentary rocks. Thus there are conglomeratic sandstones, mentioned above; argillaceous sandstones, containing an admixture of clayey material; and calcareous sandstones, in which there is an appreciable amount of calcium carbonate. In red and brown sandstones the cement is mainly iron oxide, but in white, buff, or gray sandstones it generally is silica (quartz or chalcedony) or calcite. A quartz sandstone whose cement is quartz is the most durable of building stones; a sandstone cemented with calcite is much less weather-resistant, because its cement is dissolved away by rain water charged with carbon dioxide and the stone crumbles into sand.

Sandstones are porous, and the aggregate volume of all the pores in a sandstone ranges up to 30 per cent of the total volume of the rock. As the pores are large enough to allow liquids to move freely through them, sandstones are permeable; and because of this extremely important property they are by far the most common reservoirs for petroleum and artesian water.

Arkose is a special variety of sandstone which contains so much feldspar that it resembles a granite in appearance. The abundance of feldspar, which is relatively susceptible to chemical alteration, indicates that it was not long exposed to weathering before it was deposited, and that it probably was not transported a great distance. Arkose is more commonly of continental than of marine origin, and its formation is favored by the mechanical disintegration of granitic rocks in cold or arid climates where chemical weathering is inhibited.

Shale. — Shale is a consolidated clay or mud having a characteristic flat-conchoidal or " shelly " fracture, as the etymology of the term implies (from the German *Schale*, a scale, shell, husk, slice). This fracture is parallel to the bedding and gives the shale its rude capacity to split. Between clays and shales there are all gradations, but typical shale is not plastic. Some consolidated clays and muds lack the typical shaly fracture, and the massive rocks of this kind are sometimes designated *mudstones*. Shales and mudstones are soft rocks; as the hardness increases they pass into *argillites*. Shales are much too fine-grained for the component particles to be determined with the unaided eye, or even with the hand lens. As the amount of quartz in shales increases, and the grain size increases, shales grade into sandstones. Such transitional rocks represent lithified silts; recently it has been suggested that they be called *siltstones*.

Black shales constitute a distinctive variety commonly associated with coal beds and also occurring abundantly in marine formations, where they are important as source rocks containing the mother-substance necessary in generating petroleum. The dark color of these shales is due to carbonaceous matter derived from the incomplete destruction of plant and animal organisms buried with the mud. An abundant supply of organic matter and stagnation of the water appear to be the essential requirements for the deposition of black shales, the stagnation causing a deficient supply of dissolved oxygen and so inhibiting decay. Depth is not a vital factor, though obviously any depressions in the sea floor are likely to remain undisturbed by bottom currents and so become stagnant areas where black mud can be deposited. Black muds are now accumulating in both shallow and deep water. Where black muds are forming, hydrogen sulphide (H_2S) is usually generated by sulphur bacteria and it in turn reacts with iron salts in the sea water to form pyrite (FeS_2), which is precipitated in a finely divided state, or as concretions, or in the form of replacements of fossils.

Limestone. — Limestone is the consolidated equivalent of limy mud, calcareous sand, or shell fragments. It is composed of calcium carbonate ($CaCO_3$), generally in the form of the mineral calcite.[1] Limestones are of many colors: white or light-gray, buff, brown, red, dark-gray, and black. If fine-grained and nearly pure, limestone is compact and tough and is one of the strongest of the structural stones; but with admixture of clay, limestones grade into calcareous shale, which weathers readily into clay. Many limestones are so fine-grained that they are irresolvable by the unaided eye — their texture is like that of porcelain; others are finely crystalline, and still others are distinctly granular.

Chalk is a soft, porous variety of limestone. Some chalks are composed largely of the microscopic shells of Foraminifera, the tiny animals

[1] Calcium carbonate was formerly termed *lime* carbonate; also loosely "lime" — hence the adjective "lime-secreting," applied to those animals and plants that secrete calcium carbonate. This usage is not strictly correct, since lime is calcium oxide (CaO); it is made commercially by "burning" limestone.

that make also the foraminiferal ooze of the deep-sea basins. These minute shells are extremely fragile and commonly occur much broken. In addition to the shell fragments there is normally a matrix of fine particles of calcium carbonate that is probably a chemical precipitate. Some chalky deposits, as those of Kansas and Alabama, are made up largely of such finely divided material, with an admixture of clay, and show but few foraminiferal shells.

Chalk was once supposed to represent abyssal deposits like the modern deep-sea oozes; but in spite of the fact that the foraminiferal ooze will probably form chalky deposits, it is now known that the great chalk formations were deposited in clear, shallow seas, for they inclose shells of shallow-water animals and are associated with coarse-grained sediments that could not have been washed into deep water.

Coquina is a variety of limestone made up of coarse shells and shell fragments loosely cemented.

Dolomite is a rock formed largely of the calcium-magnesium carbonate mineral dolomite, $CaMg(CO_3)_2$. There are all gradations between limestone and dolomite, and the intermediate kinds are more common than pure dolomite. Dolomite occurs in large volume, especially in the older rocks. The Dolomite Alps of the eastern Tyrol, for example, have been carved out of dolomite strata totaling 3000 to 4000 feet in thickness, and equally great masses occur elsewhere.

Limestone represents the dissolved calcium carbonate that was carried by the streams to the sea and there withdrawn from solution; but the conditions for its deposition are less obvious than those under which the clastic sediments are formed, and there is still much to learn about the relative importance of the several agents that cause the limy sediments to form.

The solubility of calcium carbonate is extremely sensitive to the amount of carbon dioxide present in the water, and anything that will decrease the content of the carbon dioxide in a saturated solution of calcium carbonate will consequently cause immediate precipitation of calcium carbonate. Rise of temperature drives off some of the carbon dioxide and thus causes calcium carbonate to precipitate; removal of the carbon dioxide by plants (algae), which under the influence of sunlight are able to utilize the carbon dioxide as a source of carbon in building their tissues, is another cause of precipitation; and certain groups of bacteria, by producing ammonia, which combines with the carbon dioxide, can cause precipitation.

Recent investigations have shown that warm shallow marine water is essentially saturated with calcium carbonate, whereas the colder, deeper water is undersaturated because of its richness in carbon dioxide.

Wherever the deeper water rises in marine currents and flows over shallow submarine banks in tropical regions, its increase of temperature drives off part of the carbon dioxide and causes the warmed water to become more and more nearly saturated with calcium carbonate.   Consequently, calcium carbonate is likely to be precipitated in such places, provided that it is not being so rapidly extracted by organisms that its saturation-point can not be attained.   As a matter of fact, these places afford the most favorable conditions for animals and plants that use the carbonate to form their shells or skeletal structures.   Corals thrive and form reefs on such tropical shoals, and with the corals are associated lime-secreting algae and a host of shell-forming creatures.

R. M. Field.

Fig. 164. — Mudflats at low tide off the west coast of Andros Island, showing the limy sediment that covers large areas of the Bahama Banks.   The sediment is a soft white paste of nearly pure calcium carbonate.

Impressed by the limy mud and coral sand formed around coral reefs, the earlier naturalists attributed to corals a predominant rôle in precipitating the limy deposits, but the corals have now been relegated to an insignificant position.   Even around existing coral reefs much of the work of calcium-carbonate precipitation is done by twelve species of lime-secreting algae.

Recent investigations have shown that calcareous sediment in the form of a fine mud is now being precipitated extensively in parts of the sea.   One of the largest areas in which such precipitation is going on is the Bahama Banks, south of the Florida Straits.   This great shoal exceeds 7000 square miles in area and the depth of the water over it averages less than 20 feet. The shoal is formed of limestone, and much of its surface is mantled by fine, white, limy mud (Fig. 164). The cause or causes of deposition of this limy material are still uncertain. Coral reefs are limited to the margins of the shoal and do not appear to contribute much to the deposit at the present time. It is thought that bacteria, chiefly those of the group that produce ammonia, cause the precipitation of the calcium carbonate, but purely inorganic processes may have coöperated, namely evaporation and increased temperature during the summer months. The relative importance of inorganic and biological agents in the deposition of the carbonate sediments is therefore still unknown.

In summary, however, we may point out that there are two extreme types of limestone: one represented by coquina, or better by the foraminiferal limestones, such as the limestone of which the Pyramids of Egypt are built, which is composed wholly or predominantly of the hard parts of organisms, and the other type, extremely fine-grained and homogeneous, which is the result of inorganic precipitation (evaporation or rise of temperature) or of biochemical precipitation, either of which modes of precipitation would produce indistinguishably similar limestones. Most limestones fall in between the two extreme types, but according to recent trend of opinion nine-tenths of all limestones are of inorganic origin.

Other Sedimentary Rocks. — *Coal,* certain *iron ores, rock salt, gypsum, phosphate rock,* and *chert* or *flint* are sedimentary rocks of special interest. Some, as coal and the marine iron ores, are of supreme economic interest, and it is easy to appreciate that the intelligent understanding of these mineral resources is increased by the growing knowledge of how the sedimentary rocks are formed. Except for the cherts, they occur in volumes so small in comparison with the enormous bulk of the shales, sandstones, and limestones that they are of little importance considered as structural elements in the constitution of the Earth's crust.

Coal and iron ore are given special consideration in Chapter XVIII of this book.

Characteristic Features of Sedimentary Rocks

In addition to the stratification which the sedimentary rocks show as a rule, they have other features that throw light on their geologic history. Among these features are fossils, mud cracks, ripple marks, and cross-bedding.

Stratification. — Most of the sedimentary rocks show stratification. Failure of a sedimentary rock to show it suggests, indeed, that the rock was formed in one of the less common ways in which such rocks are formed: glacial, eolian (loessial), or talus. The importance of stratification is so great that it deserves some further consideration here.

Stratification is commonly caused by the fact that the velocity of the transporting agent in flowing over the area of deposition changes from time to time. An obvious example is the deposition of fine silt and clay upon coarse gravels during the periods of diminished flow of water on an alluvial fan. The changes in current velocity may be diurnal, as on the outwash plain fronting an ice sheet, where the transporting competence of streams varies enormously between day and night; or it may be seasonal as a result of flood stages during the rainy seasons and low water during the dry seasons. During times of storm, sediments that had come to rest on shallow bottoms may be moved out into deeper water. An alternation of coarse and fine sediments would thus be produced. Stratification caused by changes in current velocity develops beds in which the grains are closely graded as to size, but the consecutive beds may differ little in composition.

Variations in the nature of the material supplied may develop stratification. Limestone beds alternating with shale provide an example of marked changes in the composition of the material deposited. Shifting of marine currents is one cause of such discontinuities.

Some sedimentary rocks show a regular alternation of material of two kinds, giving rise to so-called banded rocks, from the banding seen on their outcrops. Such repeated layering suggests the influence of some naturally occurring rhythm: for the thinner layers — the laminations — ebb and flood of the tide, and alternations of winter and summer have been suggested. For the thicker layers longer cycles have been suggested, but without positive results yet: the Sun-spot cycle of 11 years, the Brückner climatic cycle of 35 years, and the precession of the equinoxes of 21,000 years.

A layering due to the annual march of the seasons appears to be well developed in certain sedimentary deposits. Such an annual deposit is called a *varve*, regardless of whether it is of marine, lacustrine, or other origin. Varves generally consist of two laminae, one of which was laid down during the summer and the other during the winter. They occur in glacial clays and in some lake deposits now forming; and they are thought to have been recognized in certain marine shales, in playa clays, in dune sands, and in marine salt deposits in Stassfurt, Germany, and in Texas. The regular alternation of unlike sediments is easy to recognize, but to establish its annual origin is difficult, and so far not always possible. It is, however, a matter of great interest, for the varves give us the means of establishing eventually an absolute chronology, that is, one based on years.

A laminated lake sediment which is regarded as of varved origin is shown in Fig. 165; it is from the Green River formation of Colorado. The varves consist of a pair of laminae, one composed largely of calcium carbonate and the other much higher in organic matter, and hence much darker. During the summer, abundant calcium carbonate was produced and the peak of production of floating microscopic organisms was reached; the carbonate, because heavier, sank promptly, but the organic matter subsided more slowly and so most of it came to rest above the carbonate layer. By counting and measuring the supposed varves it is estimated that the Green River formation was deposited in 5,000,000 to 8,000,000 years.

Fossils. — Fossils (Latin *fossiles*, from *fodere*, to dig up) are the remains or imprints of animals or plants that were buried with the accumulating sediments (Fig. 166). The organisms are rarely preserved entire; generally only the hard parts, such as shells and bones, endure. These parts may be preserved without change, but commonly the original material with which the organism built its hard parts is dissolved by circulating solutions and new material

W. H. Bradley, U. S. Geol. Survey.

Fig. 165. — Laminated lake sediment from the Green River formation, Colorado. Shows probable annual layering, the light-colored laminae having been deposited during the summers and the dark laminae during the winters. Enlarged 3 diameters.

is put in the place of the removed material so remarkably that the original form and details of structure are perfectly preserved. Petrified wood is a well-known example, in which the woody tissue has been removed and silica has been concurrently put in its place. Not uncommonly the organic structure is wholly removed, leaving only an imprint or hollow mold in the rock. *Natural molds* of this sort may become filled subsequently by mineral deposits, which then form *natural casts* of the organic objects. Finally, footprints or trails made by animals crossing soft mud may under favorable conditions become preserved.

Since most fossils represent the animals and plants that were living where the sediments accumulated, they throw much light on the conditions that prevailed during the deposition of the rocks in which they occur. They show, for example, whether the beds were laid down on the land or beneath the sea, since continental sediments contain the remains of land plants, bones of land animals, or shells of river clams, whereas marine sediments contain representative marine shells. Something of the climate of the region at the time of deposition may be indicated also;

Fig. 166. — Fossil shells in rock.

for example, fossils of tropical plants and animals, such as palms and alligators, occur associated in certain formations of the Badlands of South Dakota. All these conclusions based on fossils, however, must be checked against the inorganic evidence given by the rocks, for the rocks have been formed in accordance with *changeless laws*. Fossils are of prime importance in deciphering the long history of the Earth and its inhabitants, and they are considered in detail in books on historical geology.

Mud Cracks. — Soft muddy sediments left exposed after the recession of flood-waters shrink and crack into characteristic polygonal blocks like those shown in Fig. 167. These desiccation fractures are known as *mud cracks.* Further exposure to air and sun bakes and hardens the blocks of mud. During the dry season wind-blown sand or silt may cover the surface, filling the cracks with sediment coarser than that of the mud-cracked layers. In this way the form of the polygonal blocks is preserved even after the mud-flat is again inundated. After the deposits have become hardened into rock, the beds of shale and sandstone may later be exposed by erosion, exhibiting these "fossil" mud cracks on the bedding planes. If the beds have been turned top side down during one of the many revolutions that have affected the Earth's crust, mud cracks give us a key for determining which is top or bottom: when formed

C. R. Longwell.

Fig. 167. — Mud cracks formed in the playa of Pintwater Valley, Nevada.

in their original positions they of course tapered downward. Obviously, the conditions that favor the formation and preservation of mud cracks are also ideal for the preservation of footprints of animals that have crossed the soft mud soon after its deposition, and therefore mud cracks and footprints are commonly associated in old sedimentary rocks. These conditions favor also the preservation of raindrop imprints, which record the fall of a brief passing shower while the flat was exposed to the atmosphere.

The most favorable places for mud cracks to form are the flood-plains of large rivers, the landward portions of great deltas, and the wide, flat shores of shallow interior lakes that shrink or disappear during the dry season. In spite of their alternate wetting and drying, marine tidal flats are unfavorable for the formation of mud cracks, because the mud has not sufficient time to dry out thoroughly before the return of the tide. Mud cracks may, however, form to a limited extent at the upper margins of estuaries where the spring tides reach for only a few days in each month. The mud cracks can form only when the sediment is exposed to the air and allowed to dry and shrink. They are therefore generally lacking in marine deposits.

In the early Paleozoic formations, however, there are well-known examples of mud-cracked marine limestones. They were probably formed under very special conditions that may find an analogy at present in the Runn of Cutch (p. 209) or in the Bahama Islands. During the hurricanes of the spring of 1928 the lower islands and the borders of the larger islands of the Bahama group were flooded by the seas that swept over the Bahama Banks (p. 217). It was later seen that many square miles of the resulting sediment were mud-cracked. In places, limy sand and fragments of marine shells have since blown over it. It is quite possible that in the past similar conditions have permitted marine sediments to be laid down during exceptional hurricanes over wide low coastal lands beyond the normal confines of the sea.

E. M. Kindle, Geol. Survey of Canada.

Fig. 168. — Current-formed ripple marks exposed at low tide near Windsor, Nova Scotia. The current flowed from left to right.

Ripple Marks. — Where currents sweep granular sediments along the bottom, the surface of the resulting deposit develops parallel ridges resembling the ripples on the surface of a pool of water. These are known as *ripple marks*. They are also formed on the land where sand is drifted by the wind, as on sand dunes, or under running water. Ripple marks thus produced retain their form and migrate slowly with the current, because the sand grains are rolled up the currentward or stoss side, and fall down the leeward slope. Current-formed ripple marks, therefore, have an asymmetric form, the stoss side being a gentle slope and the lee side steeper. The direction of flow of the current is thus autographed in the form of the ripple marks (Fig. 168).

Where oscillatory waves touch bottom they also develop ripple marks as a result of the to-and-fro motion of the bottom particles; but oscilla-

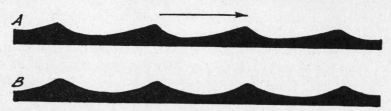

Fig. 169. — Asymmetric profiles of current-formed ripple marks (*A*) contrasted with the symmetric profiles of oscillation ripple marks (*B*).

tion ripple marks, in contrast to current-formed ripple marks, are symmetrical (Fig. 169).

Current ripple marks are formed wherever currents disturb sandy or silty surfaces, whether it be wind currents on the land, the currents of running streams, or any of the currents in the seas. Oscillation ripple marks, on the other hand, are formed only under standing water and in depths touched by wave action. Ordinary storm waves in the sea are ineffective below 200 or 300 feet, but exceptionally the bottom is ripple-marked at depths of 600 feet or more.

Cross-Bedding. — In many coarse detrital rocks, such as conglomerate and sandstone, the layers of particular beds are inclined to the general planes of stratification at considerable angles (Fig. 170). This diagonal arrangement is known as *cross-bedding*. It is produced where sand or gravel is shifted by currents in such a way as to be spilled over the front edge of a growing deposit: as the foreset edge of a delta, the front of a gravel bar in a stream, the front of a sand dune, or the front of a current ripple. The individual layers invariably come to rest on a slope inclined to the general surface of deposition.

The scale of the cross-bedding may be great or small. In dune sands single cross-bedded layers are commonly tens of feet thick, but in silts shifted by small ripples the cross-bedded layers are fractions of an inch thick. Since the inclination of the foresetting beds is invariably down-stream, it is possible to infer the direction of the currents that formed the cross-bedded deposits.

The cross-bedding in dune sands is one of the most distinctive types (Fig. 171). The oblique layers are inclined in many directions within

E. T. Hancock, U. S. Geol. Survey.
Fig. 170. — Cross-bedding in sandstone. Wyoming.

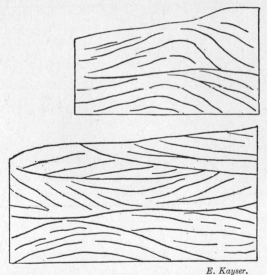

E. Kayser.
Fig. 171. — Cross-bedding in sand dunes. Ostend, Belgium.

short distances as a result of the repeated changes of direction of the winds. Few or none of the surfaces that truncate the cross-bedded layers are horizontal; and though most of the cross-bedding is concave upward, in places the layers are convex upward (Fig. 171), two features that help to distinguish eolian cross-bedding from fluvial and marine cross-bedding. The sporadic occurrence of cross-bedded layers convex upward is an inherited structure resulting from the migratory habits of dunes.

As the cross-bedding in other than eolian deposits appears to be invariably concave upward, this feature is used to determine the original tops and bottoms of beds that have been highly tilted or overturned by crustal disturbance.

C. E. Siebenthal, U. S. Geol. Survey.

Fig. 172. — Concretions which have weathered out of the shale inclosing them. Near Havre, Montana.

Concretions. — Some sedimentary rocks contain inclusions called *concretions.* These objects differ in composition from the inclosing rock and are generally round or nodular in form; some are spherical, others are flat and ring-shaped, and still others are of extraordinarily odd and fantastic shapes. They range from a fraction of an inch to many feet in diameter. They are composed of one of the minor constituents of the rock in which they occur; thus, those in chalk and limestone consist of silica and form the well-known flint nodules; in sandstone they consist of iron oxide or calcium carbonate; and in shale, of calcium carbonate or iron sulphide. Although some consist wholly of one substance, most concretions inclose much of the substance of the rock in which they occur. The bedding planes of the surrounding strata persist through some concretions, a feature which proves that these particular concretions grew in place at a time *after* the strata had formed. Some large concretions, which have weathered out of the inclosing shale, are illustrated in Fig. 172 and show this feature of the stratification passing through them.

Concretions form at any time during the origin of sediments. Manganese nodules partly encrusting sharks' teeth dredged from the depths of the sea show that some form while the sediment is accumulating. But most of them have formed after the sediments were deposited and are regarded as local phases of diagenesis. Many of them contain at their centers a fossil which acted as a nucleus around which mineral matter was precipitated. Remarkable imprints of fern leaves, insects, and marine animals are obtained by splitting such concretions. The shells and bones of even large animals occur in some of them. Inasmuch as many concretions occur in clays and shales, which are impervious to moving water, it is clear that the mechanism by which the material was aggregated to build the concretions was diffusion. Some concretions have remarkable concentric banding, which is interpreted as having been produced by rhythmic precipitation of material diffusing outward from the nuclei meeting and reacting with material diffusing inward to them.

Colors of Sedimentary Rocks

We must immediately distinguish between the color of a sedimentary rock as displayed in natural exposures and its color as seen on freshly fractured surfaces. The colors seen in canyon and cliff are the results of weathering and generally are but skin-deep, but they give country like the Grand Canyon and Zion National Park its striking picturesque qualities; as a rule, they are warmer and more brilliant than the intrinsic or proper colors of the unweathered rock as seen on fresh fracture.

The colors of sedimentary rocks are determined by the color of the predominant minerals and by the nature, amount, and distribution of the pigment contained in the rocks. Carbonaceous matter and iron compounds are the chief pigments. They are present in relatively small amounts, from a fraction of 1 per cent to several per cent, but it is probable that the thickness of the coating of these pigments around the sedimentary grains is the chief factor in producing the colors of the rocks.

Carbonaceous matter, or carbon for short, imparts dark-gray or black colors to sedimentary rocks. On exposure to light the carbonaceous matter bleaches, so that rocks pigmented with carbon are darker on fresh fracture than on natural exposures. The carbon pigment originates from the alteration of organic matter that was buried with the sediment.

The iron compounds, mainly ferric oxide and ferric hydrates, containing iron in its most highly oxidized form, are powerful coloring agents. The ferric hydrates produce the yellowish-red, brown, and maroon tones. The anhydrous ferric iron oxide (Fe_2O_3) produces red tones. A sandstone or shale containing a small percentage of the red iron pigment (Fe_2O_3) is likely to be of brick-red color. In the presence of reducing agents (carbonaceous matter, hydrogen sulphide) ferric iron becomes " reduced " to the ferrous condition, in which state it forms much less conspicuously colored compounds.

Partly because of their striking color red sedimentary rocks have long been of special interest. Red beds commonly occur with strata of rock salt and gypsum that have been precipitated by the evaporation of large bodies of salt water. They are also common as sandstones and conglomerates containing unweathered feldspars. This common association of red beds with the phenomena of arid regions has inclined many to regard all red formations as the product of warm, arid climates. Against this belief there is, however, the fact that the great areas in which red soils are now forming are in warm humid regions, whereas most of the deserts have dun or brownish soils. As the sediments transported by streams are chiefly recruited from the soil, it would seem on first thought that the greatest sources of red sediments are warm, humid lands. However, red soils form where the relief is sufficient to insure free circulation of the oxygenated water of the rainfall; but in the lower, swampy tracts, vegetation is luxuriant, the stagnant waters become depleted of their oxygen, and strongly reducing conditions exist because of the excess carbon. Therefore, even if red sediments are deposited in the swampy tracts of humid regions, the red color tends to disappear and the sediments turn dark. As sediments are generally deposited in the lowest places, it follows that there is small chance of forming red deposits in humid basins. But in the desert and in regions of seasonal rainfall, life is sparse, and the soil becomes dry and its content of humus becomes oxidized during the periods of drought. No reducing conditions obtain here, and if red sediments are washed in from the more humid uplands or slopes they are likely to remain red.

Owing to the abundance of marine life, reducing conditions generally obtain on the sea floor and, consequently, most marine sediments are not red. Nevertheless, where red sediments are swept into the sea in large quantity the organic matter on the bottom may not suffice to reduce all the ferric iron. Off the mouth of the Amazon, for example, red muds are accumulating; and examples of red sedimentary rocks can be cited in which abundant marine fossils are entombed. The brick-red and chocolate colors of the red clay of the abyssal deposits are apparently due to the sparseness of life on the deep-sea floors and to the extreme slowness of accumulation which permits thorough oxidation of the iron in the sediments.

In conclusion, red strata occur chiefly in terrestrial formations, especially in those that accumulated in warm arid or semiarid regions; but red color in itself is not proof of any one depositional environment.

STRATIGRAPHIC RELATIONS

Relative Age of Strata. — Inasmuch as the stratified rocks are formed from superposed layers of sediment, it is evident that each stratum is younger than the next below. Except where the rocks have been overturned or dislocated from their normal sequence, the youngest stratum is at the top and the oldest at the bottom of any pile of strata. Many conclusions on the structure of a region and the succession of geological events rest upon this self-evident principle. It is the first fundamental law of *stratigraphy*, as that branch of geology is termed which deals with the description, order, and position of the stratified rocks.

Grouping of Strata into Sedimentary Formations. — An assemblage of rocks into a unit convenient for the purposes of description or mapping is termed a *formation*. A succession of strata that were deposited under essentially similar conditions or without significant time breaks constitutes a sedimentary formation. It is customary to give formations geographical names based on the localities where they were first recognized. If the formation consists chiefly of rock of one kind that fact is commonly expressed in the given name, such as *Stockbridge limestone, Utica shale,* or *Dakota sandstone*. If, however, the formation is made up of a sequence or alternation of unlike kinds (for example, limestone and shale), it is given a geographical name only, as *Kansas City formation*.

Generally a formation is characterized by the occurrence in it of certain distinctive fossils or associations of fossils. These organic remains are termed *index* or *guide fossils*; they make it possible to recognize the formation and to trace it across country. This association of distinctive fossils with certain groups of strata is the second fundamental law of stratigraphy. Some formations are defined by the distinctive kinds of rocks of which they are made up, and formations thus delimited often coincide with those determined by the organic remains. This correspondence is due to the fact that the conditions of sedimentation are likely to have influenced the nature of the fauna and flora buried in the rocks.

In formations of geologically recent origin we find the remains of plants and animals of the kinds now living. Such representatives of living organisms become progressively scarcer in the older formations, and in the most ancient formations the remains consist entirely of extinct organisms. A species that has become extinct never reappears. By piecing together the evidence from the determined order of the superposed strata with the occurrence of the organisms in them, a chronology of the history of the Earth has been worked out, the larger subdivisions of which are presented in Appendix D.

The order of appearance and extinction of the fossil faunas and floras having been established, as was done first in Europe and America, it can

N. W. Carkhuff, U. S. Geol. Survey.

Fig. 173. — South wall of the Grand Canyon of the Colorado River near El Tovar, showing six sedimentary formations. They are lettered to correspond with those in the explanatory diagram.

be applied to determine the age and succession of strata anywhere, even in regions where crustal revolutions have caused the strata to stand vertically or have overturned them.

The view of the wall of the Grand Canyon of the Colorado in Fig. 173 shows a succession of six formations. The lowest formation consists of strata of sandy shale and shaly sandstone aggregating in thickness more than 1000 feet; above it is the Redwall limestone, whose massiveness

causes it to outcrop in 500-foot cliffs and to form some of the most striking scenery of the Canyon; the third is a thick series of shales and sandstones; the fourth consists homogeneously of shale; the fifth is the
Coconino sandstone, a single massive bed of white sandstone; and the
uppermost is the Kaibab limestone, so called because it forms the floor
of the Kaibab Plateau in which the Canyon is incised.

The six formations exposed by the deep incision into the crust at the
Grand Canyon total 4000 feet in thickness. They rest here in their
normal horizontal positions and in undisturbed sequence. From the fossils in them we find that the lowermost formation was laid down in early
Paleozoic time and the uppermost in late Paleozoic time; translated
into years, this means a span of hundreds of millions of years. From the
fossils we learn further that the formations represent but a fraction of
this vast span of time, and that therefore there are significant time
breaks between the successive formations, which intervals of time, although unrepresented by strata at the Grand Canyon, are represented
elsewhere.

Intergradation of Different Kinds of Sedimentary Rock. — Sediments
vary systematically in their coarseness and in their composition. The
coarser detritus begins to settle out as soon as the transporting currents
begin to slacken, and the finer material is carried farther. Thus a lateral
gradation of material is produced. Such a gradation is strikingly shown
in alluvial fans, where the bouldery wash at the apex of the fan grades
outward to fine clays on the periphery. In marine deposits, as a rule,
conglomerates are formed near the shore, shales farther out, and limestones still farther out. The change from one kind of sedimentary rock
to the adjacent rock is gradational and generally not abrupt. Therefore, sedimentary rocks grade laterally into rocks of different composition but of contemporaneous origin. In general, coarse sedimentary
rocks grade the most abruptly into the other kinds (an effect of the law
that the diameter of the particles transported by a current varies as the
square of the velocity), and are the most localized and irregular in their
distribution. Thus conglomerates that have formed in old stream channels or in shore zones occur as irregular linear deposits which extend
parallel to the stream course or the shore, but in other directions they
grade into sandstone within a few miles at the most. Coarse sandstones
as a rule are similarly inconstant, but some individual beds of shale or
limestone of constant thickness and composition may extend over thousands of square miles.

Areal Extent of Sedimentary Formations. — In view of the discontinuous nature of the areas in which the sediments are deposited, manifestly
no geologic formation can be world-wide in extent. Shales and lime-

stones make some formations several thousand square miles in area, and single falls of volcanic ash can form strata covering 1,000,000 square miles. Beds of clastic origin, as sandstone and shale, imply land surfaces from which they were derived and basins in which they were laid down; obviously they must be limited in areal extent by the borders of the basins adjacent to which they thin out and disappear. In geometrical form a group of sediments is tabular, consisting of subparallel layers or strata. If deposited in a circumscribed basin, the deposits are roughly lens-shaped, with the thickest portion of the lens in the deepest (or most rapidly subsiding) part of the basin; but if laid down along an open coast the deposits tend to be wedge-like, thickest near shore and progressively thinner seaward.

Unconformity. — One of the most important stratigraphic relations is that of *unconformity*, a subject that is treated in detail in Chapter XII. A marine unconformity records the submergence of a land mass and the deposition of a series of strata on the submerged area. As a result of the landward migration of the sea over a subsiding area, the strata that are laid down commonly have the relation of *overlap*.

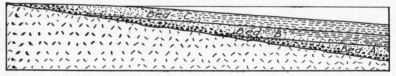

Fig. 174. — Progressive *overlap* of beds *A*, *B*, and *C* as the result of the landward incursion of the sea, from right to left, on a subsiding land mass. The normal seaward dip of the beds is much exaggerated.

Overlap. — Where the sea gradually encroaches on a land mass, the beds formed as the result of this invasion of the land have the relations shown in Fig. 174. Each layer overlaps the next layer below it, extends some distance beyond it in the direction of the landward migration of the sea, and thins out against the old land surface. This relation, known as *overlap*, is of great geologic importance. It should be noted that the gravel and sand, being near-shore deposits, grade seaward (laterally) into muds, and also vertically upward. In successive sections from right to left the gravel and sand as they follow the encroaching shoreline rise higher in the sequence of strata. In other words, the gravel and sand of Bed *C* are younger than the gravel and sand of Bed *A*. The bedding planes between *A*, *B*, and *C* are time boundaries, but the gravelly layer, being continuous from right to left, cuts across, transgresses, the time boundaries. Gravel of the kind shown in the section, when lithified, is known as a *progressive marine conglomerate*, or *basal conglomerate*, and the relation of the beds is that of *progressive overlap*.

If instead of invasion of a land mass as a result of subsidence (or rise of sea level), the land mass gradually emerges and the sea retreats, gravel and sand will be deposited on the finer sediments, thus producing a seaward overlapping of coarse clastic material on the finer sediments. Such a relation is termed a *regressive overlap* (or an *offlap*), and a conglomerate thus formed is a *regressive marine conglomerate*, or *retreatal conglomerate*.

The conglomerates of these two modes of origin record, then, the advance of the sea over a land mass and its subsequent retreat.

READING REFERENCES

1. Treatise on Sedimentation; by W. H. Twenhofel. 660 pages. Williams and Wilkins Co., Baltimore, 1926.

A source book for the study of both sediments and sedimentary rocks, with many references to special literature.

2. Deposition of the Sedimentary Rocks; by J. E. Marr. 245 pages. Cambridge University Press, Cambridge, 1929.

An excellent introductory account of the principles governing the deposition of the sedimentary rocks.

CHAPTER X

IGNEOUS ROCKS

Igneous rocks are one of the three great classes of rock that make up the crust of our planet. As their name implies, they were formed at high temperatures, and they can be defined as those rocks *which have been made by the solidification of molten matter that originated within the Earth.* Such liquids, as is well known, are discharged as streams of lava from many volcanoes the world over, and at such places we can actually see igneous rocks in the making. Grand and spectacular though volcanic eruptions are, they are only a superficial manifestation at the Earth's surface of far mightier activities of molten rock-matter within the crust. Molten material rising from the depths is more or less highly charged with gases; and these gases begin to escape because of the decreasing pressure on the liquid as it nears the Earth's surface in a volcanic vent and are almost wholly eliminated at the time when the liquid solidifies. The molten rock-matter plus its content of dissolved gases is called *magma.* Magmas have a wide range in composition; for example, the magma erupted by Vesuvius differs greatly from that discharged by Etna.

Mode of Occurrence of Igneous Rocks

Intrusive and Extrusive Rocks. — There are two principal ways in which igneous rocks occur: the *intrusive* and the *extrusive.* In the intrusive mode of occurrence, the magma ascended from the depths of the Earth to the higher levels of the crust, but its upward progress was permanently arrested before it could reach the surface; consequently it cooled and solidified under the cover of the rock masses of the outer shell. The resulting mass of igneous rock is termed an intrusive body; and manifestly such bodies become accessible to view only after they have been exposed by erosion. In the extrusive mode of occurrence, the magma reached the surface and was discharged from a volcanic vent: it was extruded upon the Earth's surface and solidified there. The resulting extrusive rocks are also known as *volcanic rocks.*

Obviously, intrusive rocks are formed in a geologic environment differing greatly from that in which extrusive rocks are formed. In intrusive bodies the magma cools and solidifies slowly; in extrusive bodies it is drastically chilled by exposure to the atmosphere and solidifies rapidly. Correspondingly great differences in appearance therefore distinguish the intrusive from the extrusive rocks.

Although the distinction between intrusive and extrusive rocks is generally valid, in some places the rocks of the two classes grade into each other. For example, magma that issues at the Earth's surface as a lava flow has come up through a passageway from below; and if the passageway remains filled, the magma in it eventually solidifies into rock. Consequently the extrusive body — the lava flow occurring on the surface — is connected with an intrusive mass below. The connection of an extrusive mass with its root can rarely be seen, however, because as a rule the extrusive mass either covers its root or else it has been separated from it by erosion, whereby the former continuity has been destroyed.

Intrusive Bodies

The intrusive igneous bodies are structural elements in the architecture of the crust, and according to their shape or form and their structural relations to the inclosing rocks there are six principal kinds: *dikes, sills, laccoliths, volcanic necks, stocks,* and *batholiths.* The simplest form of intrusive body is the dike and it therefore will be considered first.

Dikes. — A *dike* is a tabular mass of igneous rock that fills a fissure in preëxistent rocks. Consequently, it has walls that are parallel or nearly so. Dikes are inclosed in rocks of all kinds — igneous, sedimentary, or metamorphic — and they are said to "cut" the rocks that inclose them. Dikes occurring in layered rocks must by definition cut the layers at an angle; for if a tabular igneous mass lies parallel with the layers it is termed a *sill.*

Dikes range in length from a few yards to many miles; they range in thickness from a fraction of an inch to thousands of feet. An illustration showing three dikes cutting a series of stratified rocks at right angles to their stratification is seen in Fig. 175.

Some fissures extended to the Earth's surface and discharged magma as streams of lava, and after the discharge ceased the magma in the fissure solidified and thus formed a dike that reached to the Earth's surface; other dikes did not reach the surface and have later become exposed to view by erosion. Some dikes fill the channels through which were fed larger intrusive bodies at higher levels in the crust, such as the sills and laccoliths next to be described. During erosion, some dikes resist more strongly than the inclosing rocks and hence are left projecting as walls; but other dikes are less resistant and form ditches; from these features the name is derived, especially from the resemblance to the more prominent wall, for dike means both *ditch* and *wall.* The rock of some dikes is divided into blocks or columns by joints, and these columns are perpendicular to the walls of the dike, resembling a pile of cordwood, an arrangement whose origin is described later under *columnar structure*.

Dikes occur at many places in more or less well-defined systems; and in some localities parallel dikes are so numerous and closely spaced as to form dike-swarms. Around volcanic centers they generally have a radial arrangement, extending out from the central crater like the spokes of a wheel.

N. H. Darton, U. S. Geol. Survey.

Fig. 175. — Dikes cutting sedimentary beds at right angles. Alamillo Creek, New Mexico.

Dikes, especially those cutting sedimentary rocks, are bordered by zones of hardened, baked, or otherwise altered rock, which are the results of the high temperature to which the rocks were subjected by the molten magma. Similar effects are produced by all intrusive rocks, and they give us a means for determining the intrusive nature of an igneous mass.

Sills. — A *sill* is a tabular mass of igneous rock lying parallel with the layers of the inclosing rocks (Fig. 176). Sills range in thickness from a foot or so to several thousand feet. Magma insinuated itself between two layers and lifted the overlying rocks through the distance now represented by the thickness of the sill. It can be easily appreciated that the magma of a thick sill, intruded deep within the crust and having an areal extent of several thousand square miles, must have been injected by an enormous impelling force.

As the term sill implies, the name was originally given to horizontal intrusive sheets, such as the famous Whin sill of the north of England, which is traceable for 80 miles and averages 90 feet in thickness. The Whin sill has remained in its horizontal position since it was injected, but other sills have been tilted from their original horizontal position; and some tabular masses were injected into strata or other layered rocks that were already inclined at the time the magma was forced in between them. The essence of the definition of a sill is therefore not in the horizontality of the tabular mass, but in its parallelism with the inclosing layers.

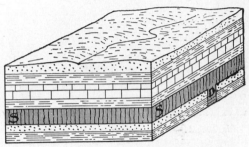

Fig. 176. — The sill *SS* was intruded between horizontal strata; the dike *D* represents the conduit through which the magma was forced up. Vertical joints were formed as the sill cooled. The block is about 1 mile wide, the sill 50 feet thick.

Undoubtedly the best-known sill in America is the Palisade sill, on the west side of the Hudson River fronting New York City. The palisade structure to which this sill owes its name is the result of the vertical columns developed in it by shrinkage-cracking during cooling, like columnar jointing in dikes. Such columnar structures, as explained in Chapter XII, invariably develop at right angles to the walls of the dikes and sills.

Laccoliths. — A *laccolith* is typically a lens- or dome-shaped mass of igneous rock that was intruded into layered rocks. It has a flat floor and is more or less circular in ground plan. If the magma, after it has insinuated itself between the layers in the form of a sill, arches up the overlying layers, instead of continuing to spread laterally away from the supply channel, a lens of liquid rock will be produced, and this lens on solidifying forms a laccolith. An ideal section of a laccolith is given in Fig. 177, *A*, in which is shown the dome-shaped mountain produced by the lifting of the rocks that overlie the laccolith.

Many laccoliths, however, depart from the typical form. Instead of being circular in ground plan, some are oval or quite irregular; and in section some have the shape of a wedge instead of the symmetrical form shown in Fig. 177, *A*. As the amount of uparching of the overlying layers decreases, the resulting laccolith approximates nearer and nearer to a sill in form. Some laccoliths locally break across the layers. Some thin out into sills, or are accompanied by sills on the flanks of the arches, and thus are compound in form.

Laccoliths, more or less exposed by erosion, are conspicuous features in many parts of western North America (Fig. 177, *B*). They were first discovered by Gilbert in the Henry Mountains of southern Utah, where they rise above a plateau of undisturbed horizontal strata. They form a complete series showing the progressive stages of denudation: from laccoliths still covered by their roof-rocks and whose presence in depth is inferred from the dome-like hills produced by the uparching of the strata, to laccoliths so deeply dissected as to show the undisturbed horizontal strata underneath them. These laccoliths were intruded at estimated

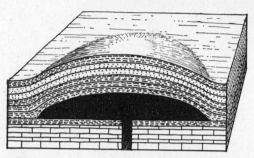

Fig. 177, *A.* — Laccolith, showing the typical form of the igneous mass and the doming of the overlying beds. The block is about 2 miles wide.

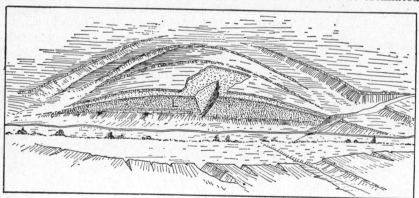

L. V. Pirsson.

Fig. 177, *B.* — Laccolith (*L*), from which the roof-rocks have been partly stripped off by erosion. Warm Spring Creek, cutting across the laccolith, has exposed the horizontal floor on which the laccolith rests. The laccolith is 1 mile in diameter. Judith Mountains, Montana.

depths of 10,000 to 14,000 feet in the crust: depths that on the one hand give some measure of the enormous force that propelled the magma and enabled it to dome up the overlying strata, and on the other hand indicate the large amount of erosion that had occurred before the laccoliths became visible.

Subsequently, laccoliths have been found in many parts of the world and are therefore a not uncommon form of intrusive body. Some of the more recently recognized laccoliths are of immensely greater size than the classic laccoliths of the Henry Mountains, the largest of which has a diameter of 4 miles and a volume of 10 cubic miles. The great Duluth laccolith on the northwest shore of Lake Superior is estimated to represent the injection of 50,000 cubic miles of magma.

The floor of a large laccolith as a rule is not horizontal but dips from the perimeter inward toward a point under its center, just as if the floor had sagged from loss of support. Such loss of support is conceivably the result of the emptying of a magma reservoir below the laccolith.

Volcanic Necks. — When a volcano becomes extinct, the column of magma that filled the conduit leading upward from unknown depths

C. E. Dutton, U. S. Geol. Survey.

Fig. 178. — Volcanic necks. Zuni Plateau, New Mexico.

solidifies and forms a cylindrical mass of igneous rock which is known as a *volcanic neck* (Fig. 178). It is circular in ground plan and may be from a few hundred yards up to a mile in diameter. The rocks surrounding a volcanic neck are generally cut by a radiating system of dikes, and if the rocks are stratified they are commonly injected with sills. The further description of volcanic necks is postponed to Chapter XI.

Batholiths. — A *batholith* is a huge intrusive body of igneous rock. Large size and invading relation to its inclosing rocks are its distinguishing features (Fig. 179). Furthermore, a batholith appears to extend indefinitely downward into the Earth's crust; it is without known floor, in contrast to a laccolith, which rests on a floor.

Batholiths, like other intrusive bodies, become accessible to human observation only as the result of their exposure by erosion. Accordingly, the size of a batholith as we customarily speak of it depends on the depth to which erosion has uncovered it. The largest batholith in the United

States is the Idaho batholith of central Idaho, exposed over an area of
16,000 square miles.   Had erosion stripped off less of the roof-rocks that
formerly covered the batholith, its exposed area would be smaller; and
had erosion extended a mile or two deeper its visible portion would have
been much larger.   Another great batholith is the Coast Range batholith, which extends for 1100 miles from the Canadian border northward
into Alaska and has an exposed width of 80 to 120 miles.

Many mountain ranges have batholithic cores, or backbones of igneous rock.   The home of the batholith is in the world's mountain belts,

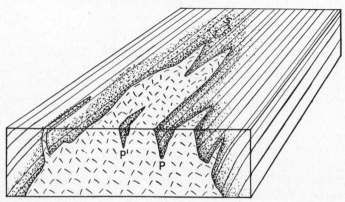

Modified from R. A. Daly.

Fig. 179. — Batholith, partly uncovered by erosion; *P* and *P'* are masses of invaded
country rock projecting deeply downward into the batholith.   They are termed *roof-*
pendants; at *P* the continuity with the main body of country rock has persisted, but at
P' the connection has been removed by the downward progress of erosion.   The batholith is of the *discordant* or *transgressive* type, as it cuts across the structure of the invaded
country rock.   Stippling indicates metamorphism of the older rocks near the borders of
the batholith.   The block is about 20 miles wide.

in the zones of acute deformation of the crust.   The enormous bodies of
magma were intruded either at times of crustal deformation or shortly
after.   A batholith intruded during a crustal revolution tends to have
concordant contacts, *i.e.*, the roof-rocks arch over the top of the batholith just as the roof-rocks arch over a laccolith; whereas a batholith intruded at the end of a period of crustal deformation has discordant contacts: it breaks across the general structure of the rocks it has invaded.
Structurally, then, there are two types of batholith: *concordant* and
discordant.

Granite is the chief rock of which discordant batholiths are composed,
and granite gneiss (a modification of granite due to the roughly parallel
arrangement of its component minerals, chiefly expressed by the orientation of the biotite flakes) makes up the concordant batholiths.

As granite is formed at some depth in the crust, it is exposed at the surface only after erosion has stripped off the covering rocks; hence it is seen chiefly in those parts of the continents bared by erosion — that is to say, in mountains or in regions so deeply eroded that the roots of the mountains are visible.

Granite is the main constituent of the foundation of the continental masses. These foundation granites occur as batholiths of very ancient origin, of Pre-Cambrian age, and constitute a floor upon which the sedimentary rocks of later age were deposited. Granite of younger age also occurs abundantly as stocks and vast batholiths that are intrusive into the younger rocks, for epochs of granitic intrusion have occurred time and time again during the long span of the Earth's history. The Idaho and Coast Range batholiths already cited are grand examples of such younger intrusions. On account of this prevalence in the crust, granite is by far the most voluminous of the intrusive igneous rocks.

From many points of view batholiths are of extraordinary interest. They are structural units of the first magnitude in the architecture of the crust. The source of the heat, the origin of the magma, the forces that set the magma in movement, and the manner in which such stupendous masses of molten rock-matter make room for themselves in the higher levels of the Earth's crust are among the most fundamental and fascinating problems of geology. The concordant batholiths appear to make room for themselves by lifting and shouldering aside the rocks of the crust, like laccoliths of immense size; but the mode of intrusion of the discordant batholiths is much less clear. Many brilliant explanations have been suggested: foremost among these is the hypothesis of magmatic stoping, so called from a certain analogy between the process by which the magma is conceived to make room for itself in the crust and the miner's process of extracting ore. The hot magma in coming into contact with the rocks it is invading shatters these rocks above the junction zone and spalls off blocks of rock; and as soon as these fragments are engulfed in the magma they sink, because the fragments of solid rock are heavier than the liquid magma. By the progressive spalling-off of these blocks and their sinking in the magma, the magmatic chamber becomes enlarged and the magma works its way upward into the higher levels of the crust. Although it is abundantly clear that this process of magmatic stoping has been effective around the borders of discordant batholiths, it has not yet been demonstrated that the immense chambers occupied by the batholiths were formed entirely in this way.

Stocks. — *Stocks* are the smaller intrusive igneous bodies without known floors. There is no fundamental difference between a stock and a batholith. A stock differs from a batholith only in its much smaller size; arbitrarily, an intrusive igneous body less than 40 square miles

(100 square kilometers) in areal extent is called a stock; if larger than 40 square miles, a batholith. Some stocks, as indicated at S in Fig. 179, are merely dome-like protuberances from the body of an underlying batholith; they have been aptly called *cupolas*.

Stocks as a rule are circular or elliptical in ground plan. As they are likely to form hills or mountains after being exposed by erosion, they are sometimes called *bosses*, especially those that are circular in plan. The distinction from a volcanic neck is not one of size, though necks tend to be smaller than stocks, but that the term "neck" is used only when there is evidence that the igneous body occupies a channel that functioned as the supply conduit of a volcano. Some stocks doubtless were necks, but this can not now be proved.

Extrusive Bodies

Extrusive bodies are those formed by magma that reaches the Earth's surface. Magma is discharged at the surface in two ways, depending on the quantity and activity of the gases contained in it: the *quiet*, in which it wells out as a liquid and solidifies into rock, and the *explosive*, in which it is violently blown into the air and falls in the form of fragments.

Lava Flows. — Magma that issues at the surface is known as *lava*. The liquid discharge, as well as its solidified equivalent, is commonly spoken of as a *lava flow*. Liquid flows are poured out from volcanoes. The ejections of a few volcanoes, like those in Hawaii, consist almost wholly of liquid lava, but at most volcanoes the outpouring of lava alternates with the ejection of fragmental material.

Some lava flows were not erupted from volcanoes, however, but have welled out quietly from fissures. In the geologic past such *fissure eruptions* have occured many times on a huge scale. Among the most notable of these enormous lava floods are those of the Columbia River region in the northwestern United States and of the Deccan region in western India. In each of these regions the resulting pile of lava flows is thousands of feet thick and covers an area of 200,000 square miles.

Not infrequently lava flows have been buried under sedimentary deposits of various kinds. Such buried flows are sheet-like in form and therefore resemble sills, but they can be distinguished from sills by the facts that they have not baked the sediments above them and that their upper surfaces generally show the features common to the surface of lavas, such as the scoriaceous and ropy structures, which are described in Chapter XI. Furthermore, the layer of sediments resting directly on a buried lava flow is likely to contain pebbles or boulders eroded from the upper part of the flow before it was completely covered.

Tuffs and Breccias. — If magma in the conduit of a volcano is viscous and highly charged with gases, its eruptive activity becomes explosive, and fragmental material is hurled into the air. During the explosions not only fragments of hot, still-fluid magma are ejected, but also cold solidified lava torn from the crater walls is blown into the air in immense amount. The coarser material falls around the vent; the finer material, carried by the wind, tends to fall after the coarser and at greater distances from the vent. The coarser material, when converted into rock, is termed *volcanic breccia,* and the finer material is known as *tuff.* Both are termed *pyroclastic* rocks (p. 270) to distinguish them from the fragmental or clastic sedimentary rocks.

Tuffs and breccias are distributed the world over, occurring wherever volcanism is active or has been active, and their presence is, indeed, one of the surest indications of former volcanism in places where it has long since died out.

Determination of the Age of an Igneous Rock

The geologic date at which a given mass of igneous rock was intruded or erupted is determined by ascertaining the relations of the mass to the rocks with which it is in contact. Thus, if an igneous body such as a dike cuts through another body of rock, it is manifestly the younger of the two. If it cuts through sedimentary beds, it is younger than they are; and as the age of sedimentary beds can generally be determined by the fossils that occur in them, it is clear that the dike is younger than the age indicated by the fossils, *but how much younger must be ascertained from other evidence,* unfortunately not as a rule obtainable. Suppose, however, we

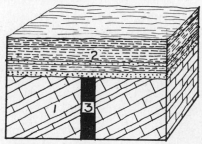

Fig. 180. — Determination of the age of an igneous rock. The dike (*3*) is younger than the limestones (*1*) it intersects, and older than the strata (*2*) that rest on it.

have the fortunate conjunction of circumstances indicated in Fig. 180. The dike there shown cuts limestone beds, which from the fossils in them are known to be of Carboniferous age; by erosion these beds with the dike in them were worn down and a series of fossiliferous Triassic beds were deposited on them. The dike, therefore, is younger than the Carboniferous beds and is older than the Triassic; in geologic parlance we say it is post-Carboniferous and pre-Triassic.

Lava flows are of course younger than the rocks on which they lie. If a pile of flows contains interbedded layers of tuff and breccia, these pyroclastic deposits may inclose fossils, the remains of plants or animals that were overwhelmed by the volcanic eruptions; and by means of these fossils the flows can as a rule be precisely dated.

If a sheet of igneous rock lying concordantly between strata has baked the strata both above and below it (p. 236), it is younger than both. Such evidence of baking is positive proof that the sheet has been injected at some time after the inclosing strata were formed and is therefore a sill. If a sheet has not baked the stratum overlying it, it probably is a lava flow and at any rate is older than the overlying strata.   It is thus usually easy to tell whether an igneous mass is younger than other rocks by examining its contacts with them.   The attempt should always be made to find whether the massive igneous rocks, which unlike the pyroclastic rocks can not contain fossils, are older or younger than the fossiliferous rocks with which they may be in contact.

Texture and Composition of Igneous Rocks

Basis of Classification. — Igneous rocks occur in immense variety, partly because the magmas from which they were formed differed in composition and partly because the physical conditions under which the magmas solidified differed greatly.   They are classified on the basis of two properties: first, their texture, and second, their composition.[1]

Texture. — The most obvious thing about an igneous rock is its texture.   By *texture* is meant the appearance of a rock as determined by the size, shape, and arrangement of its constituent mineral grains. Thus, if the grains are as large as peas, we say that such a rock has a *coarse-grained* texture; if the grains are the size of those in granulated sugar, we say that the rock is *fine-grained*; whereas, if the particles are so minute that they can not be discriminated by the unaided eye and the rock looks as if it were a homogeneous substance, we say that it is *aphanitic* in texture.[2]

The grain size depends on the *rate at which the magma cooled*.   If the magma is extremely hot, the minerals dissolved in it can not crystallize out; that is, the atoms and atomic groups in the magma can not arrange themselves to form organized solid compounds (the minerals).   No minerals begin to crystallize out until the temperature has fallen far enough; then they begin to separate from the magma and, if the cooling is slow, they have time to grow to large size, thus forming a coarse-grained

---

[1] See Appendix B for the classification and description of the common igneous rocks.

[2] *Dense* is often incorrectly used in America as a synonym for *aphanitic*.   It is also used correctly to mean "of high density," and this double usage leads to ambiguity. For example, a "dense" felsite (in the sense of an extremely fine-grained rock) is a rock of low density.

rock. But if cooling proceeds rapidly, more and more centers of crystallization form spontaneously, and, instead of a few such centers growing to large crystals, many begin to grow simultaneously; none of them can therefore attain large size, and consequently the resulting rock is fine-grained in texture. If cooling is still more rapid, the crystals become so minute that they are invisible to the unaided eye, and the resulting rock is aphanitic. Under conditions of extremely rapid cooling the magma solidifies into a homogeneous substance before any crystallization occurs.

In this event the product is a *glass*, a result by no means uncommon.

To sum up, igneous rocks are *coarse-grained*, *fine-grained*, *aphanitic*, or *glassy* in texture, the grain size being coarser the more slowly the magma cooled.

Porphyry: Porphyritic Texture. — So far it has been tacitly as-

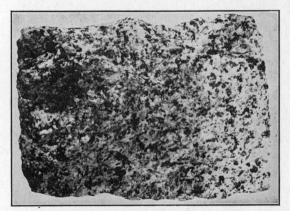

Fig. 181. — Even-granular igneous rock.

sumed that all the mineral grains in a given rock are of uniform size, *i.e.*, that the rock is *evenly granular* (Fig. 181). Not all igneous rocks, however, are evenly granular. Many of them are composed of grains of two sizes: in part of large conspicuous crystals and in part of much smaller grains, which form a matrix in which the large crystals are imbedded. An igneous rock of this texture is called a *porphyry* (Fig. 182). The matrix of a porphyry is termed the *groundmass*, and the large crystals imbedded in the groundmass are called *phenocrysts* (clearly discernible crystals). In porphyries certain minerals occur in *two* generations: in a first generation as the phenocrysts and in a second generation as constituents of the groundmass.

Porphyries are abundant and comprise many kinds. The groundmasses of the various porphyries have a wide range in grain size; they are medium-grained, fine-grained, aphanitic, or glassy. Most commonly they are aphanitic, as in the extrusive rocks, which generally are porphyritic rocks with aphanitic groundmasses. The phenocrysts also have a wide range in size — from those several inches in diameter to those so small as to be barely visible to the unaided eye; and they may be abundant or comparatively few. In all porphyries, however, the phenocrysts contrast conspicuously in size with the grains that make up the ground-mass, and it is this contrast that is the essential feature of a porphyry. The porphyritic texture is *not* a contrast of colors; thus a rock consisting of grains of light-colored quartz and feldspar, through which are scattered a few crystals of black mica, all grains being of about the same size, is *not* a porphyry.

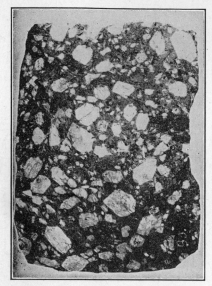

Fig. 182. — Porphyry, showing abundant white crystals of feldspar set in an aphanitic groundmass.

Relation of Texture to Geologic Mode of Occurrence.

— Inasmuch as the texture of an igneous rock depends chiefly on the rate at which the magma cools, anything in the geologic environment of a magma that influences the rate of cooling must affect the resulting texture. Obviously an *intrusive* mass of magma that is surrounded and blanketed above by other, older rock masses must lose heat much more slowly than an *extrusive* one, which is poured out on the Earth's surface as a lava flow. Therefore because a coarse-grained texture is produced by slow cooling, we naturally associate it with intrusive masses, and, conversely, we regard the aphanitic and glassy groundmasses as characteristic of extrusive rocks — the lava flows. The volume of an intruded mass greatly influences the rate of cooling, because a large mass cools more slowly than a small one. Thus, the rocks that make up great batholiths are coarse-grained, whereas the rocks of dikes and sills tend to be much finer-grained. On the other hand, the central portion of a thick lava flow cools slowly enough to develop a medium-grained texture, whereas a magma that was injected into a narrow fissure in cold rocks is chilled so quickly as to cause it to solidify as an aphanitic or glassy rock. Thus modifications of the general rule according to particular conditions can easily be conceived; nevertheless, the general rule holds true that the intrusive rocks range from coarse- to medium-grained and the extrusive rocks range from fine-grained to aphanitic.

An important deduction from the rule just cited is that the coarse-grained rocks, because they were formed within the crust, become visible at the Earth's surface only after erosion has stripped off the rocks that covered them.

Although the rate of cooling is the most important factor determining the texture of igneous rocks, as discussed above, it is not the only one. Chemical composition is also important. Under similar conditions of cooling, *basic* magmas (those low in silica and high in iron and magnesia) solidify as rocks of coarser grain than do the *silicic* magmas composed of much silica, alumina, and alkalies. The reason is that the basic magmas are much more fluid than the silicic magmas, and consequently while they are solidifying, the crystal grains easily grow to larger sizes than they can in the silicic magmas.

That the kind of texture formed during solidification is influenced by the geologic mode of occurrence is perhaps most vividly shown by the extrusive rocks. The large conspicuous crystals — the phenocrysts — were mainly formed before the magma was extruded on the Earth's surface and the fine-grained groundmass solidified after extrusion. The porphyritic texture thus developed records a sudden change in the environment in which the rock was formed, whereby the rate of cooling was enormously speeded up and the dissolved gases could readily escape.

The presence of the gases, especially the water contained in magmas, increases the fluidity of the magma and thereby promotes a coarser crystallization to an astonishing degree. This enhanced power of crystallization is very notably shown by certain dikes associated with intrusive masses of granite. The dikes are made up of large crystals of quartz, feldspar, and mica, individuals several feet in diameter being not uncommon. The very coarse igneous rocks of this composition are known as *granite pegmatites*, and from them are obtained the plates of mica that are used commercially. In allusion to their giant grain size, granite pegmatites are sometimes called giant granites.

The rock of a volcanic neck is likely to be comparatively coarse-grained in spite of the small volume of the neck, because the constant upward passage of molten material to the surface greatly heats the rocks surrounding the conduit, thus causing slow cooling of the last charge of magma that occupied the conduit and solidified there when the volcano became extinct.

Composition of Igneous Rocks. — The composition of an igneous rock obviously depends on the chemical composition of the magma from which it solidified. As already emphasized, a magma is made up of two parts: a volatile part, consisting chiefly of gaseous water, with carbon dioxide, sulphur fumes, and others, amounting to a few per cent, and a non-volatile part, consisting of the fixed constituents, chiefly molten silicates. The volatile part is highly important in rock formation because of its power of increasing the fluidity of the magma, but it is almost completely eliminated during solidification, and it is the molten silicates that by their solidification form the rocks.

Many thousands of igneous rocks from all parts of the world have been analyzed, with the following results, which show the ranges in the amounts of the various constituents. These results are reported by the chemist in terms of oxides, and it has accordingly become conventional to speak of the chemical composition of rocks as if the rocks were actually composed of these oxides. For example, when we say that a rock is high in silica we really mean that its chemical analysis shows a large amount of silica; but this mode of expression implies nothing as to the state of chemical combination of the silica in the rock.

Silica, SiO_2, invariably present; ranges from 35 to 80 per cent.
Alumina, Al_2O_3, ranges from 0 to 25 per cent.
Oxides of iron, FeO and Fe_2O_3, generally both; 0 to 20 per cent.
Magnesia, MgO, 0 to 45 per cent.
Lime, CaO, 0 to 20 per cent.
Soda, Na_2O, 0 to 16 per cent.
Potash, K_2O, 0 to 12 per cent.

As we shall see presently, certain general laws govern the associations of these oxides as they occur in the rocks. It will be noticed that one acid-forming oxide (silica) is present; but the other oxides are oxides of the six metals (aluminum, iron, magnesium, calcium, sodium, and potassium) and are in general bases. Oxides of other elements occur in small or minute quantities, but are so much less important that they can be neglected.

Silicic Rocks and Basic Rocks. — Silica is abundant in all igneous rocks and metallic oxides occur in all, but the particular metallic oxides present range from almost nothing to large amounts. However, a rough general rule governs the composition of igneous rocks; without going into details we can say that igneous rocks, although they form a series that varies continuously in composition between the extremes known to occur in nature, can be divided into two classes: one in which the silica content is high and the alkali-metal oxides — soda and potassa (Na_2O and K_2O) — predominate among the metallic oxides; and the other in which, conversely, the silica content is relatively low and lime (CaO), iron oxides (FeO and Fe_2O_3), and magnesia (MgO) predominate among the metallic oxides. Rocks of high silica content are termed *silicic*. Rocks of low silica content are termed *basic*, because of their abundant content of the bases lime, iron, and magnesia.

As a rule silicic rocks are light-colored, whereas basic rocks are dark or black, and heavy because of their content of iron-bearing minerals. The silicic rocks are sometimes termed *acidic*, because the acid-forming radicle silica (SiO_2) predominates in them; the *basic* rocks because of their high content of bases are relatively low in silica, carrying about 50 per cent.

Crystallization of Minerals from Magmas. — It is a familiar experiment that, if a liquid containing a salt, zinc sulphate for example, is boiled down and concentrated to a certain point, not all the zinc sulphate can continue to remain dissolved in it, but begins to appear as a solid in the form of crystals. If the hot solution is allowed to cool, more crystals of the salt are formed, since hot solutions as a rule can contain more salt than cold ones. In analogy with this, a magma can be regarded as a solution; it contains dissolved in it various salts (mineral molecules) more or less electrolytically dissociated. If the magma cools slowly enough, the dissolved matter in it separates from it as crystals. This crystallization proceeds as the temperature falls until the whole magma has turned into a solid mass of crystal grains. The molten liquid has become *rock*. The minerals separate from any given magma in a definite order, which is governed by their solubility in that magma.

Minerals Common in Igneous Rocks. — The minerals that make up most of the igneous rocks are the following:

Light-colored Group (Feldspar Group)	*Dark-colored Group (Ferromagnesian Group)*
Orthoclase feldspar	Biotite (black mica)
Plagioclase feldspars	Pyroxene
	Hornblende
	Olivine
Quartz	Magnetite

Of these minerals, *feldspars, quartz, pyroxene, hornblende,* and *biotite* are the most common in igneous rocks, and they should therefore be carefully noted. For details regarding them see Appendix A.

Since magmas differ in chemical composition, not only the kinds of minerals separating from them but also the relative amounts of these minerals must differ. Thus, a silicic magma, in which silica, with some Na_2O, K_2O, and Al_2O_3, are the chief substances, forms a rock consisting mostly of feldspars, whereas a basic magma, in which lime, magnesia, and iron are abundant makes a rock containing abundant pyroxene, hornblende, and other *ferromagnesian* minerals, as they are called in allusion to the iron and magnesium in them.

These variations in mineral composition largely determine the different varieties of igneous rocks, and mineral composition is one of the two factors here used in classifying the igneous rocks. By employing the criterion of texture the principal classes of igneous rocks are obtained, and these classes are then subdivided into species on the basis of mineral composition. The results are shown in tabular form in Appendix B. They can be recapitulated here in somewhat simpler form.

In general, the intrusive rocks, especially those occurring in batholiths, are coarse-grained equigranular in texture; such rocks are commonly called *plutonic* rocks. They have formed as the result of slow cooling, and the pressure of the overlying rocks favored the retention of the gas content in the magma until a late stage in its solidification, thereby greatly facilitating crystallization and the development of a coarse-grained texture.

On the other hand the extrusive rocks have been formed by drastic chilling and loss of gas content at the Earth's surface and are characterized by either fine-grained or aphanitic groundmasses. Exceptionally drastically chilled magmas, or those which have lost their gas content, or those to which both of these contingencies have happened, solidify to glasses.

Thus a high-silica magma slowly cooling in a batholithic environment solidifies to a granite. The same magma, however, erupted at the Earth's surface solidifies to a rhyolite, a rock vastly different in texture from a granite. Rhyolite is, then, the extrusive equivalent of granite.

A magma of medium silica content solidifies at depth as diorite, but if extruded at the surface it solidifies as andesite. Andesite is therefore said to be the extrusive equivalent of diorite.

A magma of low silica content — a basic magma of about 50 per cent silica — solidifies at depth as gabbro, but the same magma when erupted commonly solidifies as basalt. Basalt, then, is an extrusive equivalent of gabbro. On account of the ease with which basic magmas crystallize, however, especially in thicker flows, some extrusions of basic magma solidify as dolerite.

Diorites and gabbros, although abundant as intrusive masses, do not commonly occur in extensive batholiths as the granites do. They are more common as stocks, sills, and dikes.

Problems of Igneous Geology. — The igneous rocks, and their mode of occurrence in the crust as well as on the crust, present many alluring problems. The source and origin of the various kinds of magmas and the causes for their ascension are fundamental problems. Some of the most suggestive evidence is furnished by the magmas that reach the Earth's surface and there give rise to volcanic phenomena; and as volcanism is an important part of igneous geology, consideration of these questions is postponed to the following chapter.

READING REFERENCES

1. The Natural History of Igneous Rocks; by Alfred Harker. 385 pages. The Macmillan Co., New York, 1909.

2. Igneous Rocks and Their Origin; by R. A. Daly. 563 pages. McGraw-Hill Book Co., New York, 1914.

3. Rocks and Rock Minerals; by L. V. Pirsson (2d edition by Adolph Knopf). 426 pages. John Wiley & Sons, New York, 1926.

CHAPTER XI

VOLCANOES AND VOLCANISM

Volcanoes

General Description. — A *volcano* is a vent from which hot or molten material is ejected from the Earth's interior. The term appears to have been first applied to Mount Etna, which was regarded as one of two sites where stood the forge of Hephaestus, later identified with Vulcan, the Roman god of fire. According to traditional concept a volcano is thought of as a steep conical mountain having a crater at its top, from which at intervals are ejected gases, rock fragments, bombs, and lava flows. A world-wide survey shows, however, that many volcanoes diverge from this traditional picture. The essential feature of a volcano is the conduit that connects the interior with the exterior of the Earth. The conduit is often referred to as the volcanic pipe or chimney.

The ejection of material is termed an *eruption*, and to the human mind volcanic eruptions are perhaps the most impressive of all geologic phenomena, from the immensity of the forces displayed, the magnitude of the results achieved, and the disastrous consequences that they frequently entail.

Volcanoes range in size from small cones hardly larger than a beehive to some of the loftiest mountains on the globe. Some of the highest peaks of the Andes are volcanoes; a few of these are still active, as Cotopaxi in Ecuador, 19,600 feet in altitude, with a crater half a mile wide and 1500 feet deep; but others, like Aconcagua, on the border between Chile and Argentina, and Chimborazo in Ecuador, which apparently have no craters and are not now active, have become extinct in the recent geologic past. These volcanoes stand upon a dissected platform of much older rocks, above which they rise 10,000 to 12,000 feet; but certain volcanoes that occur in mid-ocean are of still vaster size. The volcanoes of the Hawaiian Islands rise from the bottom of the Pacific Ocean at depths of 14,000 to 18,000 feet, and as their highest summits project 14,000 feet above sea level, they attain a total height of 30,000 feet. The higher peaks of the Cascade Range, beginning on the north with Baker, Rainier, and Adams in Washington; Hood in Oregon (Fig. 183); and Shasta in northern California, are volcanoes which are now dormant or have recently become extinct. Lassen Peak, at the south

Fig. 183. — Mount Hood, Oregon. A composite volcanic cone, somewhat modified by glacial erosion.

A. M. Prentiss.

end of the Cascade Range in California, is the only active volcano within the continental United States. Mount Etna, on the coast of Sicily, rises 11,000 feet above sea level and is 30 miles in diameter at the base of its cone. Its lower slopes are gentle and are studded with hundreds of small " parasitic " cones.

Character of Eruptions. — Materials of three kinds are ejected from volcanic vents: gases, liquids consisting of molten rock, and solid material in the form of fragments. The nature of a volcanic eruption depends largely on the proportions of these three things. If the eruption is explosive, then gases are the chief factor and solid fragmental material is the main product; if, on the other hand, the eruption proceeds quietly, liquid rock, or lava, is the main product, and the gases are less important. We may roughly classify volcanic eruptions as *explosive* and *quiet*. When we examine actual volcanoes according to this difference in operation, we find that, although good examples of both occur, most are *intermediate* in their eruptive activity; that is, at times they erupt violently and at other times they quietly discharge flows of lava.

Explosive Type. — The most extreme eruptions of this type are appallingly disastrous. Enormous quantities of gas are suddenly ejected into the atmosphere, so thickly charged with comminuted rock (dust and " ashes "), as to form vast clouds of dense appearance and dark color. The greatest known explosion was that of Tamboro, on Sambawa Island, east of Java, in 1815. About 35 cubic miles of material were blown into the air. This material caused darkness during three consecutive days for a distance of 300 miles from the volcano and dust fell over an area of 1,000,000 square miles. Krakatoa, a volcano in the Strait of Sunda near Java, became violently active in August, 1883, after a repose of two centuries. Following on the premonitory outrushes of gas, great explosions occurred, which blew into the air more than 4 cubic miles of dust, ash, and rock fragments. A vast dark cloud rose 17 miles into the atmosphere, by its density completely hiding the sun over an enormous area, and the finest part of the dust eventually attained a height of 30 miles and traveled around the world several times, causing brilliant red sunsets during three years after the eruption. The ejected material rained down on an area of 320,000 square miles. The noise of the terrific detonations was heard as far as Australia, 1750 miles distant; and the disturbance in the atmosphere was registered by barometers over the whole world. Huge waves, up to 100 feet above tide, were generated in the sea and rushed along the low-lying coasts of Java and Sumatra, sweeping far inland and destroying towns, villages, and the lives of 36,000 people; these waves were perceptible 3000 to 4000 miles away.

In May, 1902, the volcano of Mont Pelée on the island of Martinique in the West Indies, after small premonitory symptoms, began to erupt in a series of violent explosions. No lava was poured out, but an enormous dense black cloud of superheated steam and suffocating gases heavily charged with incandescent particles of rock rushed down the mountain slopes to the sea. Annihilating all life in its course, the cloud swept

A. Lacroix.

Fig. 184. — Cloud from Mont Pelée, Dec. 16, 1902, arriving at the sea. Height of cloud is 13,000 feet.

through the town of St. Pierre 6 miles from its point of origin and instantaneously destroyed the town and its 28,000 inhabitants. Almost at the same time La Soufrière on St. Vincent, 90 miles away, ejected a similar cloud; it killed 2000 people and devastated a broad tract of country. For many months after, Mont Pelée continued at irregular intervals to eject these clouds, one of which is shown in Fig. 184 reaching the sea. The 1902 eruption of Pelée directed attention to a phenomenon previously unrecognized. The French investigators termed the remarkable clouds ejected *nuées ardentes*, which has been more or less unsatisfactorily translated as "incandescent" or "glowing clouds," and as "descending eruption clouds." As they were not incandescent but were of inky blackness, it seems best to refer to them as *Peléean clouds*. The extraordinary features of a Peléean cloud are that it is emitted as a horizontal blast from beneath the lava plug in the summit of the volcano; that it carries with it an enormous amount of rock fragments, including blocks many yards in diameter; and that all this material is deposited chaotically together, instead of raining down according to size, as from other volcanic clouds.

Intermediate Type. — Most volcanoes are intermediate in their eruptive activity. Their periods of activity are likely to begin with explosions, manifested by the discharge of gases in great quantity accompanied by solid fragmental material. In a succeeding phase liquid material appears; lava either is ejected as fragments by the gases or it breaks through the crater wall and flows out as streams of lava, some of which are of large volume. Finally the volcano becomes quiet, its energy for the time being having become exhausted; the lava column sinks in the conduit and a period of quiescence and recuperation intervenes before the next eruption. Although this sketch gives the general succession of events, not all volcanoes of this class are alike in their eruptive action, nor does the same volcano always pass through a similar set of phases at each eruption, for there is great variability in these respects.

Vesuvius, which long and careful study has made the best-known volcano in the world, goes through fairly well defined cycles of activity. It is on the site of an older volcano, which in the time of the Romans seemed to be extinct, for, although they recognized its nature, they had no traditions of its having been active. In the year A.D. 79 the volcano became violently active in eruptions that destroyed the towns of Herculaneum and Pompeii on its seaward flanks. Much of the older cone on the side toward the sea was blown away or engulfed, and in its place the new center of activity, the modern Vesuvius, began to be built. This building up has continued until Vesuvius has become 4000 feet high. Partly inclosing it is the crescentic ridge of Monte Somma, the remains of the rim of the older crater (Fig. 185). Vesuvius is in a state of almost constant mild activity, with irregular periods of violent eruption. The last great eruption occurred in 1906.

Quiet Type. — Volcanoes in the phase of quiet eruptivity tranquilly discharge flows of liquid lava, unaccompanied by the explosive disengagement of gases and the ejection of fragmental material. The lava of these eruptions is very hot and highly fluid. More or less gas constantly escapes from it but without the catastrophic violence of the previous types. The best examples are in Hawaii.

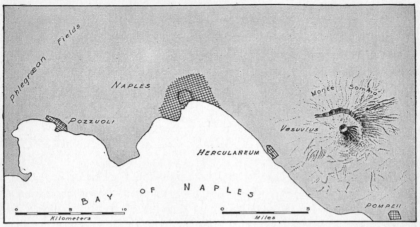

Fig. 185. — Map of Vesuvius and vicinity.

The island of Hawaii consists of a vast mass of lavas surmounted by five great volcanoes: Kohala; Mauna Kea, now extinct (13,800 feet

Hawaiian Volcano Observatory.

Fig. 186. — Halemaumau, the fire-pit of Kilauea. October, 1921.

high); Hualalai (8300), active in 1801; Mauna Loa (13,700), now active, some of its modern lava streams having flowed 50 miles; and Kilauea (4000 feet). On the eastern slope of Mauna Loa, 20 miles from its top, is the great pit in the summit of Kilauea, rudely oval in shape and 9 miles in circumference. In the floor of this pit is Halemaumau, a circular depression, which before 1924 was 1300 feet in diameter, and was occupied by a lake of liquid lava, " boiling " and fountaining from the escape of gases (Fig. 186). The temperature of the lava ranges from 1000° to 1200° C., the higher temperatures prevailing at times of increased activity. In 1924 the lava column in the pit of Halemaumau dropped suddenly 700 feet, and this subsidence was followed by explosive eruptions, the first since 1790. Avalanching from the sides of Halemaumau began and enlarged the pit, so that it became 3000 by 3400 feet across and 1340 feet deep. After the eruption the pit began to fill again with lava, but up to the year 1930 the rise of the lava column had been only 300 feet.

Mauna Loa is the " monarch among modern volcanoes." It exceeds all others in its mighty size and in the magnitude of its eruptive activity. At times immense columns of white-hot molten lava play as fire-fountains several hundred feet high and afford a spectacle truly sublime. Its crater is at an elevation nearly 10,000 feet higher than that of Kilauea. Its outflows of lava as a rule issue from its flanks rather than through the crater rim, and sometimes they occur below sea level.

Relation between Eruptivity and Composition of Magmas. — When magma issues at the Earth's surface, the liquid material, as well as the rock formed from it are called lava, as already pointed out. The solidified lava, however, is not exactly of the same composition as that of the magma from which it congealed. For a deep-seated magma contains, besides the mineral substances of which the solidified lava is made, great quantities of gases, especially gaseous water, which are held in it under pressure. As the magma rises to the Earth's surface and consequently the pressure on it diminishes, the gases escape more or less explosively and produce the spectacular features of volcanic activity. As the different types of volcanoes and of the lavas they discharge depend in large measure on the magmas producing them, it is necessary at this point to consider the influence of temperature and composition of the magmas on eruptive activity.

The magmas that produce the silicic lavas are, after their gaseous constituents have escaped, extraordinarily viscous liquids, even at very high temperatures, as high as 2000° C., as experimentally ascertained. Parenthetically, it may be remarked that 2000° far exceeds the temperatures that occur at existing volcanic vents, which are generally between 1000° and 1100° (about the temperature of molten gold) and rarely reach 1200°. The extreme viscosity of the silicic magmas is due chiefly to the high percentage of silica they contain, in some kinds being as much as 75 per cent of the bulk composition. When silicic magma rises into the upper part of the volcanic vent where the pressure is small, it begins to lose its contained gases and as a result becomes stiffly viscous, and the remaining gases escape with difficulty and usually with violence, giving rise to explosive eruptions. Hence volcanoes that yield silicic lavas are likely to be highly explosive, as Mont Pelée. On the other hand, the basaltic magmas, containing 50 per cent of silica, are very much more fluid, and they remain fluid down to much lower temperatures, 800° C. or thereabouts. The gases escape from them readily, but without explosive violence, as illustrated by the lava lake of Kilauea in Hawaii. Hence the basaltic magmas produce volcanoes that as a rule are quietly eruptive.

The above statement indicates the general rule; it does not mean that basaltic volcanoes never erupt explosively, for a basaltic magma may cool by standing in the conduit and in consequence become viscous, and thus its content of gases can escape only with difficulty and explosive violence. The explanation applies chiefly to the two extremes and indicates what is probably the most effective cause for the explosive and quiet types of eruptions. The intermediate type of activity may be due in part to the intermediate kind of magma erupted, or to this factor combined with variations in viscosity at different stages during the eruption as well as variations in the amount of gases. Sudden accession of ground water into the volcanic pipe, as undoubtedly occurred at Kilauea in 1924 as the result of the lava column in the pipe dropping abruptly to great depth, will cause an explosive eruption even in a basaltic volcano.

PRODUCTS OF VOLCANOES

Gases. — It has been shown that the products yielded by volcanoes fall into three general classes: gases and vapors, solid fragmental material, and liquid lava. These products will be considered in more detail, beginning with the gases. The quantity of steam discharged by active volcanoes is immense and is indicated by the height and volume of the cloud with which many eruptions begin. This cloud consists of the dust and ashes borne aloft by the uprushing column of gases. The great quantity of steam thus discharged into the atmosphere condenses and causes heavy downpours of rain in the vicinity of the volcano; but part of the downpour is probably due to condensation from moisture-laden air that was sucked up to high altitudes by the up-draft created by the discharge of the volcanic gases. Owing perhaps to the friction of the particles and to atmospheric disturbance, the eruptions and rains are accompanied by conspicuous electrical displays and lightning. Although the composition of the gases during an actual volcanic eruption is not directly known, and it probably varies at different volcanoes and at different stages of an eruption, it is inferred with good reason from indirect evidence to consist chiefly of gaseous water, or steam. As an instance of the quantity of water that some believe is discharged, Fouqué estimated that one of the subsidiary cones of Mount Etna discharged in 100 days in the form of steam the equivalent of over 460,000,000 gallons of water.

In addition to the steam, the other gases and volatile products exhaled by volcanoes make a long list. Not only are they given off from the vent itself, but the flows of lava, for weeks and months after their extrusion, continue to emit gases as they cool and harden. Carbon dioxide, hydrochloric acid, hydrofluoric acid, and hydrogen are given off, and to the mixture of the hydrogen with oxygen and its sudden combustion are sometimes ascribed the explosions in the conduit. Sublimed sulphur and various compounds of sulphur, such as hydrogen sulphide (H_2S) and sulphur dioxide (SO_2), are emitted by some, but not all, volcanoes.

Chlorides, especially ammonium chloride, are formed abundantly at many volcanoes during eruptions. In fact, it was the abundance of chlorides at the Italian volcanoes that suggested the idea that eruptions are due to marine water leaking into magma at depth; but no chlorides occur at Kilauea, which is on an ocean-girt island.

Fragmental Products. — These are the volcanic projectiles, the materials blown into the air by the explosive liberation of the gases. They are derived from the crust, or plug, of hardened lava left in the upper part of the conduit after a previous eruption; from rock material torn from the walls of the conduit; or from lava ejected from the top of the liquid column by the violent escape of the gases from the magma. Although clots of lava start their aerial flight in a liquid condition, they generally harden and fall as solid fragments. The pieces of rock and the clots of molten lava blown out and solidified have a wide range in size: from dust so fine that it floats in the atmosphere for several years, to large masses weighing many tons. According to size, they are roughly classified as follows: pieces the size of an apple or larger are called *blocks*, if ejected as solid fragments, and *bombs*, if ejected as particles of still-fluid magma; those the size of a nut are termed *lapilli* (Latin for *little stones*); those the size of a pea are *volcanic ashes*, and the finest are *volcanic dust*. The ashes and lapilli are frequently spoken of as *volcanic cinders*, and the cones made of them as *cinder cones*. Although these terms are used to describe the appearance of the products, the " ashes " and " cinders " are *not* products of combustion. A volcanic bomb is illustrated in Fig. 187; its spirally twisted ends prove that it was still liquid during its flight.

The ejected products in part are composed of compact solid rock and in part are of a spongy, cellular, or vesicular character. This vesicular condition is due to the fact that, while most of the gas is escaping into the air and carrying the fragments with it, a minor part is expanding within the particles of liquid, puffing them up into the cellular forms. Although the bombs, lapilli, and most of the ashes fall near the vent and thus help to build up the cone, the dust is carried by the prevailing winds long distances, hundreds of miles or more, and thus is spread over an immense area. Huge quantities are discharged during great erup-

Fig. 187. — Volcanic bomb; Hawaii. Shows spirally twisted ends.

tions, amounting to many millions of tons. Such dust showers are very destructive to vegetation and even to animal life, but the soil ultimately yielded by them is exceedingly fertile.

Liquid Material: Lavas. — In volcanoes whose periods of eruption begin explosively, the liquid lava generally issues later, after the vent has been cleared. A volcanic cone is not a structure of great strength, and is easily fissured by the explosions and by the pressure of the lava column; hence the magma is not likely to flow out over the lip of the crater, but to issue through fissures in the sides of the cone. It may even happen, especially if the cone is composed of cinders, that, unable to withstand the hydrostatic pressure of the lava column in the vent, one side gives way and allows the lava to rush out through the breach thus made.

The appearance and character of a lava stream and the rock resulting from its solidification depend on several things: on the chemical composition of the magma, on its viscosity, and on the extent to which it retains its dissolved gases. The chemical composition determines the nature of the resulting rock, whether it will be a light-colored lava or a black basalt, or of intermediate character as previously explained. The viscosity determines the rate at which the lava flows, the distance it flows, and in large measure the appearance its surface presents. When the lava issues, it is red- or white-hot. It soon cools on the surface, darkens, and crusts over. If very viscous, the under part may still be moving while the upper part crusts over and breaks up into rough, angular, jagged blocks, which are borne as a tumbling, jostling mass on the surface of the slowly moving flow. When eventually the flow comes to rest, the lava sheet is extremely rough and difficult to traverse. A "cin-

W. C. Mendenhall, U. S. Geol. Survey.

Fig. 188. — Lava cascade, Hawaii. The basaltic lava has solidified into the corded type termed pahoehoe.

dery" lava flow of this kind is sometimes called *aa*, from its Hawaiian designation.

In marked contrast, other lavas harden with smooth surfaces, which have curious ropy, curved, and billowy forms, as seen in Fig. 188. "Corded" lava of this kind the Hawaiians term *pahoehoe*, in reference to its glistening, satiny surfaces. The difference between the two kinds of solidified lava is determined in some way yet unknown by differences in the physical conditions during solidification, for a flow may begin as pahoehoe and end as aa.

Very fluid lavas move rapidly, especially on steep slopes (Fig. 3); the rate rarely exceeds 10 or 12 miles an hour. As they cool and become viscous the motion may be almost indefinitely slow, the stream creeping onward, possibly for several years.

Sometimes on a slope, after a lava flow has crusted over, the still-liquid portion in the interior runs out at the lower end, thereby producing a long tunnel, a so-called lava-tunnel. The natural drainage of some volcanoes passes into these tunnels, disappears from view, and issues lower on the slopes as springs. Such may be in part the cause of the springs around Mount Shasta.

Some magmas when ejected are too viscous to flow; they then pile up over the vents in great domes. Such doming is confined chiefly,

E. O. Hovey.

Fig. 189. — Spine of Mont Pelée, March 25, 1903.

though not wholly, to the silicic lavas. The essential condition to form a dome is that the magma be in a highly viscous, pasty state, because of low temperature or low gas content, or both. Domes of lava occur in central France, Bohemia, Germany, and elsewhere. There are thirteen domes within an area of 50 square miles in Lassen Volcanic National Park, the largest being Lassen Peak itself. After the violent eruption of Pelée in 1902, the column of silicic lava that filled the vent hardened into rock at the surface but remained highly viscous in the interior, and the whole mass was pushed up so that it rose like a vast tower above the volcano, until it attained a maximum height of 1200 feet above the crater rim, a year after the destruction of St. Pierre. As viewed from the northeast, the tower resembled a gigantic spine and therefore was often called the spine of Mont Pelée (Fig. 189). Gradually it crumbled into a mass of blocks as a result of continuous explosions of gases.

Effect of Contained Gases: Vesiculation of the Lava. — That the lavas, even after they issue from the volcanic vent, still contain dissolved gases is amply shown not only by the clouds of steam that issue for weeks and months from them but also by the structures they assume as they solidify into rock. Thus the upper part of a flow, especially of the viscous, silicic lavas, may become so inflated by the innumerable bubbles of gas in it expanding on relief of pressure that it is transformed into a veritable froth. Such rock froth, which is generally white or light-colored, is known as *pumice*.

In more fluid lavas, especially those of the basalt class, the gas cavities or vesicles are larger, and if the vesicles are so abundant as to be closely crowded, the resulting *vesicular rock* is coarsely cellular like a sponge. The highly porous, cindery form of lava is called volcanic

C. R. Longwell.

Fig. 190. — Cinder cone. Near Santa Fe railway, Amboy, California.

scoria. It is commonly dark to black, or reddish. Pumice, scoria, and other vesicular products are characteristic features of the tops of lava flows, and they comprise also the major part of the coarser fragmental ejecta, such as bombs and lapilli, that build up the volcanic cone.

VARIETIES OF VOLCANOES AND CRATERS

Cinder Cones. — The nature of the structure built up around a volcanic vent depends on the material of which it is formed. If made wholly of fragmental ejecta, the resulting cone is high and steep relative to the area it covers. This steepness is due to the high angle of repose for lapilli and volcanic cinders; such material is rough and angular, and slopes of 40° are attained before the angle of repose is exceeded and the accumulating mass begins to slide. Cones of this kind are termed *cinder cones,* and they are characteristic results of explosive eruptions. They are relatively small; none of them reach a height of 1000 feet (Fig. 190).

Shield Volcanoes. — In contrast with the cinder cones are the volcanoes that have been built largely or entirely by the piling up of lava flows one on the other around a central vent. They are low in proportion to the immense area they cover, and on top are gently convex plateaus; hence they are called *shield volcanoes* (Fig. 191). They are built up by the emission of flows of highly fluid lavas, which spread widely as thin, nearly horizontal sheets, and as they are well represented in the Hawaiian Islands are referred to as volcanoes of the Hawaiian type. Mauna Loa, 13,675 feet in elevation, is a grand example of a shield volcano: it is a colossal, gently sloping dome; its slope near its base is 2°, increasing summitward to 10°, but flattening above an altitude of 10,000 feet.

I. C. Russell, U. S. Geol. Survey.

Fig. 191. — Shield volcano. Snake River Plains near Arco, Idaho.

Composite Cones. — However, most volcanoes, including most of the world's largest volcanoes, have cones that are intermediate in form between those just described. They are built up by the fall of fragmental ejecta around their vents when they are explosively active and by the discharge of lava flows when they erupt quietly. As a result of their composite construction the volcanic cones of this origin have a characteristic profile of great beauty: concave upward, with gentle slopes near the base that steepen upward to the summit crater. Mayon, the most active volcano in the Philippine Islands, is regarded as the finest example of a composite cone (Fig. 192). Many others the world over have similar graceful contours, but the most famous is Fujiyama, the sacred mountain of Japan, towering 9000 feet above its surroundings. Within our own country are the majestic cones of the Cascade Range — Rainier, Adams, Hood, Shasta — which give that range its distinctive scenic grandeur.

The eruptions that break out on the lower flanks of the larger volcanoes build up smaller " parasitic " cones. Etna has several hundred on its flanks, some of which are 700 feet high. As an active volcano grows in size, the earlier parasitic cones are likely to be buried and concealed under later accumulations; or, in the declining stage of activity, the last eruptive energy may manifest itself by building them.

Fig. 192. — Mayon, Philippine Islands; height, 7900 feet. One of the finest examples of a composite cone.

Calderas: Explosion and Subsidence Basins. — The term caldera, the Spanish word for *caldron*, is applied to crater-like basins of great size, especially those which are very broad as compared to their depth. The term is taken from the huge pit in the Canary Islands, called La Caldera, which is 3 to 4 miles wide and is bounded by lofty cliffs 1500 to 2500 feet high, except on one side where the encircling wall is breached. As seen from a distance, the mountain inclosing La Caldera resembles a huge cone truncated far below its apex.

Many such calderas occur throughout the world. Some of them were caused by gigantic explosions that have blown away the tops of former volcanic cones as dust and ashes, and the resulting pits mark the sites of these wrecked volcanoes. Thus the stupendous explosive eruption of Tamboro in 1815 blew away a good part of the original volcano and formed a caldera nearly 4 miles in diameter.

Perhaps more generally calderas are formed by the subsidence of the column of magma in the conduit of the volcano, leaving a great cavity into which the superstructure of the cone has subsided. The truncated remnant of the cone makes the rim of the caldera. A caldera of this origin is occupied by Crater Lake in southern Oregon. This marvelously beautiful lake occurs at the summit of a volcanic mountain in the Cascade Range, and is 6 miles long by 4 miles wide, 2000 feet deep, and encircled by steep cliffs 500 to 2000 feet high (Fig. 193). An island in it — Wizard Island — is the unsubmerged top of a small but perfect volcanic cone, and indicates that eruptive activity was feebly renewed through the floor of the caldera after the principal subsidence. The caldera, if emptied of the water now in it, would appear as a great basin. The reason for believing that the caldera was formed by the collapse and engulfment of the top of a former cone as the result of the subsidence of the lava column in the pipe of the volcano, rather than by explosion, lies in the absence of the débris — about 18 cubic miles of material — that so gigantic an explosion would have spread over the adjacent outer slopes. The former volcano, to which the name Mount Mazama has been given, is conceived to have had the size and general character of Mount Shasta and to have been heavily capped with snow and glaciers during the Ice Age.

There is no sharp demarcation between a crater and a caldera. The essential feature of the caldera, however, is that its diameter is generally enormously larger than that of the supply pipe of the volcano. During periods of repose of a volcano, avalanching into the crater occurs, thereby increasing its upper diameter. Subsequently this fragmental material may be blown out. During continuous blow-offs of gas, such as characterized the great eruption of Vesuvius in 1906, avalanching and enlargement of the crater may lead to gigantic results.

A. M. Prentiss.

Fig. 193. — Crater Lake, Oregon: a caldera occupied by a lake. The island — Wizard Island — is the top of a small volcano that was built after the collapse of the main volcano.

Finally, some calderas, such as the great circular depression in the top of Kilauea, are definitely known to be the results of downfaulting.

Explosion Pits. — In some places volcanic activity has gone no further than to drill a vent through the country rock. The material blown out, therefore, consists largely of fragments of the country rock with only a trifling admixture of volcanic ejecta and makes a low ridge around the pit, but no real cone was built (Fig. 194). Such pits range in width from a few hundred feet to possibly two miles; most of those in humid regions are filled with water and form lakes. Some of the best examples are west of the Rhine in Germany, in the region known as the volcanic Eifel. They are called *maars* (German, *Maaren*).

A pit strongly resembling a maar occurs near Flagstaff, Arizona. It is sunk into a plateau and is 4000 feet across and 500 feet deep. The presence of meteoritic iron in and around it and other cogent evidence have proved that it is not of volcanic origin, and have led to the view that it was caused by the impact of a huge meteorite. Hence it has been named Meteor Crater.

Modified from F. Rinne.

Fig. 194. — Explosion pit, or maar, occupied by a lake. The fragments blown out consist chiefly of the country rock perforated by the volcanic vent. Maars are sometimes called embryonic volcanoes.

Rebuilt Volcanoes. — After a caldera has formed, volcanic activity may revive and begin building one or more new cones within it. As we have seen, this has occurred at Crater Lake, where Wizard Island is the unsubmerged top of a new volcanic cone that stands on the floor of the caldera formed by the collapse of Mount Mazama. One of the best examples is at Vesuvius, which is built within the caldera of Monte Somma. By the building of new cones within an old crater or caldera, a cone-in-crater structure, or nested-crater arrangement, is produced. Many of the vast crater-like pits so common on the Moon show this arrangement, suggesting an analogous origin for them. Conceivably Vesuvius, before it becomes extinct, will increase in size until the old caldera is obliterated: it will then be a completely *rebuilt volcano*.

STRUCTURE AND EROSION OF VOLCANIC CONES

Structure of a Composite Cone. — When magma nears the surface of the Earth, the relief of pressure causes it to begin discharging its dissolved gases. Conceivably the pressure of the dissolved gases may be too great for the strength of the outermost portion of the Earth's crust to hold them in the magma until the magma reaches the surface; consequently the outermost portion of the crust may be blown into the air and a vent drilled ahead of the rising column of magma. Arrived at the surface, the magma may flow out quietly, or, if it is too viscous to do this, explosions will continue and fragments be shot upward. By the falling of fragments around the vent a cone is built up (Fig. 195). The pieces can not, of course, fall back against the uprushing column of gases and cover the vent; they fall outside of it — the heaviest and largest first and nearest to it, the smaller and lighter later and farther away.

The distribution of the ejecta depends much on the direction and strength of the wind. Thus the cone grows as a circular ridge upon whose crest most of the ejecta are deposited. This material tends to roll and slide

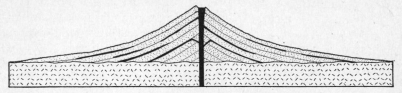

Fig. 195. — A composite cone, showing its internal structure. Flows alternating with layers of fragmental ejecta dip away from the central vent. The profile is that of Mayon (Fig. 192).

both outward away from the vent and inward down the crater toward the vent. This process forms the cone and crater, and certain features of their structure follow as a consequence of this mode of formation.

Tuff and Breccia. — The deposits of successive eruptions are marked by layers, some of coarser, some of finer material, in each of which, if not

W. T. Lee, U. S. Geol. Survey.

Fig. 196. — Part of volcanic cone near Trinchera, Colorado, showing inclined beds of tuff and breccia.

composed of uniform-sized particles, there is a gradation from coarser at the bottom to finer at the top. Thus there arises a rude bedding, the beds sloping down and out from the crater edge (Fig. 196). The blocks, lapilli, and ashes composing the beds gradually become compacted by their weight and by the infiltration and deposition of cementing substances. They are thus transformed into a more or less porous rock called, if composed of the coarser materials, *volcanic breccia*, and if of the finer dust and ashes, *tuff*. In the crater the fragments are larger, generally large blocks of rock, and they commonly form a chaotic mass with intermingled finer material; such material is called *agglomerate*. Any such material whose fragmentation was caused by igneous action is referred to as *pyroclastic* (p. 243).

Lava Flows and Dikes. — In addition to the beds of tuff and breccia, liquid lava flows down the outer slopes of many volcanic cones, and when these streams harden into rock they protect the less coherent layers of pyroclastic material from erosion and give strength to the edifices. As the lava rarely flows over the lip of the crater, but, especially in high volcanoes, issues from fissures on the sides of the volcano, these fissures also become filled with lava, which hardens into rock, forming dikes; they radiate outward from the vent as a center, and they serve as ribs to strengthen the volcanic cone. Thus a vertical section through a volcano shows a central core of massive igneous rock surrounded by beds of tuff and breccia with intercalated flows of lava, which are cut by a radial system of dikes. This is the general structure of a typical composite cone; but there are many variations from it.

Erosion of Volcanoes. — During all stages of its existence a volcano is subject to weathering and erosion. Its height and appearance at any given time are the results of the balance between these destructive forces and the constructive power of volcanism. Even active and growing volcanoes are trenched by ravines and gulches. After eruptions, when the cones are freshly covered with dust and ashes, the loose ejecta become so saturated with water from the rainfall that they slide down as flows of liquid mud, forming gullies, which become enlarged by subsequent storms.

As soon as a volcano becomes extinct, the ravages of erosion are unchecked, and the period of destruction ensues. The tuffs and breccias are carried away easily and rapidly; the harder, more resistant flows and dikes and the parts protected by them are eroded more slowly. It is surprising, however, for how long a time some cones that are built of loosely piled cinders will resist erosion and retain their form. They resist erosion so well because of the porosity of the material, which lets the rainfall sink through it without causing runoff.

As erosion progresses, the volcanic neck consisting of the material filling the central conduit becomes exposed to view. If the column of magma in the conduit had not drained off before the volcano became extinct, the neck consists of massive igneous rock; but if the magma column did drain off, the neck consists of a mass of agglomerate. As erosion goes on and the cone is demolished, the volcanic neck, because of its greater resistance, generally forms a conspicuous prominence; and, when erosion has finally swept away all external evidence of the cone and has bitten deeply into the underlying rocks, it remains projecting, a monument to the vanished volcano.

Extinct volcanoes occur in every quarter of the globe, many of them in regions where volcanic activity has long ceased. Every stage of demolition is represented among them: from cones only slightly worn to those so greatly eroded that the original shape has been entirely destroyed, but whose central rock shaft (the volcanic neck), outlying concentric masses of lavas, tuffs and breccias, and radial dikes still plainly show that they were once volcanoes. The evidence showing the sequential stages in the demolition of a volcano is even more impressive when it can be seen within the area of a single volcanic field, in which, because of the accidents of erosion, some volcanoes have been left nearly intact, others have had their outer framework removed, and others have been nearly wholly destroyed. Obviously, the internal structure of an active volcano is incompletely shown. Rarely are we given such an opportunity as at Krakatoa, where the catastrophic explosion of 1883 blew away half the cone and revealed the anatomy of the volcano. In general we must depend on erosion for our information on the internal structures of volcanoes. In this way it has been ascertained that the supply pipes of some volcanoes change into dikes at depth.

Some confirmatory evidence has been gathered from actual mining operations. A few volcanic necks contain economically valuable substances: the famous diamond-bearing pipes of South Africa are the most noted examples. There a certain volcanic neck filled with diamond-bearing breccia has been followed down to a depth of 3500 feet; this neck narrows somewhat in depth, i.e., is funnel-shaped; and a few necks were found to grade downward into dikes, the breccia-filling of the necks concurrently changing into massive rock.

Relation of Volcanoes to Deep-Seated Bodies of Magma. — Volcanism is only one effect, the surface manifestation, of the rise of magma from unknown depths to the upper levels of the Earth's crust. The present volcanism throughout the world is but the continuation of an activity that has persisted since the beginning of geologic time, though not on the present sites. Although magma has reached the surface in places and has been ejected, much of it has not reached the surface but has remained intruded into the rocky crust, and on cooling and solidifying has formed bodies of igneous rock, which range in size from insignificant to enormous dimensions. Such deep-seated bodies of igneous rock are the intrusive masses previously described, and every extinct volcanic conduit, could it be traced downward, would be found to join an intrusive mass below, or, if the conduit is feeding an active volcano, to extend into a body of magma — the volcanic reservoir — which in time will solidify as an intrusive mass.

LIFE AND DISTRIBUTION OF VOLCANOES

Age of Volcanoes. — The span of life of active volcanoes differs greatly in different individuals. From written testimony we know that Etna has been erupting for the last 2500 years very much as it does now. Because of its great volume we estimate that at least 300,000 years have been required to build this grand volcano. From the human standpoint that is an immense lapse of time. On the other hand, we know from geologic evidence that Etna did not begin to erupt until the middle of the Quaternary, the most recent of the geologic time-periods. From this standpoint Etna is a comparatively recent structure.

It is difficult to judge whether a volcano is extinct or is merely dormant, because hundreds of years may elapse between eruptions. In the Middle Ages, Vesuvius had been dormant so long that its crater was overgrown with vegetation and it gave no sign of life. But in 1631 it became violently eruptive, and has since been intermittently active.

New Volcanoes. — Within the period of recorded human knowledge a number of volcanoes have begun their existence, and many of them are still active. Vesuvius is generally regarded as an example, but it stands on the site of the older volcano, Monte Somma. Jorullo in Mexico came into being September 28, 1759, in the midst of a cultivated plain; the initial explosions blew out fragmental materials, Peléean clouds were emitted, and lavas were discharged. Four cones were formed, of which the highest, Jorullo, attained an elevation of 1300 feet above its surroundings. Izalco in Salvador, which began in 1770, has been almost continuously active since then, and in its short life has already discharged more lava than any other Central American volcano; it rises 2600 feet above its base. All the new volcanoes broke out in volcanic areas; no new volcano has been born in a previously non-volcanic area.

Volcanic Activity at Lassen Peak. — No well-authenticated volcanic eruption was witnessed within the limits of the United States proper until May, 1914, when explosive eruptions, which have since continued at intervals, began at Lassen Peak in northern California. The eruptions have been chiefly of gases, ashes, and stones. In 1915 there were two enormous explosions — two great blasts that blew out horizontally from beneath the lava plug in the top of the volcano and laid waste a wide swath of country. Lassen Peak, although active, is a decadent volcano, whose explosiveness appears to be stimulated by water from melting snow gaining access to the still-liquid magma which is solidifying and crystallizing within the conduit.

Geographic Distribution of Volcanoes. — The present active volcanoes are about 430; but those that because of their slightly eroded condition can be considered dormant or but recently extinct amount to several thousand. Volcanoes tend to be grouped in long belts on the Earth's surface. The most marked of these belts encircles the Pacific Ocean; it extends northward along the Andes, through Central America into Mexico, through the United States and Canada to Alaska, then along the Aleutian chain to Asia, and, turning southward through Kamchatka, Japan, and the Philippines, it crosses the East Indies, and by various island chains again passes into the Pacific. Portions of this belt, like the Andes and the Aleutian chain, are remarkably linear and well developed. Another great belt extends east and west: from Central America it extends through the West Indies; it then continues through the Atlantic by the Azores, Cape Verde, and Canary Islands, runs through the Mediterranean, through Asia Minor and Arabia, and continues along the chain of the East Indies, where it crosses the circum-Pacific belt, and extends out into the Pacific (Figs. 197, 198). This linear arrangement occurs not only on a large scale, affecting series of volcanic groups, but on a small scale as well, causing the volcanoes of individual groups to occur along lines.

Volcanoes occur both on the continents and in the oceans. They are notably abundant in the Pacific; many are extinct or dormant, but many are still active; in fact, three-fifths of all active volcanoes are in the Pacific alone. Here also many of the volcanoes occur along lines and stand on submarine ridges that rise from the ocean floor. A superlative example is the Hawaiian ridge, extending for 1800 miles and crowned with mighty volcanoes, active and extinct. From their linear arrangement it appears that volcanoes are in general situated on, or near, lines of weakness marked by fracturing and folding in the Earth's crust (p. 335).

Lines of fracture have undoubtedly been favorable sites for volcanic action for long geologic periods, and thus they have greatly influenced the origin, situation, and arrangement of volcanoes. On the other hand, a volcano, or a group of volcanoes, may originate where a connection between them and a fracture line appears not to exist. Moreover, in some groups the volcanoes have no linear arrangement. The volcanic forces appear to have been sufficiently powerful to make their own outlets without needing the aid of a fracture in the outer crust. A good example of this is in the Highwood Mountains, a group of extinct and deeply eroded volcanoes situated on the great plain of central Montana. Although the remaining tuffs, breccias, lava flows, and dikes composing this group and their arrangement and attitudes indicate clearly the cones that once stood here, the cones have been eroded so deeply that their shapes have been destroyed, the central conduits now filled with massive

L. V. Pirsson.

Fig. 197. — Distribution of active and recently extinct volcanoes in the Eastern Hemisphere.   (On Penfield's stereographic projection.)

rock are exposed, and their relations to the stratified rocks through which they were forced are laid bare.   The foundation on which the volcanoes stood shows no evidence of profound breakage or displacement that might have determined the positions of the vents, nor have the conduits of the several volcanoes linear arrangement.

A striking instance of how little influence surface topography may have in determining the site at which volcanic action will perforate the crust can be seen at the Grand Canyon of the Colorado.   Uninfluenced by its

5000 feet of depth, volcanoes have broken out upon its very rim, instead of in the bottom of the canyon, and their lavas have spilled over the brink of the canyon and flowed down into it.

That almost all active volcanoes are either situated in the sea, or in a general way around its borders, and when inland are in or near lakes, has led many to believe that there must be a necessary connection be-

L. V. Pirsson.

Fig. 198. — Distribution of active and recently extinct volcanoes in the Western Hemisphere. (On Penfield's stereographic projection.)

tween the surface waters and the cause of volcanic activity. This question is considered later in discussing the origin of volcanoes.

Submarine and Sublacustrine Eruptions. — From the great number of volcanic islands in the sea, it is evident that tremendous eruptions and vast outpourings of lava have occurred on the sea floor. The volcanic chain of the Hawaiian Islands is an example of this. Actual eruptions beneath the sea have been recognized by the issuance of vapors and ash from the water. Thus, in 1831 a volcano was formed in the midst of the Mediterranean Sea, making a new island called Graham's Island. Being composed of light cinders, it was soon destroyed by the waves and reduced to a shoal. The three Bogoslov volcanoes of the Aleutian chain formed in 1796, 1883, and 1906, are other examples.

Such eruptions have occurred repeatedly in the past, and their products, mingled with sediments from the land, have been laid down on the sea bottom, as seen in many places where the sea floor with these deposits has since been raised and become a land surface. The submarine volcanic products do not differ essentially from those formed by volcanoes on the land. It is probable that many of the cones formed beneath the sea, and thus protected from erosion, are of great geologic age and have served as the foundations for coral islands (p. 196).

Eruptions occur also on the floors of bodies of fresh water. Streams of lava flow from the land into the sea or into lakes. Under certain conditions basaltic lavas that have been erupted subaqueously or have flowed into bodies of fresh or marine water take on a curious internal structure during solidification. They resemble a pile of pillows, the individual pillows along their contacts showing mutual indentation and accommodation. Such lavas are expressively termed *pillow lavas*. Consequently, when we find such pillow lavas intercalated between sedimentary rocks, we infer that they were erupted into a body of water.

Fissure Eruptions. — Basaltic lava has been poured out in several regions on such a gigantic scale and has deluged such immense tracts of country that it can not be referred to the eruptions of any volcanic cone or group of volcanoes. Moreover, the cones from which they might have come are apparently wanting. These great floods of lava were discharged from fissures in the Earth's crust. The result of this flooding is that there have been formed broad plains or plateaus consisting of superposed horizontal sheets of basalt lava with a few intercalated beds of tuff.

Basalt plateaus of this origin are the great lava fields of the Columbia River in the far Northwest of the United States, which cover 200,000 square miles and are in places 4000 feet thick (Fig. 199); the Deccan *traps* (basalts) of western India, which are at least 200,000 square miles in extent and reach a maximum thickness of 6000 feet; the northern British Isles, which in part, with the outlying island groups, appear to have been carved by the sea from a great basalt plateau that may have extended to Iceland. The horizontal layering of these lava sheets is evidently due to the extreme fluidity of the issuing magma, which permitted them to flow on nearly level surfaces for many miles before congealing. Another result of the easily fluent nature of the lavas is that the average flow is only 20 to 40 feet thick. It is the vast outpourings of the fissure eruptions in the form of the plateau basalts, which occur in other regions as well as in those mentioned, that exhibit the grandest effects of volcanism.

An historical example of a fissure eruption was afforded by the activity at Laki, Iceland, in 1783. From a fissure 20 miles long there welled forth 3 cubic miles of lava, the greatest discharge in historical time. Explosive activity occurred during the extrusion, but the pyroclastic material ejected was of insignificant topographic effect.

Although we have distinguished between fissure ("linear") eruptions and eruptions from volcanic centers ("central eruptions"), in nature there is a complete gradation between them. Etna, for example, is

Simmer Studio.

Fig. 199. — Columbia basalts, showing the superposition of flow on flow. Crescent Bar, Columbia River, Washington.

growing in size mainly by discharges from fissures on its flanks, not by material ejected from its summit crater. The Hawaiian volcanoes, also, are being built up partly by the escape of lava from fissures on their flanks and partly by overflows from the central craters.

Areal Eruptions. — Theoretically it appears possible that eruptions might occur through great openings formed in the crust by the collapse of the roofs of large magmatic reservoirs. Lava might thus well out on a stupendous scale. Examples of this mode of eruption are thought to have been recognized but have not been definitely established.

In conclusion, then, we recognize three kinds of eruptions based on the nature of the orifice: (1) central eruptions, from definite centers or points; (2) linear eruptions, from fissures; and (3) areal eruptions, from broad areas.

Origin of Volcanism

Origin of the Heat. — At the present time the prevalent view regarding the source of the heat necessary to produce the magmas is that it is original, in the sense that the heat is residual from a globe that was once molten and is still intensely hot in its interior. Some, however, think that the heat is generated by the gradual contraction and compression of the Earth through the force of gravity.

Some have urged that the crushing together of the Earth's outer shell as the result of its collapse upon the shrinking nucleus generates heat in enormous amount. Such compression and crushing have taken place during the formation of mountain structures (p. 394), and it is inferred that through this process melting has occurred and volcanoes have been made. There are two objections to this view. The first is that many volcanoes occur where there has been no crushing of the crust, or at least, not for an immense period of geologic time antedating the birth of the volcanoes, as at San Francisco Mountain and other volcanoes on the high plateau of Arizona. The other is that the compression and folding that occur during a crustal revolution take place very slowly, and although an enormous amount of heat undoubtedly is generated, it has not been shown why it would not be dissipated as rapidly as it is generated or be absorbed in doing chemical work. How could it become accumulated and concentrated sufficiently to produce melting and volcanoes?

The discovery of radioactivity has shown that some of the chemical elements are spontaneously disintegrating and breaking down into other substances, as for example, uranium is disintegrating into helium and lead, with the concurrent evolution of heat in notable quantity. Accordingly it has been suggested that the radioactive changes that are going on within the Earth produce the heat necessary for volcanic action and even for such vast-scale igneous manifestations as are represented by the enormous intrusive bodies beneath the surface. The distribution of radioactive matter throughout the rocks is universal; in fact, if the rocks deeper in the crust contain as much radioactive matter as those at the Earth's surface, then the amount of heat evolved is so large that the Earth is not only not cooling off, as was hitherto thought to be true, but is actually heating up and in time will become molten. It is highly probable, however, that the amount of radioactive matter diminishes in depth. Manifestly, the radioactive content of the crust is of profound importance to its thermal condition, but it is too early yet to come to positive conclusions based on these revolutionary discoveries.

Origin of the Magma. — This is a complex problem. Different volcanoes erupt lavas of different kinds. Vesuvius erupts one kind, Etna another. More remarkable still, neighboring volcanoes may erupt very unlike lavas. Stromboli and Vulcano are in the Lipari Islands north of Sicily: Stromboli ejects basalt but Vulcano ejects rhyolite — lavas about as far apart in composition as it is possible to be.

Furthermore, many a long-lived volcano has erupted a variety of lavas. For example, Lassen Peak, which is regarded as an old and dying volcano, has erupted lavas of four different kinds: rhyolite, dacite, andesite, and basalt. Did the supply pipe of Lassen Peak tap four different reservoirs containing four different magmas? It is believed that originally there was a homogeneous magma beneath Lassen Peak and' that by a series of internal changes this magma yielded the other magmas. This process by which a magma of initially homogeneous composition splits up into unlike fractions is called *magmatic differentiation*. It is to this process that appeal is made to account for the diversity of lavas erupted, not only at Lassen Peak but at all other volcanic centers. The methods by which magmas differentiate are many but need not be explained here.

Magmatic differentiation, although accounting for the variety of magmas erupted at the various volcanic centers, does not explain the origin of the initially homogeneous magma, the parent magma from which the diverse magmas were derived. It is thought that the parent magma the world over is' basaltic in composition. One of the cogent reasons for this belief is that the great fissure eruptions that have discharged such enormous volumes of lava at intervals throughout the whole span of geologic time are of basaltic composition; and the ample source of basaltic magma thus demonstrated is held to indicate that a layer of basalt in a potentially liquid condition underlies everywhere the visible crust. We say " potentially liquid " because the evidence from the study of earthquakes, as shown in Chapter XV, demonstrates that the material at the depth of the supposed basaltic layer has rigidity, a property foreign to liquids. It is probable that because of the tremendous pressure reigning in the Earth's depths the material, although very hot, is not liquid but rigid. Therefore, if the pressure on the layer of potentially liquid basalt is relieved at any place, as for instance, by upward buckling of the Earth's crust or by reduction of the superincumbent load as the result of deep denudation, or by both, then melting would ensue and a body of magma would form.

Origin of the Gases. — The chief magmatic gas is steam (also variously referred to as water vapor, superheated steam, or simply water); as a rule, water makes up more than 80 per cent of the total content of gases dissolved in the magma. This water may have been part of the original substance of the Earth, in short, of primitive origin — " telluric

water " (Latin *Tellus*, the Earth); or formed by the union of primitive
hydrogen with oxygen of atmospheric or other origin; or it may have
been atmospheric water absorbed by the magma from the surrounding
rocks; or it may have been acquired by the magma in melting up rocks
containing water-bearing minerals.   A quantitative evaluation of these
possibilities is beyond the present powers of science.   A magma that
has dissolved much limestone would become highly charged with carbon
dioxide, which is one of the important volcanic gases.   Such absorption
of limestone would generate enormous pressures, and such local development of pressure, it has been ingeniously suggested, may have determined the sites of certain volcanic vents.

The combustible gases — hydrogen, sulphur, hydrocarbons — appear
to be original constituents of the magma.   Their combustion, especially
that of the hydrogen, produces the only true flames seen at an eruption,
and the heat liberated makes the magma somewhat hotter than it is at
greater depth in the vent.

The fact that most volcanoes are in or near the sea or lakes was formerly considered strong evidence that the gaseous water contained in
the magma has been obtained from descending surface water.   But this
evidence when examined loses its force in part.   The nearness of some
volcanoes to the sea, like those of North and South America, is only
relative to the size of the continents.   Actually they are far inland: in
South America from 100 to 250 miles, and this includes some cones still
active — like Cotopaxi — which are not near any inland water body;
in North America from 30 to 130 miles or more, and, although most of
these are extinct, it can be shown that when active most of them were
not near any bodies of water.   However, volcanic cones are permeable
edifices and ground water can move freely through them; and the present trend of thought regards it as highly probable that magma standing
in the crater and supply pipe of a volcano absorbs water from the surrounding rocks and thereby enhances enormously its explosive poten-
tiality.

Cause of the Rise of Magma to the Earth's Surface. — The fact that
the great volcanic chains are situated on those belts of the Earth's crust
along which movement and disturbance have taken place is significant.
For these belts are zones of weakness in the crust, and have manifestly
afforded favorable places for the rise of magma and its escape to the surface.   The Earth's crust is divided into great blocks, or segments, and
these have at times moved up or down with respect to one another
(Chap. XII).   In some regions where great blocks of this kind, measuring hundreds or thousands of square miles, have sunk, this subsidence
has been attended by the rise of magma and outpouring of lava.   Such

crustal subsidence and concomitant volcanic activity have occurred in the depressed tracts that form the great rift valleys of East Africa and the valley of the Rhine. The mechanism of ascension of the magma in this way is likened to the action of a hydraulic press.

Formerly it was thought that the Earth has a hot, liquid interior and that the collapse of the cold, solid crust on the shrinking nucleus forces this liquid out and thus causes volcanism. The evidence of seismology and other geophysical considerations prove, however, that there is no liquid interior, at least in the depths from which volcanoes and fissure eruptions draw their magmas. Nevertheless, this old idea can be reframed to conform with modern knowledge by assuming that a zone of potentially liquid magma occurs at depth and that the collapse of the outer shell is the ultimate cause of the rise of this material to the surface.

The source of the magma appears to be at different depths for different volcanoes. In general, volcanoes are fed from reservoirs at smaller depths than are fissure eruptions. Evidence based on the earthquakes attending volcanic eruptions indicates that the magmatic hearths or reservoirs tapped by volcanoes are at relatively shallow depths — a few miles. Fissure eruptions, however, appear to tap the basaltic substratum, which from earthquake data and other evidence is believed to lie at a depth of 20 miles or more.

FUMAROLES AND HOT SPRINGS

In the foregoing description of volcanoes it was shown what an active rôle gases, especially superheated steam, play in their eruptions. But long after a volcano has ceased to be active and has passed into a dormant or dying stage these gases continue to issue from its crater, or from its flanks, or even from places in the surrounding country. In the same way thick flows of lava continue for years to exhale steam and other vapors. Large bodies of magma that have ascended to the higher levels of the crust without reaching the surface or forming volcanoes have, in solidifying, given off their dissolved gases, which escape through fissures to the Earth's surface. The emanations may issue at the surface either as gases or as liquids. The gaseous emanations will be considered under the general heading of *fumaroles*, the liquid emanations under *hot springs*.

Fumaroles. — The term *fumarole* (from the Latin *fumare*, to smoke) is applied to fissures or holes in the rocks from which steam and other gases escape with more or less force. The fume or " smoke " of the fumarole is thus mainly steam. Although steam predominates, generally forming 99 per cent of the total, other gases, such as carbon dioxide, hydrochloric acid, hydrogen sulphide, hydrogen, methane, and others also occur.   Fumaroles that give off sulphurous vapors are termed *solfataras*, from the Italian word for sulphur.

In addition to the substances already mentioned, the gases emitted by some fumaroles carry metallic constituents, such as iron, copper, and lead.   These metals have been rendered volatile by the presence of chlorides and fluorides in the magma and consequently are able to leave the magma and escape into the surrounding rocks.   As they approach the Earth's surface they begin to react with the other fumarolic gases and are deposited in the form of metallic minerals in the fissures through which the gases are streaming.   Hematite is probably the commonest mineral formed in this way.   During one of the eruptions of Vesuvius a fissure 3 feet wide was thus filled with hematite in a few days.   Galena, the chief ore mineral of lead, is occasionally formed at Vesuvius by the mutual action of the lead chloride and hydrogen sulphide contained in the fumaroles.   Ores as it were are actually being deposited under our eyes; in fact, it was the contemplation of these phenomena on the flanks of Vesuvius that first suggested the fruitful idea that there is an intimate relation between igneous rocks and the occurrence and origin of ore deposits throughout the world (p. 448).

The gases issuing from some fumaroles are exceedingly hot.   In the remarkable fumarole field known as the Valley of Ten Thousand Smokes, which came into existence in 1912 at the time of the catastrophic eruption of the volcano Katmai in Alaska, temperatures as high as 645° C. have been measured.   A view of several fumaroles occurring within the crater of Katmai is shown in Fig. 200.

The volcanic cone near Naples known as Solfatara last erupted in 1198, since when it has been merely discharging steam mingled with sulphur vapor;   and hence the term *solfataric stage* is applied to volcanoes that are quiescent or dying.   Some of the great cones of the Cascade Range, like Shasta, are in a feebly solfataric stage.   In Yellowstone Park the solfataric condition still prevails and fumaroles abound.   Although the steam given off by a fumarole is probably in the main of magmatic origin, the amount is often increased by descending surface water that becomes vaporized, either by contact with hot rocks or by the hot gases of the fumarole itself.   This is probably the condition in Yellowstone Park.

Carbon dioxide gas is given off copiously in many places where volcanic activity still abounds, and in many where volcanism has long since died out.   In some places the carbon dioxide issues directly from the ground as a gas spring, and such occurrences are known as *mofettes*. Being heavier than air, the carbon dioxide collects during still weather in depressions near the vent; and, as it is colorless, tasteless, and odorless, pools of such gas, by suffocating the creatures that enter them, are deadly traps for animals. Their deadliness is attested by " Death Gulch " in Yellowstone Park, where animals as large as grizzly bears have become asphyxiated.

The carbon dioxide exhaled in volcanic areas is likely to encounter ground water on its way upward, however, and thus give rise to a carbonated spring which, if it passes through limestone, will dissolve some

C. N. Fenner.

Fig. 200. — Fumaroles within the crater of the volcano Katmai, Alaska.

of the limestone and is therefore likely to deposit calcium carbonate as travertine at the Earth's surface. Some carbonated springs, however, derive their carbon dioxide from the action of acid on limestone.

Hot Springs

Hot springs as well as fumaroles are likely to occur in volcanic regions. There is an intimate relation between hot springs and fumaroles: in many regions as the dry season comes on some of the hot springs become fumaroles, and when the wet season returns the fumaroles become hot springs. This evident seasonal variation leads to the theory that hot springs are chiefly fed by ground water that has become heated by magmatic steam: hot springs are " drowned " fumaroles. The water circulation of the hot spring is in principle like the hot-water heating system in a house, but instead of a furnace in the basement supplying the thermal energy, magmatic steam furnishes the heat.

It is impossible in general to tell how much of the water (and steam) of hot springs and fumaroles is of surface and how much is of magmatic origin. The proportion contributed by each source doubtless varies in different regions. It is estimated that the hot springs at Lassen Peak consist of 10 per cent of magmatic water and 90 per cent of water of surface origin. Hot springs in the rainless arid interior of some deserts are regarded by some as of magmatic origin. That magmatic emanations have contributed to such waters is indicated by the presence in them of such substances as arsenic, boric acid, and other constituents in quantities and under conditions that show that they could not have been leached out from the surrounding rocks of the country. Most of the

J. K. Hillers, U. S. Geol. Survey.

Fig. 201. — Beehive group of geysers. Upper Geyser Basin, Yellowstone National Park.

water of the hot springs of Yellowstone Park probably is of surface origin, which becomes heated in depth by the condensation of magmatic steam in it and returns in this heated condition to the Earth's surface.

Although there are many kinds of hot springs, according to temperature or substances in solution, the most interesting are boiling springs and geysers. Warm carbonated springs that deposit travertine have been already described in Chapter VI.

Boiling Springs. — Actively boiling springs are a feature of many volcanic regions. They are abundant in Yellowstone Park, especially in the various geyser basins (Fig. 201). They grade from pools that are hot but rarely boil, or else simmer quietly, into springs that boil strongly and steadily, and even some that boil more or less violently and with somewhat explosive energy, interrupted by short periods of repose. The violently boiling springs form transitions to geysers. So long as a spring has a sufficient supply of water to maintain an overflow, it remains limpid, and it is usually deep-blue or green; but if the evaporation through boiling is equal to the inflow, the water becomes more or less turbid from particles of disintegrated rock, and eventually becomes a mass of boiling mud. Exceptionally the mud is white, but more commonly it is tinted yellow, red, purplish, or black by oxides of iron and manganese; such hot springs are called "paint pots," or "mud pots."

As the mud increases in amount it becomes so thick as to prevent continuous boiling, but because the steam pressure builds up during times of quiet, the paint pot boils explosively at intervals, the mud being blown into the air and accumulating in considerable masses around the vent. Such an eruptive mud spring is known as a *mud volcano*, or mud geyser. It generally marks the declining stage in the life of a hot spring.

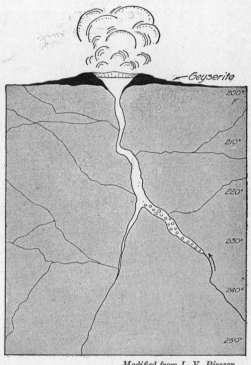

Modified from L. V. Pirsson.

Fig. 202. — Vertical section to illustrate conditions necessary for geyser action.

Geysers. — The term *geyser*, from an Icelandic word meaning to gush, is applied to a hot spring that at intervals erupts a column of hot water and steam. Depending on the size of the geyser and its special peculiarities, the height to which the column of water is ejected ranges from a few feet up to several hundred; the eruption lasts from a few minutes to several hours; the quantity of water discharged is small or it is many thousands of gallons; the jet plays steadily and continuously straight up, or it is fitful, is composed of minor jets, or is thrown in inclined directions. Some geysers erupt at regular intervals, but most erupt at irregular intervals, ranging from minutes to hours, days, or weeks. In general, the geysers that have regular periods overflow only during eruptions, whereas those that are irregular have continuously overflowing vents.   As geysers are boiling springs of a special kind, they are not common; in fact, they are confined almost wholly to three principal regions: Yellowstone Park, Iceland, and New Zealand.

Some geysers erupt into pools, which are several feet or yards across and may be rather deep.   The sides and edges of most of the pools are beautifully ornamented by the deposits of silica, called *geyserite*.   From the bottom of each basin a tube or fissure connects with the heated

C. D. Walcott.

Fig. 203. — Geyserite cone of Lone Star Geyser, Yellowstone National Park; 1915.

depths below, as shown in the diagram (Fig. 202).   The tubes and basins are filled, except immediately after eruptions, with water at or near the boiling-point.   Other geysers have built cones of silica around their orifices, from a foot to several yards high, which form upward extensions of the pipes (Fig. 203).

Of the geysers in Yellowstone Park the most celebrated is " Old Faithful " (Fig. 204), which has a regular interval of 65 minutes between eruptions.   In 1929 a drill hole was put down in the basin of Old Faithful to a depth of 406 feet, where the temperature was found to be

170° C. (338° F.). The drill went first through geyserite, then through glacial gravel, and then into more geyserite — a sequence indicating that the geyser began working before the last glaciation.

Since the Park first became known to the white man in 1871, a few geysers have become extinct, and several new ones have come into being. These changes and the declining activity of other geysers and springs do not mean any immediate diminution of thermal action in this region,

Haynes Studio.

Fig. 204. — Old Faithful in eruption at sunrise. Yellowstone National Park.

but merely indicate that the underground system of pipes and fissures that supply the hot water is undergoing change. Altogether there are several dozen fine geysers in the Park, and the hot springs, fumaroles, and thermal vents of various kinds exceed three thousand.

Cause of Geyser Action. — The intermittent eruptive action of geysers depends on the relation between pressure and the boiling point of water, as was pointed out by Bunsen as a result of his studies of the great geyser in Iceland. The boiling point of water under the ordinary pressure of the atmosphere at sea level is 212° F.; increase of pressure raises it, a decrease lowers it. Consequently, the boiling point at the bottom of a column of water is raised by the weight of the water above it. As shown in Fig. 202, the boiling temperature gradually increases in the tube of the geyser from the surface downward. If the tube is large and regular in form, the water below rises as it becomes hotter; convection currents are thus established, mixing the water, so that it becomes nearly, though not quite, of the same temperature in all parts of the tube, and a boiling spring results. But if the tube is narrow or tortuous, convection is retarded or prevented, and the water reaches its boiling point in the deeper levels at increased temperatures corresponding to the increased pressures. Suppose that at the point 230° in the figure heat is being supplied by fumarolic steam entering the geyser tube. At first the steam condenses to water. The temperature of the water gradually increases until it is at the boiling point corresponding to the depth and pressure, and the steam no longer condenses. Finally, when a sufficient volume of steam has formed, the expansive power of this steam lifts the column sufficiently to cause some of the water to overflow. This overflow lowers the pressure, and the water in depth, being now above the boiling point for the diminished pressure, immediately flashes into steam, and a column of mingled steam and hot water is driven roaring out of the pipe into the air. After the eruption is over, the system fills again by the inflow of ground water into the geyser tube, and the process is repeated.

It was found by accident that adding alkaline substances, such as soap or lye, to the waters of geysers causes some of them to erupt very quickly. The Federal Government had to put a rigorous ban on the " soaping " of the geysers of the Yellowstone Park, in order to prevent the geysers from being ruined.

That the geysers and hot springs of the Park derive their heat from a deep-seated source is shown by their occurrence along the shores and within the area of Yellowstone Lake, an immense body of cold water, beneath which the rocks must have cooled to a considerable depth. The deep-seated source probably is a consolidating magma, from which superheated steam issues along fissures; and where these fissures cut the ground-water circulation, hot springs and geysers are formed.

Hot-Spring Deposits. — It has been previously shown that warm springs, especially those containing carbon dioxide in notable quantity and coming up through limestone beds, deposit calcareous tufa, or travertine (Chap. IV). The waters of the boiling springs and geysers that come up through the rhyolite lava that underlies most of the Park carry *silica* (SiO_2) in solution, which they deposit as a whitish material. This geyserite or siliceous *sinter* varies from compact to highly porous. It forms the geyser cones, and is deposited as an incrustation, much of it of great beauty, in and about the margins of the hot-spring and geyser basins. The geyser waters are dilute, in fact, so dilute as to be tasteless. The rate of deposition of silica from these extremely weak solutions is very slow when it occurs only by evaporation but is hastened due to its secretion by low forms of plant life (diatoms and algae, the latter related to seaweeds), which flourish in the warm waters and even in the hot waters. The beauty of many of the pools is greatly enhanced by the rich coloring given them by the growths made by these organisms. Deposits of considerable size and thickness have been and are being made in this way.

Besides silica, the hot springs deposit other substances. The waters of some springs are acid and deposit sulphur and alum salts; and from other springs sulphides of arsenic and of metals are deposited. They thus demonstrate that extremely dilute hot-water solutions can transport metals from the depths of the crust and subsequently deposit the metals; and they thereby throw light on one of the chief processes by which ore bodies are formed.

Economic Utilization of Fumarole Fields

In recent years it has become apparent that fumarole fields can be developed so as to yield large supplies of steam for power generation. The fumarole field in the volcanic area of Tuscany, north of Rome, was the first to be developed. Wells have been put down to depths of 600 feet, and the flow of steam, as well as the temperature of the steam, has been found to increase as depth is gained. About 16,000 horsepower is generated and is transmitted to Florence, 60 miles away, Pisa, and other cities.

At " The Geysers " in the Coast Ranges of California, 40 miles north of San Francisco, is an area of 35 acres containing a few feeble fumaroles and some small but very hot springs. The name " Geysers " is a misnomer, however, as none of the hot springs is periodically eruptive. In 1921 the idea was conceived of drilling wells in this area to develop a flow of steam for power purposes. So far eight wells have been put down, the deepest being 650 feet, and copious supplies of superheated steam have been developed. In fact, it is estimated that four of the wells will on the average deliver more than 1300 horsepower each. As in Tuscany, the deeper a well is drilled the greater the flow of steam and the hotter its temperature.

The power possibilities of the fumarole fields in Java also are being investigated. One of the fields was bored in 1926. The most promising well, 220 feet deep, yields steam sufficient to generate 1200 horsepower.

Many fumarole fields remain to be bored in Java, as well as others in the near-by islands of Sumatra and the Celebes.

READING REFERENCES

1. Volcanoes; by G. W. Tyrrell. 252 pages. Thornton Butterworth Ltd., London, 1931.

This booklet gives in readable form an authoritative account of volcanoes and their activities.

2. Physics of the Earth — I, Volcanology. 71 pages. Bulletin of the National Research Council, Washington, 1931.

A stimulating presentation of the present status of our knowledge of active volcanism.

3. Volcanoes: Their Structure and Significance; by T. G. Bonney. 3d edition. 379 pages. G. P. Putnam's Sons, New York, 1913.

Accurate, readable, fairly up-to-date book on volcanoes.

4. Hawaii and its Volcanoes; by C. H. Hitchcock. 314 pages. The Hawaiian Gazette Co., Honolulu, 1909.

Describes the Hawaiian volcanoes, especially Kilauea and Mauna Loa.

5. Volcanoes of North America; by I. C. Russell. 346 pages. The Macmillan Co., New York, 1897; reprinted 1924.

An interesting, well-written account of the volcanoes of North America, but unfortunately much out of date.

6. Der Vulkanismus; by F. von Wolff. I. Band: Allgemeiner Teil, 711 pages, 1913–1914. II. Band: Spezieller Teil, 1923 (still in progress). Ferdinande Enke, Stuttgart.

Technical; exhaustive, with ample bibliographies.

7. Vulkankunde; by Karl Sapper. 424 pages. J. Engelhorns Nachf., Stuttgart, 1927.

The best general book on volcanoes.

8. The Volcanic Activity and Hot Springs of Lassen Peak; by A. L. Day and E. T. Allen. 190 pages. Carnegie Institution of Washington, 1925.

Well-illustrated account of a highly interesting volcanic area.

CHAPTER XII

DEFORMATION OF THE EARTH'S CRUST

Although the strength of rocks and the stability of " terra firma " have become proverbial in popular fancy, the Earth's crust is weak in a geologic sense, and at one time or another every part of it has suffered movement in some degree. Evidence of such movement is largely circumstantial, but in part it is direct. Within historic times, and even in the present century, there have been abrupt, catastrophic shifts along fractures that penetrate bedrock to great depth. From historic records it is known also that gradual movements have occurred, with results that are perceptible only after a long time interval. Back of human history we find in the geologic record of all continents evidence of ancient movements on a gigantic scale, which repeatedly changed the geography of the globe. The bedrock has been fractured, bent, or squeezed, and in general the oldest rocks have suffered most severely, because they have been subject to deformation repeatedly during geologic time.

All movements of the lithosphere, resulting in relative vertical or horizontal changes of position and in deformation of rocks, are comprehended under the general term *diastrophism*. Movements that affect all or a large part of a continent are termed *epeirogenic* (from the Greek *epeiros*, continent); more localized disturbances related to mountain building are designated as *orogenic* (from *oros*, mountain). These terms are useful in discussion; but crustal disturbances are extremely complex, and are not subject to description by any simple, rigid classification.

MOVEMENTS IN HISTORIC AND LATE GEOLOGIC TIME

Earthquakes. — Abrupt movements in the lithosphere generate strong vibrations, which repeatedly remind us that our planet is unstable. Scarcely a day passes without records of shocks from some part of the world. Earthquakes are of such significance to science and are so important in human history that they are discussed in some detail in a later chapter (Chap. XIII).

Changes of Level. — The most conspicuous known movements of the land are in the vertical direction; and to determine the extent and rate of change it is necessary to have a convenient horizontal surface of reference. The average level of the sea is the most logical surface for this purpose, as the shoreline at mean tide level is essentially horizontal throughout its whole extent. Any local or differential movement, upward or downward, of land bordering the sea is clearly evident to one who observes the peculiarities of shorelines.

The idea that the sea surface is undistorted and permanently fixed is not strictly correct. Adjacent to high continental borders the water is attracted laterally and upward by the land mass, and the water surface is slightly farther from the center of the Earth in such localities than it is along low, flat coasts or adjacent to oceanic islands. Moreover, the sea level has varied within recent geologic times, first through withdrawal of much water from the sea during the accumulation of continental ice sheets, and later through restoration of this water by wastage of the ice (p. 153). If the water now locked up in the Antarctic and Greenland ice sheets should be liberated by the advent of warmer polar climates, sea level all over the Earth would rise 80 or more feet. Further, there are reasons for believing that the sea has increased in size and depth through geologic time by the constant addition of magmatic water (p. 279); and it is probable that the deep-sea basins have changed appreciably in size many times through upward or downward bowing of their floors and by slow filling in of sediment, with consequent change of sea level. But such changes are gradual, and their effects in shifting shorelines are essentially uniform all over the Earth; whereas many movements of the land are relatively rapid, and all such movements vary in amount from one place to another.

Elevation. — The most striking proofs of uplift of the land consist in the locally elevated position of features that we definitely associate with the sea or its edge. Thus in various parts of the world outcrops of rocks with attached shells or skeletons of dead marine organisms, such as barnacles and corals, are found high above sea level. In some localities the rocks are pierced by tubes that were drilled and lined by a peculiar rock-boring marine animal (*Lithodomus*). Excellent evidence of continuous or recurrent elevation is furnished by certain islands of the East Indian Archipelago. In shallow waters off the coast of Timor, corals are building extensive reefs. Similar reefs, strikingly fresh, extend from the shore zone to the higher ground above the reach of the highest tides (Fig. 205); and still others, showing various degrees of weathering, occur at different levels up to several hundred feet above sea level. A classic example of changes in land level is furnished by the temple of Jupiter Serapis built by the Romans near the seashore in the vicinity of Naples. The three columns left standing are bored by lithodomi to a height of about 20 feet above the temple floor, and the shells of the animals remain in some of the holes. From this we infer that after the temple was built the land subsided more than 20 feet, carrying the temple into the sea, and that later there was uplift of about the same amount. This conclusion is confirmed by historic record.

Strong testimony is given also by the abnormal position of conspicuous features made by erosion and deposition along a coast. In parts of California, Chile, Scotland, and numerous other coastal regions, raised beaches, wave-cut benches, and wave-built terraces make nearly level platforms terminated inland by former wave-cut cliffs. Typical sea caves pierce the cliffs, and old stacks, now high and dry, rise abruptly

G. A. F. Molengraaff.

Fig. 205. — Uplifted coral reefs on the Island of Letti, Netherlands East Indies.   Two stages of uplift are recorded.   The reefs at the level of the palms were lifted above sea level and then undercut by waves.   The lower reefs (sloping to the right) grew while the sea was forming the undercut cliff; they also are well above present sea level (shown at extreme right).

from the benches (Fig. 142). Such a combination of elevated shore features is often spoken of as a raised *strand line*, since it commonly appears as a more or less distinct topographic line or level, approximately parallel with the present shoreline and above it.

Other evidence, of a direct and positive character, is supplied by careful observations made year by year. Thus in countries bordering the Baltic Sea an uplift has been under observation for a long period, and has been measured by marks placed on the shores. In some places the elevation has been as much as 3 feet in a century, but the rate varies

from one part of the region to another. All the facts indicate that the
Scandinavian peninsula has risen gradually for a long period, so that the
northern part of Sweden is about 900 feet higher than it was at the close
of the Ice Age. Raised strand lines are a noticeable feature in many
northern regions. There is similar proof on a large scale that within
recent geologic time the west coast of South America has experienced
very considerable elevation; and probably the uplift is still in progress.

Depression. — Evidence of subsidence below sea level is less striking
than that of elevation, but not less convincing. It is necessary to use
care in drawing conclusions, however, because encroachment of the sea
upon the land is not in itself a proof of subsidence, as it may result merely
from cutting back of the land by waves and currents, or from a general
rise of sea level. Submergence of features that are definitely characteristic of land surfaces constitutes the best proof, if it is clear that the submergence is not world-wide but is limited in extent. Increasing depth
of average water level over well-known rocks or reefs in certain harbors
gives evidence of slow sinking still in progress in some regions.

Evidence of subsidence of the land is furnished also by some irregular
shorelines formed by the drowning of valleys, with formation of bays
and estuaries (p. 419). The seaward extension of river channels, such
as that of the Hudson, for long distances across a submerged continental
shelf, demands the same explanation; for manifestly these great trenches,
now sunk in the sea floor, could not have been cut while the continental
shelf was covered with water, but only by fluvial or glacial erosion, or
both, when the shelf stood at a higher level and was a land surface. The
submerged channel of the Hudson has been outlined by closely spaced
soundings south of New York harbor. It has the definite form of a
valley, extending more than 100 miles southward from Sandy Hook to
the steep continental slope. The subsidence has affected the continent
far inland, as shown by the fact that the tide now reaches up the Hudson
as far as Albany. In the present valley the amount of sinking is
suggested by alluvial fill, hundreds of feet thick, resting on the old
bedrock floor (Fig. 206). This material was deposited by the Hudson
during and after the subsidence.

In many parts of the world thick deposits of sediment are being laid
down by streams in subsiding basins adjacent to coasts. Borings into
deltas pass through alternating marine and freshwater deposits, or even
through sediments entirely nonmarine, to a great depth below present
sea level. For example, wells sunk into the delta of the Po near Venice
pass through four separate layers that contain abundant remains of
plants similar to those now growing in the marshlands along the Adriatic.
One of the layers is about 300 feet below sea level. At shallower depths

some of the sands, gravels, and clays contain shells of marine molluscs, and other layers yield freshwater types such as land snails. In the delta of the Ganges, near Calcutta, pieces of wood and bones of land animals are found hundreds of feet below sea level. Deep wells in the Great Valley of California furnish similar evidence. Facts of this kind suggest

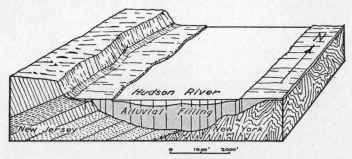

Fig. 206. — Section through the Hudson River at New York, showing the great depth of sediment deposited after submergence of the valley. The land once stood several hundred feet higher, as shown by the present position of the bedrock floor of the valley, shaped by stream erosion. Vertical lines show positions of drill holes.

that subsidence has been going on for a long period, not at a uniform rate, but as an interrupted process whose variations permitted alternating freshwater and marine deposits to be formed.

Evidences of Elevation or Depression Inland. — Movements of the lithosphere involving changes of level are not confined to the sea coasts; they occur also in the interiors of the continents. For example, in 1811 large areas of the Mississippi floodplain near New Madrid, Missouri, sank far below their former level and now are occupied by lakes. Trees that grew on the plain were killed by the flooding, and for a long time

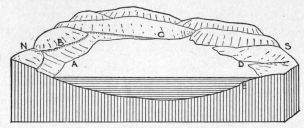

Fig. 207. — Tilting of a lake basin from north (*N*) to south (*S*). *AD*, present lake level; *BC*, raised shoreline, disappearing under water at *C*; *CD*, evidence of drowning; *E*, profile of former shore, now under water.

their dead trunks or tops, projecting above the water, testified to the recency of the catastrophe.

An excellent illustration of tilting on a large scale is afforded by the Great Lakes. To the northeast the land has risen since the disappearance of the great ice sheet, and as a result the lake basins have been tilted southwestward. The old strand lines are several hundred feet above the present water level on the north and northeast, and slope toward it as they are followed west and south. Since the lakes discharge to the east, the raising of their outlets has caused them to enlarge, expanding them to the west and south. As a result of the tilting, the mouths of streams on the south and west sides of some of the lakes (especially Erie and Superior) have been drowned (Fig. 207). The tilting movement is still in progress and has been accurately determined. It is at the rate of 5 inches per hundred miles per century. Small as this rate seems, in 1600 years it would cause the upper Great Lakes to discharge by way of the Chicago River into the Mississippi drainage.

Horizontal Changes of Position. — In addition to the vertical movements discussed above, important horizontal shifts have been detected. In 1906 the ground on opposite sides of a great fracture in California moved in opposite directions; the shift was indicated by abrupt offsetting of roads, fences, and similar features that crossed the fracture (Fig. 250). Knowing that movements of this kind occur repeatedly in the Coast Ranges, the Coast and Geodetic Survey has established stations at critical points whose relative positions have been determined by precise measurements. At intervals of several years the measurements are repeated, and thus the direction and amount of horizontal movement is determined.

Significance of Recent Vertical and Horizontal Movements. — It is obvious that changes of position on the Earth's surface must be accompanied by bending or fracturing of the lithosphere. In fact, surface movements merely record deep-seated processes that lead to slight changes in the form of the globe. Commonly the movement is a broad warping that affects wide areas; locally there is sharper bending, or the rocks actually break under enormous strain. Probably some of the striking recent elevations, such as those observed in various lands bordering the Pacific Ocean, represent small steps in the uplifting of mountain ranges whose growth will continue for long ages.

In considering effects of this kind we are impelled to inquire at once into their ultimate cause; but discussion of this question will be postponed until more of the essential facts and conditions have been presented. It does not seem strange, however, that a globe so large as the Earth, which spins rapidly on its axis and whirls through space, which experiences chemical and physical changes in its outer and probably also in its deeper parts, should be subject to slow and almost continuous deformation. Volcanoes testify to local unstable conditions, which result in the melting and moving of rock material. Erosion and sedimentation through long periods result in the transfer of great loads at the surface; and this process undoubtedly sets up enormous strains in the lithosphere. These well-known processes would in themselves cause some slow deformation of the crust; and probably more profound changes in progress in the deep unknown parts of the Earth are responsible for still greater deforming forces.

ANCIENT CRUSTAL MOVEMENTS

It is neither desirable nor possible to distinguish sharply between recent and older deformation. Certain features at the surface bear unmistakable witness to very recent crustal disturbances, even if there is no direct record of the events in human history. On the other hand, we see in the rocks many fractures and folds that date from very early periods in Earth history, as is shown clearly by their geologic relationships. Between these two extremes are found indications of disturbance in every geologic epoch, showing that movements of the same or similar kinds have been continuous or recurrent throughout recorded geologic time. In general, the latest movements are recorded in forms and features on the Earth's surface, such as the elevated beaches, drowned valleys, and tilted lake basins described above. All surface forms are ephemeral because of erosion; and as they become fragmentary or disappear, the most reliable guide to former crustal movements is found in the structure of the underlying rocks.

EVIDENCE IN SURFACE FORMS

Certain topographic features that result from gentle warping of the crust develop slowly and persist for a very long time. For example, when a peneplane is arched up widely the streams become deeply incised and their old meander patterns are thus preserved in the deepened valleys (Fig. 315). As the deepest incision occurs in the area of greatest uplift, the middle portion and the edges of such a great arch can be recognized by study of the incised valleys. Furthermore, remnants of the uplifted peneplane persist for a long time between the valleys. By study of the valleys and the remains of old surfaces it is determined that the Appalachian region is an irregularly arched peneplane undergoing dissection. It is obvious that evidence of this kind, used for recognizing warping movements that are quite old, is similar to that by which recent uplift is determined.

Further explanation of surface features as indicators of crustal movement is given in the discussion of land forms (Chap. XVII).

EVIDENCE IN SEDIMENTARY ROCKS

The significance of thick masses of unconsolidated sediments like those in the Great Valley of California has been mentioned (p. 295). Similar evidence for earlier geologic periods is furnished by old sedimentary formations, especially by the thick sections exposed in dissected mountains or plateaus. In the Appalachian region the sedimentary strata, now greatly disturbed and eroded, are made in large part of sediments that were deposited on shallow sea floors near land. Although the total thickness of the strata is several miles, the evidence is conclusive that the sea was never deep and that at times it actually disappeared, only to return again. Obviously there was continuous or recurrent subsidence of the area while the sediments were accumulating.

In some sections of sedimentary rocks a pronounced change in the character of sediments indicates either uplift or subsidence. Thus in the high plateau of southern Utah a thick formation made of sand deposited by streams and by the wind shows that the region was above sea level for a long period. Above the sandstone a formation of shale and limestone containing marine fossils records a period of widespread submergence. In the Catskill region of eastern New York a series of marine limestones and shales is succeeded by an enormous thickness of conglomerate and sandstone. Evidently the land adjacent to the old seaway was elevated so that quantities of coarse gravel and sand were rushed into the basin where fine mud and limy sediment had been accumulating.

" Breaks " in sedimentation, caused by uplift, erosion, and resubmergence, are of great importance in reading the history of a region. This aspect of sedimentary rocks is discussed later in the chapter, under the heading *unconformity*.

EVIDENCE IN STRUCTURE OF ROCKS

The most lasting effect of crustal movement is the disturbance of rocks beneath the surface. Sedimentary rocks are particularly useful in preserving the records of diastrophism because they are formed in nearly horizontal strata, and therefore even a slight bending or breaking is easily detected. Igneous rocks are in general less favorable for this purpose, since they are characteristically massive and irregular in their original form. Lava flows and ash beds are an exception, as they have some degree of layering, although this original structure is usually less regular than in sedimentary beds. Thin sills of igneous rock intruded into sedimentary rocks bend or break with the strata and so help record the amount of deformation. On the other hand, the great size and the nearly uniform structure of granite batholiths make them poor recorders of Earth movements.

The principal types of structural features acquired by the bedrock from crustal movements are (1) broad warps, (2) folds, (3) fractures, (4) cleavage. Since cleavage results from fundamental change or *metamorphism* of rocks, it is explained in connection with that subject (Chap. XIV). Careful attention to the results of deformation has great practical importance, since such a study is essential in locating and tracing coal beds, mineral veins, and strata containing oil and gas. There is also broader interest and value in the structural features of the Earth, because they furnish the clue to important events in the history of a region.

Broad Warps

A wide board exposed to the weather becomes twisted or warped from its original flat form. On a much larger scale, rock strata are permanently warped by irregular uplift or depression of a region. In the Colorado Plateau of Utah and Arizona a thick blanket of old marine strata lies thousands of feet above sea level and is dissected by deep canyons. In a general way these strata are nearly horizontal; but if any one layer is followed in detail it is found to bow gently upward into irregular domes and bend downward into shallow basins. It is clear that this wide area of sedimentary beds, many hundreds of miles across, was not lifted up with absolute uniformity, but was distorted somewhat. The original surface of the uplifted mass has been entirely destroyed by erosion; but a record of the distortion is preserved in the form of each layer of stratified rock beneath the former surface.

Warping is the commonest form of rock deformation near the Earth's surface. All the old marine strata that now lie on the continents are more or less warped, where they have escaped more violent disturbance, because uplift of the former sea floors was extremely irregular.

Folds

Anticline and Syncline. — In many places the stratified rocks have been buckled into more or less regular plications or *folds*. Some of these are on a small scale and can be seen directly (Fig. 208); but commonly the folding is on such a great scale, and exposures of the rocks are so discontinuous, that it is necessary to study and piece together the structure of certain distinguishable layers over many miles before the form of the folds becomes clear. The nature and scale of the folds in mountain regions can be appreciated best by study of maps and cross-sections that have been prepared by geologists in the field.

Two terms are used constantly in descriptions and discussions of folds. Like regular swells on the sea, rock folds ordinarily occur in a series, with alternating crests and troughs. The crests of the folds — that is, the upfolds — are *anticlines*; the troughs, or downfolds, are *synclines* (Fig. 209). Initially the anticlines form ridges, the synclines form valleys; but if the original surface crests are subsequently carried away by erosion, and the whole reduced to a level plain, we still call the upfolded portions below the surface anticlines, the downfolded portions

A. W. Rogers.

Fig. 208. — Folded strata along the Buffels River, north side of the Cape Ranges, Cape Province, South Africa. The folds are overturned toward the right (north).

synclines, and in imagination reconstruct the missing parts. Thus it should be clear that anticlines and synclines *are features not of surface form, but of structure.* Commonly the original configuration of the surface is actually reversed by erosion, so that valleys now occupy the positions of the former crests, and ridges or mountains are in the places of the troughs; but the original structural terms still apply (Fig. 210).

It is cause for some wonder that strong, brittle rocks can be bent into sharp folds. If we should try to bend a rock slab by compressing the opposite edges in a powerful vise, the slab would be broken in two or crushed to bits. Probably two conditions are essential for making the rock folds found in nature. The tremendous forces that cause deformation act through very long periods of time, and the rocks yield slowly instead of fracturing abruptly; furthermore, the folded strata that we now see at the surface lay at some depth in the crust when they were deformed, and the confining pressure of the rock above and around them prevented the layers from breaking as the folding took place.   If there

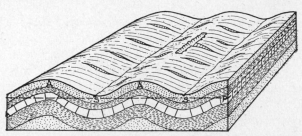

Fig. 209. — Anticlines (*A*) and synclines (*S*).   The diagram assumes that the folding occurred so recently that running water has had time to cut only a few small valleys in the anticlines; hence the anticlines form ridges and the synclines valleys.   Even if erosion proceeds until a peneplane surface is produced, as represented by the broken line through *P*, the anticlines and synclines will still exist as structural features beneath the surface.

is sufficient time for adjustment the most brittle rocks under strong confining pressure can be forced to bend as if they were soft and plastic.

Besides the bending of individual layers an important necessary adjustment in the folding of thick sections of strata is brought about by slipping of each layer over those adjacent.   True folding is restricted to

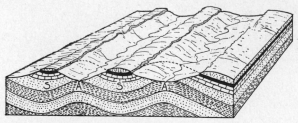

Fig. 210. — Illustrating an advanced stage in erosion of folded strata.   Anticlines (*AA*) have been cut down until valleys occupy their crests; a resistant stratum (black) protects the synclines (*SS*), so that ridges exist along these structural troughs.   The original position of the resistant stratum across the valleys is indicated by the broken line.

stratified rocks because in massive bodies, such as granite batholiths, there are no parallel planes on which adjustment by slipping can occur.

Method of Studying and Mapping Inclined Strata. — Only the ideal relation of simple, upright, regular folds has been considered above.   A series of folds approximating this form is by no means uncommon in nature, but usually the folding is much more complicated.   The varied kinds of deformation which the rocks have suffered in any region determine the *geologic structure* of that region, and it is important that the geologic structure of every country should be known so far as possible and represented accurately on maps. If the surface of the Earth were everywhere naked bedrock, this would be a comparatively easy matter; but since the rocks have been greatly eroded and are largely covered with mantle and vegetation, or with water, snow, and ice, the natural difficulties of the task are large. The structure in a region is determined by a careful study and comparison of the outcrops. If the ground were perfectly level and the strata horizontal, the outcrop would be the flat surface of the uppermost rock stratum, and we should learn little from it; but on slopes and cliffs bordering stream valleys we may inspect the outcropping edges of many horizontal strata, as in the Grand Canyon (Figs. 4 and 173).

On the other hand, if the strata have been inclined by folding and later eroded, their edges are exposed even on a nearly flat land surface. Com-

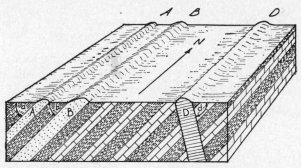

Fig. 211. — The *strike* of two resistant strata, *A* and *B*, and of a dike, *D*, is indicated clearly by the trend of the ridge formed by each. The strike in each case is exactly north. *A* and *B* dip west (the dip angles are *a* and *b*); the dike dips east (angle of dip *d*).

monly the edges of the harder, more resistant beds project to form the more prominent outcrops. In mountain districts, particularly in arid regions, soil and other concealing débris usually decrease in amount with increasing height; and exposures of rock grow in prominence correspondingly, until each of the upper rocky ridges and peaks is a vast outcrop (Fig. 115). Because of the excellent exposures and the great depth of the section visible in canyon walls and on cliffed slopes, mountains furnish the most favorable opportunities for determining geologic structure.

Dip and Strike. — The inclination of a rock layer is called the *dip*. If the stratum is resistant, its projecting edge trends across flat country as a definite ridge (Fig. 211). The compass direction of this ridge is called the *strike* of the stratum. In precise terms, *the strike is the direction of the line formed by intersection of the plane of bedding with the hori-*

zontal plane. The diagram, Fig. 212, illustrates the definition. Intersection of a horizontal water surface with an inclined bedding plane makes a horizontal line (*SS*), and the direction of this line, or of any other horizontal line, as *AB*, on the inclined plane, is the *strike* of the rock layer. This direction is determined with a compass, and the out-

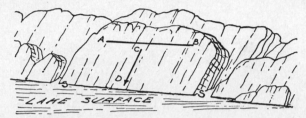

Fig. 212. — Strike and dip of tilted strata. The line of intersection (*SS*) of the horizontal water surface with a bedding plane gives the strike; or any other horizontal line on the bedding, as *AB*, also represents the strike. The dip is measured along a line (as *CD*) at right angles to the strike.

crop of the stratum can then be represented accurately on a map. In Fig. 211 the strike of all the strata and of the dike *D* is north-south. The dike and the two strata *A* and *B* are resistant and so form prominent ridges whose directions are easily determined.

The inclination or *dip* of a rock layer is the angle between the surface of the layer and the horizontal plane. In Fig. 211 the surface of the

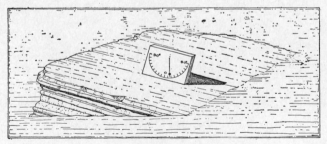

Fig. 213. — Measurement of dip angle with a clinometer. The pendulum of the instrument swings freely on an axis, and therefore is always vertical when the box is on edge. When the edge of the box rests on a bedding plane in the direction of dip, the dip angle (in this case about 16°) is read directly on the graduated arc.

ground is supposed to be horizontal except for the three projecting ridges. Then the angle *a* (50°) gives the amount of dip of layer *A*, *b* (50°) of the layer *B*, and *d* (80°) of the dike *D*. But it is important to give the direction as well as the amount of dip. *A* and *B* dip 50° *west*, *D* dips 80° *east*. The direction of the dip is at right angles to the strike.

The amount of dip is determined with a clinometer, which is essentially a pendulum swinging over a graduated arc (Fig. 213). For geologic purposes the compass and clinometer are combined in one instrument, to permit ready determination of the strike and the direction and amount of dip.

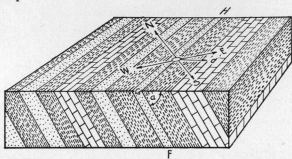

Fig. 214. — Determination of strike and dip. The compass (*O*) is placed on the edge of a bedding plane of the stratum *FGH*. The arrows *N*, *E*, *S*, *W*, indicate compass directions; *d* is the direction of dip, and the angle *a* is the amount of dip.

The full procedure in determining strike and dip is illustrated in Fig. 214. At one edge of the inclined stratum *FGH* the compass shows the angle *NOH* between the edge of the stratum and the north-south

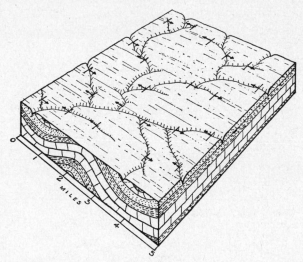

Fig. 215. — Diagram of a land surface underlain by folded strata. In making a geologic map of this area, the strike and dip of each outcrop are noted in the proper position, by use of the conventional symbol. The symbols in the figure mark the positions of outcrops in stream valleys; the strikes and dips at these locations, recorded on a map, indicate an anticline and two synclines, which are shown in section at the end of the block.

line. If this angle is 45°, the strike is recorded as north 45° east (abbreviated N 45° E). The direction of dip is at right angles to the strike, or south 45° east (S 45° E), shown in the diagram by the angle

SOd. With the clinometer the angle of dip, *a*, is found to be 50°, and the dip is recorded as 50° S 45° E. The meaning of this shorthand record is clear if it is kept in mind that the first angle — 50° — is the *amount* of dip, measured downward from the horizontal, whereas the second angle — 45° — gives the *direction* in which the stratum dips, in relation to the north-south line.

Dip and strike are represented on geologic maps by a conventional sign |→, in which the direction of the bar, as placed on the map, indicates the direction of strike, and the arrow points in the direction of dip. Ordinarily the amount of dip in degrees is written in; *e.g.,* |→ 30°.

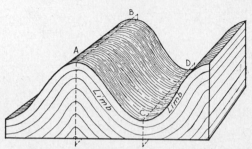

Fig. 216. — Simple upright folds. The line *AB* is the axis of the anticline; *CD* is the axis of the syncline. The imaginary planes indicated by broken lines are the *axial planes* of the two folds.

The practical use of dip and strike in studying folded strata is illustrated in Fig. 215, which represents a flat, soil-covered area where the only outcrops of bedrock are in the stream valleys. By studying these outcrops and plotting the strikes and dips in the proper positions on a map, it is found that the strata are folded into an anticline and two synclines, as shown in the section at the end of the block diagram.

Pitching Folds. — The sides of a fold are called the *limbs* (Fig. 216), and the median line between the limbs, along the apex of an anticline or the trough of a syncline, is the *axis* (Figs. 216, 217). This line extends

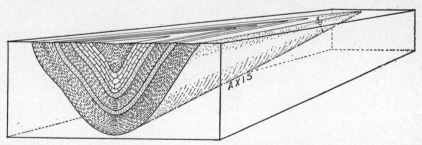

Fig. 217. — A syncline tilted along the axis and eroded. The angle (*P*) between the tilted axis and a horizontal plane is the *pitch*.

along a bedding surface, or along this surface restored if it has been partly eroded. When folds that have horizontal axes are eroded deeply, the ridges made by the edges of resistant strata are nearly parallel as shown in Fig. 218; but if the axes are not horizontal, on a nearly flat erosion surface the outcropping edges of strata in the limbs of any anticline or syncline converge and finally meet (Figs. 217, 219).   The result

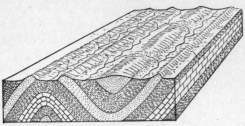

Fig. 218. — Land surface developed by erosion of folds whose axes are horizontal.   Edges of resistant strata form parallel ridges.   Front of block say 3 miles long.   Compare Fig. 219.

is a hairpin turn in the outcrop in either kind of fold; but there are two general ways for distinguishing one from the other.   In the ordinary syncline, dips are consistently inward toward the axis, and the younger strata lie inside the hairpin; in an ordinary anticline, dips are outward from the axis, and the older strata lie inside the hairpin (Figs. 219, 220).

Folds whose axes are not horizontal are known as *pitching* or *plunging* folds.   The angle between the axis and the horizontal plane is called

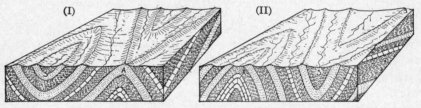

Fig. 219. — Land surfaces developed by erosion of folds whose axes are tilted.   In (*I*) the anticline and syncline pitch toward the front of the block; in (*II*) the pitch is toward the back of the block.   Front of each block say 2 miles long.   Compare Fig. 218.

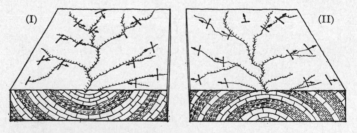

Fig. 220. — Dips and strikes in scattered outcrops, showing a syncline (*I*) plunging toward the observer and an anticline (*II*) plunging in the opposite direction.

the *pitch* of a fold (Fig. 217).   Use of dip and strike observations in detecting and mapping plunging folds from scattered outcrops is illustrated in Fig. 220.

Other Variations in Fold Structure. — Thus far we have considered only regular, upright folds.   An imaginary plane passed through the center of a fold and its axis, as in Fig. 216, is called the *axial plane* of the fold. In a regular or *symmetric* fold, this plane is one of symmetry; that is, the parts to left and right of it are symmetrically disposed, or each point on the left of the plane is the mirror image of a corresponding point on the right of it. If the fold is upright the plane is vertical (Fig. 216). However, some folds are not upright but have been pushed over until the axial planes are inclined. A fold of this kind is said to be *overturned* (7 in Fig. 221). In some folds the overturning has gone so far that the axial plane is nearly or actually horizontal; and the fold is then termed *recumbent*.

Some overturned folds break at the apex or on one limb; and on breaking, the parts are likely to be displaced with respect to one another, or *faulted*. Faulting, however, is so important a phenomenon that it deserves especial consideration in another place.

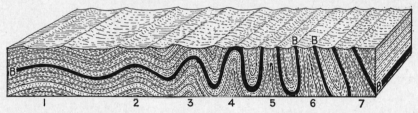

Fig. 221. — Folded strata, considerably eroded. The anticlines *1* and *2* are *open* folds; to the right of *3* all the folds are *closed*. At the right of the block the folds are *isoclinal*. The layer *BBB*, which can be traced through the entire series of folds, serves as a useful key. Length of block about 50 miles.

If folds are so sharply flexed that the limbs are nearly or quite parallel, they are said to be *closed*; in this condition the horizontal distance across the strata, or the width of the fold, can not be further reduced without squeezing or mashing of the beds (*4* to *7* in Fig. 221). If the limbs make a large angle with each other (as in *1* and *2*, Fig. 221) the fold is *open* and the strata can be further folded without mashing.

In *isoclinal* (equal-inclination) folds the strata are compressed until, on both sides of a fold, and perhaps throughout a series, they are parallel and have the same dip (Fig. 221, *5* to *7*). When the crests of such folds are cut away by erosion, considerable skill is required for correct interpretation of the structure, since there is no difference in general appearance between anticlines and synclines. The general principle followed is to determine the positions of axial planes by study of the strata. The oldest exposed strata are repeated at the middle of an eroded anticline, and the youngest strata at the middle of a syncline. For example, in Fig. 221 the sandstone layer *B*, seen at the left, can be traced entirely through the series of folds. In the anticline *6*, layers below and hence older than *B* are repeated on opposite sides of the axial plane; in the synclines adjacent to *6*, layers above and hence younger than *B* are similarly repeated.

A special kind of fold is the *monocline*, in which the strata are bent in one direction only (Fig. 222). A true monocline is a one-limb flexure, on either side of which the strata are horizontal or have uniform gentle dips.

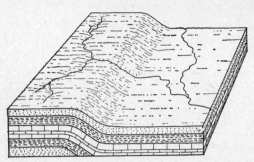

Monoclines are particularly well developed, as isolated features, in the nearly flat strata of the Colorado Plateau in northern Arizona and New Mexico.

Geosynclines and Geanticlines. — Long belts within a continent or on the sea floor have been warped down to form *geosynclines*, whose dimensions are measured in hundreds of miles. Corre-

Fig. 222. — A monocline. It is assumed that the fold developed rapidly and recently; therefore it is little eroded. Length of block about 2 miles.

spondingly great upwarps are called *geanticlines*. The prefix in each case (from the Greek word *geos*, meaning Earth) emphasizes the scale of these features. In contrast with ordinary folds, the flexures responsible for geosynclines and geanticlines are very gentle.

The geosynclines of the past have been the great basins for the accumulation of sediments like those exposed in the Appalachians (Fig. 285) and the Alps. Slow downwarping of the floor of a geosynclinal basin continues as sediments accumulate, until in the middle portion the thickness of deposits reaches several miles. It is only by the later folding, uplift, and dissection of these deposits that the original nature of the geosyncline is revealed.

Geanticlines also grow slowly, and their crests are eroded away as the warping continues. A good example, on a moderate scale, is the Cincinnati Arch in Ohio and Kentucky, where the Paleozoic strata dip gently away from a median axis in an area 250 miles wide.

Joints and Faults

In the outer shell of the Earth the rocks are traversed in all directions by fractures, which vary from microscopic crevices to important breaks on which large displacement has occurred. Such fractures have great geologic importance, because they are clues to important events in the history of a region, and particularly because of the aid they give to vari-

ous geologic processes. We have considered the large influence of fractures on the weathering and erosion of rocks (Chaps. II, III), and on the
circulation of ground water (Chap. IV); and we shall consider their
importance also in connection with mineral deposits (Chap. XVIII).

A fracture on which there has been no appreciable displacement parallel with the walls is a *joint*. If there has been relative displacement of
the walls parallel with the fracture, so that corresponding points on
the two sides are distinctly offset, the fracture is known as a *fault*.
Many joints and faults are closed so tightly that little or no space is visible between the walls. If the walls are distinctly separated the term
fissure is sometimes applied to the fracture. Some fissures are open,
and others have been filled with mineral matter deposited by circulating
water.

Joints in Stratified Rocks. — Field examination shows that joints are
common, but that they are much more numerous in some places than
in others. Where they are abundant, commonly they are arranged in
more or less definite *sets*; that is, the divisional planes running through
the rock fall into groups according to direction. In many places there
are two prominent sets of joints, intersecting at a large angle. Such a
combination of two or more intersecting sets constitutes a joint *system*.
Combined with natural divisional bedding planes, a well-defined system
of joints divides stratified rocks into series of closely fitting blocks. The
finer the grain of the rock, as a rule, the more perfect the jointing and
the more sharply defined the resulting blocks. In some beds of shale
and limestone the jointing is exceptionally perfect (Fig. 223).

Some jointing probably results from the tension caused by contraction in beds of sediments when they are elevated from the sea floor to
form land masses and are partially dried as a result. A more common
probable cause of regular fracturing is the warping and twisting experienced by the strata during crustal movements. In regions where the
strata have been folded, as in many mountain zones, unquestionably the
force that plicated the beds also produced many joints.

Strike joints are parallel with the strike of the beds, or nearly so; *dip
joints* are essentially in line with the dip, and therefore at right angles to
strike joints. Some sets of joints extend for long distances across a
thick series of beds, and are known as *master joints*. They are contrasted
with minor fractures, some of which are limited to a single stratum.

Joints in Igneous Rocks. — A common type of jointing in igneous
rocks is due to the contraction resulting from the cooling of the original
magma. This occurs during and just after solidification from the liquid
state. It may manifest itself in one of several ways, depending on the
rate of cooling, the size and shape of the igneous body, and other fac-

tors.   Large intrusive masses of granite and similar rocks are character-istically cut by joint planes that divide them into large blocks or prisms. Finer-grained rock in sills, laccoliths, and dikes commonly are divided into small angular fragments by closely spaced joints.   Some laccoliths and similar dome-shaped intrusions have a shelly jointing on a large scale, parallel with the domed surface.   This appears to have been caused by nearly uniform cooling of the mass from the periphery, with resulting separation into sheets.

The most striking kind of contraction-jointing in an igneous rock results in development of *columnar structure*, which is characteristic of

I. C. Russell, U. S. Geol. Survey.

Fig. 223. — Joints cutting horizontal beds of limestone.   There are two sets of joints, nearly vertical and at right angles to each other.   Drummond Island, Mich.

tabular masses.   Many dikes, sills, and lava flows are made up of closely fitting prisms subdivided by inconspicuous cross-joints.   The prisms have a variable number of sides, but commonly they tend to be hex-agonal, and some of them have remarkable regularity of form.   They range from several inches to a number of feet in diameter, and up to 500 feet in length.   The Giant's Causeway on the north coast of Ireland is one of the most celebrated examples of this columnar structure (Fig. 224).   The columns form at right angles to the chief cooling surface, and consequently in a level intruded sheet or a flow of lava they stand vertically, whereas in a vertical dike they are nearly horizontal.   Thus some dikes, exposed as walls by erosion, resemble regularly piled cord-wood.   In igneous bodies that have curved surfaces the position and form of the columns depend on the form of the periphery of each individual mass.

In addition to the joints caused by cooling, later fractures caused by crustal movements also affect igneous rocks; but wherever a prominent columnar structure or other well-defined fracture system is original in the rock mass, later stresses are more likely to be relieved along these existing breaks than to form additional fractures.

Jointing in Metamorphic Rocks. — As a rule, metamorphic rocks are much jointed. This might be expected because of the extensive deformation to which such rocks have been subjected. The character of the

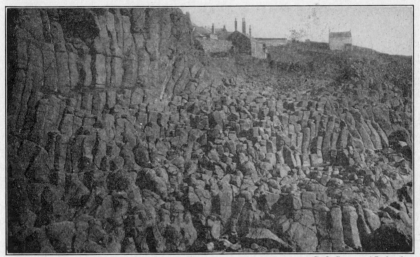

Geol. Survey of Ireland.

Fig. 224. — Part of the Giant's Causeway, Ireland. Columnar jointing in basalt, caused by contraction through cooling of the lava.

jointing varies considerably with the nature of the rock. Many of the massive gneisses have joint systems like those characteristic of granite; whereas the fissile and schistose rocks, such as slates, have joints more like those found in sedimentary rocks. (See Chap. XIV.)

Practical Importance of Joints. — Joints are a matter of great importance in all quarrying, tunneling, and mining operations where rock work enters as an important factor, since the jointing obviously facilitates the work of excavation. Without them, every rock fragment would have to be broken or blasted loose from bedrock. However, joints may also be a serious inconvenience, especially if large blocks of quarried stone are desired. Perfect monoliths 50 or 100 feet in length can be obtained from comparatively few localities.

General Features of Faults. — Displacement of rock masses along a fault (p. 309) may occur at the time of the break, or at some later time. Faults are common features in rocks of all kinds. They are most evident in stratified formations, since the offsetting of definite layers makes a break conspicuous and directly measurable. However, massive igneous rocks are faulted as well; and as mineral veins and other features of economic value are displaced by such fractures, it is extremely important from a practical as well as a scientific standpoint that the nature of faults be well understood.

C. R. Longwell.

Fig. 225. — Part of an old fault surface, with slickensides, uncovered by erosion. The striations and flutings indicate that the movement was directly down the dip of the surface. Spotted Range, Nevada.

A surface of fracture along which movement and dislocation has occurred is often spoken of as a fault plane. Although a limited part of it may be nearly plane, it is rarely flat for any considerable distance, but more or less curved and irregular. Therefore it is better, and causes less misapprehension, to term it a *fault surface*. Rather commonly a faulting movement occurs, not upon one surface, but upon a number of more or less closely adjacent breaks, producing a *fault zone*, in which the various offsets make in the aggregate the total displacement. The masses of rock involved in fault movements generally are of such size and weight, and are so compressed together, that the motion of one fault face on the other takes place under tremendous pressure. As a result of the friction the rock faces are smoothed and striated, and not uncommonly receive a high polish. Such polished and grooved surfaces are

known as *slickensides* (Fig. 225).   The line of intersection of the fault
with the plane of the horizon is called the *strike* of the fault, just as we
speak of the strike of inclined strata.   The surface of faulting is rarely
exactly vertical; usually it is inclined, and in some important faults it
approaches horizontality.   The angle between the fault surface and the
horizontal plane is the *dip*.   In an inclined fault the side that overhangs
is known as the *hanging wall*, the other as the *foot wall* (Fig. 226).   If
one were to descend along a fault, as in an inclined shaft of a mine, the
appropriateness of these old mining terms would be evident.

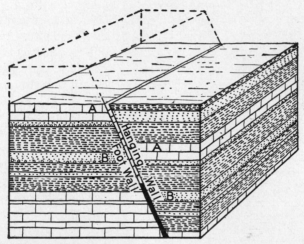

Fig. 226. — Fault relations and terms. The strata have been displaced by a fault,
and a vein of mineral (black) has formed along the fracture. Mining operations have
removed the mineral to a considerable depth, exposing the hanging wall and foot wall of
the fault. Part of the upthrown side has been removed by erosion, as shown by broken
lines. Corresponding strata on opposite sides of the fault are indicated by *A–A, B–B*.

Generally the fracture is closed tightly; but parts of it may have been
open at one time, and have been filled with mineral matter deposited
from solution.   Along many faults the grinding of the walls upon one
another has produced a zone of broken and crushed rock known as *fault
breccia*.   Commonly the finely powdered rock directly along the fault
forms a thin seam of clay-like material, known as *gouge*.   In the displacement of stratified rocks the friction usually causes bending of the
layers near the fault surface.   This feature, referred to as *drag*, is a useful aid in determining the relative direction of motion on the two sides
of the fault (Figs. 238–240).   Practically it is of the highest importance
as an aid in finding the dislocated segment of a coal bed or a mineral
deposit.
   The features explained so far have to do chiefly with faults as seen

below the surface of the ground.   Ordinarily a fault breaks the surface as well as the rocks beneath; and if one side of the fault is elevated with relation to the other, the result is a cliff, or *fault scarp* (Fig. 228).   With the passage of time the original scarp is modified or even removed by erosion (p. 320).

FIG. 227

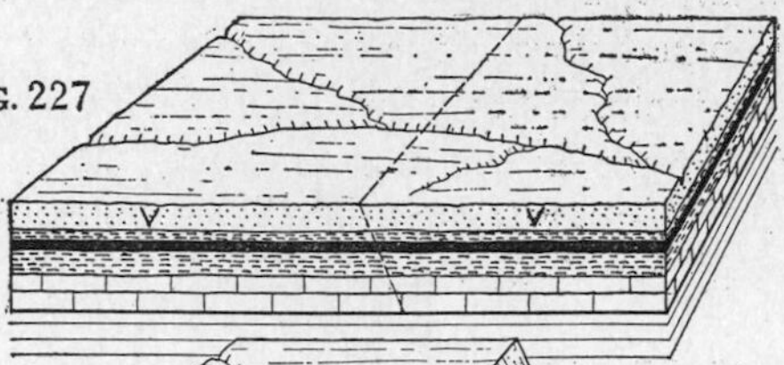

FIG. 228

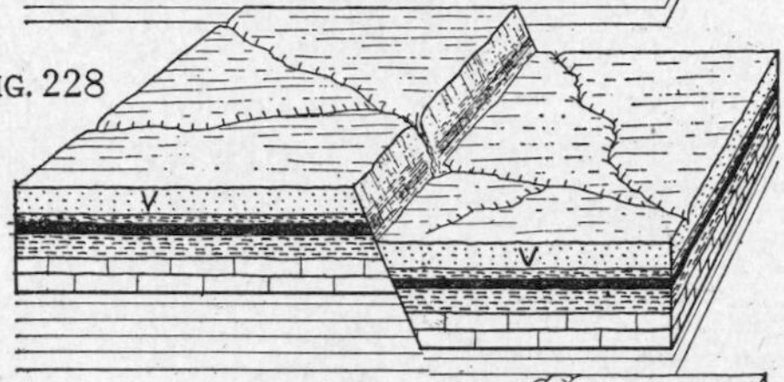

FIG. 229

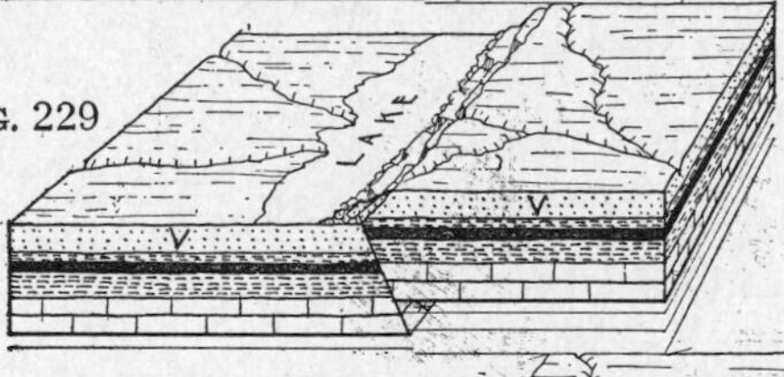

FIG. 230

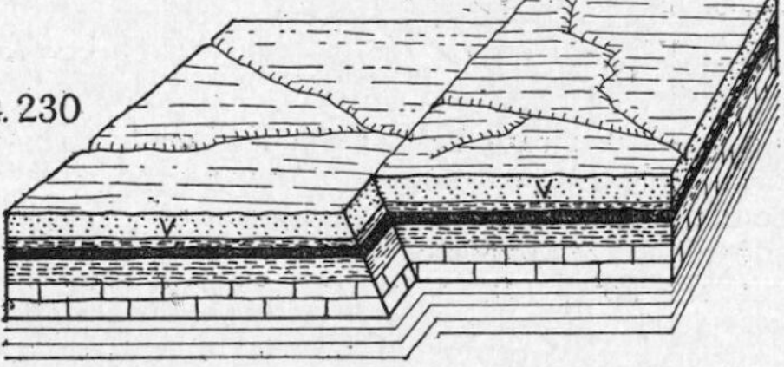

Figs. 227–230. — Types of faults.   Relative movement indicated by the broken bed V–V.

Fig. 227. — Before movement.   Position of the fracture shown by broken line.

Fig. 228. — Simple normal fault, making a scarp which the stream descends in a cascade.

Fig. 229. — Reverse fault.   The projecting edge of the hanging wall breaks off and slumps under its own weight.   The stream is obstructed and forms a lake.

Fig. 230. — Strike-slip fault, with no vertical displacement.

Movement on a Fault. — Generally there is no means of telling how much actual movement there has been on either side of a fault.   Even if a definite, recognizable object, such as a crystal or pebble in the rock, has been cut in two by the fracture and the halves carried apart a measurable distance, we cannot determine whether one side of the fault stood still while the other side experienced all the displacement, or whether both sides shared in the movement.   Conceivably we might know the exact position of every point on the ground before the faulting and later check the positions on each side of the break.   Such a check is being attempted along some active faults in California.   Generally, however, we lack the precise information necessary for such a study of modern displacements; and most faults with which we have to deal are old features whose original expression at the Earth's surface was long ago destroyed by erosion.   The actual walls of such faults usually are seen only in mine tunnels or in other excavations of limited size.

Nevertheless an attempt is made to classify faults according to the apparent or relative displacement on the two sides as indicated by off-set strata, dikes, or other recognizable features.   Thus in Fig. 228, it is evident, from the displacement of the layer VV, that the hanging wall has gone down with relation to the foot wall (although actually the foot wall may have moved up while the hanging-wall block stood still, or both blocks may have moved).   A fault that has this relation between hanging wall and foot wall is called a *normal* fault.   If the hanging wall appears to have been crowded up over the foot wall, as in Fig. 229, the fault is called a *reverse* fault.

Generally the movement on a fault surface is more or less oblique, as suggested in Fig. 231, instead of straight up or down the dip of the surface.   Not uncommonly the motion is chiefly or entirely horizontal, parallel with the strike of the fault (Fig. 230). Such a fault is called a *strike-slip* fault.   If it cuts only horizontal strata there is no measure of the movement except in displaced features on the ground, since the strata are not offset.   Displacement of a steeply in-clined dike, however, would record both the direction and the amount of movement.

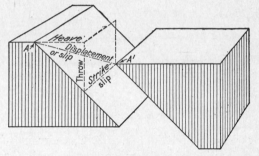

Fig. 231. — Oblique movement on a fault; points A and A' have moved apart along the fault surface.   Broken lines show the *displacement* (*slip*), and its three components — *throw, heave,* and *strike-slip* — measured along axes at right angles to each other.

The simplest possible examples are shown in Figs. 228–230.   Strata and other features of bedrock commonly are inclined and hence are off-set by either vertical or horizontal movement along most faults.   Therefore the offsetting of rock layers, taken by itself, is not a safe criterion in solving fault problems.   Some of the possible complications are discussed in a later paragraph.

Since generally we do not see much of the fault surface, it is necessary to calculate the displacement from the effects seen on the ground, on the side of a valley cut through the fault, or on some other chance plane. Therefore the displacement on a fault is described geometrically, by its components in three dimensions.   These three components are named and explained in Fig. 231.

Faults in Stratified Rocks. — Certain terms are used to define faults in relation to the structure of sedimentary beds that are affected.   Thus in a *strike fault*, the strike of the fault and that of the strata are parallel, or nearly so (Fig. 232); *dip faults* cut directly across the strike of the strata, or nearly so (Fig. 233); *oblique faults* cut diagonally across the strike of the strata. The figures show only normal faults; but similar principles apply to reverse faults. The figures also indicate no real

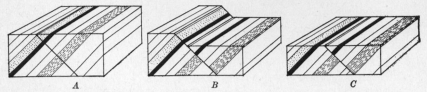

A B C

Fig. 232. — Repetition of strata by normal strike faulting and later erosion. *A*, before faulting; *B*, directly after faulting; *C*, surface leveled by erosion.

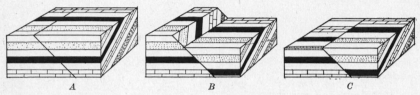

A B C

Fig. 233. — Offsetting of strata by dip faulting and later erosion. *A*, before faulting; *B*, directly after faulting; *C*, surface leveled by erosion.

strike-slip, but in Fig. 233, *C*, there is offsetting of beds, with a false suggestion of strike movement. Such abrupt offsetting of tilted strata is one of the surest indications of dip or oblique faulting. Strike faults

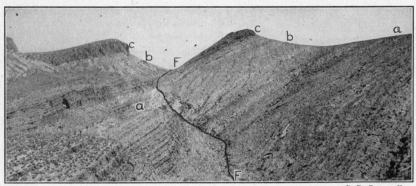

C. R. Longwell.

Fig. 234. — Repetition of formations by a normal strike-fault (*F–F*). *a*, *b*, and *c* are three distinct formations, broken and dislocated as shown. Erosion has removed much of the rock on both sides of the fault since movement occurred. Spotted Range, Nevada.

are more difficult to perceive and are easily overlooked; not uncommonly they cause deception as to the thickness of strata by producing repetitions (Fig. 232, *C*; and Fig. 234). In traversing strata the repetition of a certain set should lead to suspicion of strike faulting. On the other hand, some strike faults conceal strata after erosion has occurred. Thus in Fig. 235, which represents a reverse fault with later erosion, there is no outcrop of the stratum A at the surface. This layer might contain petroleum, or some valuable deposit of ore, which could be discovered only by a fortunate accident or by modern geophysical prospecting (p. 445).

Displacement on some faults is attended by rotary or pivotal motion (Fig. 236). A fault of this general nature is known as a *rotary* fault; or, if the displacement dies out gradually up to a definite point, it is a *hinge* fault. After erosion has leveled the surface,

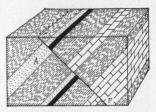

Fig. 235. — Concealment of strata by reverse strike faulting and subsequent removal of the scarp by erosion. *F–F–F*, trace of the fault. The bed A and higher beds have been eroded from the hanging-wall block.

C. R. Longwell.

Fig. 236. — Rotary fault, Spotted Range, Nevada. The fault runs from left to right, between the tilted rocks and the steep cliff on nearly horizontal strata. Displacement decreases toward the right, increases toward the left. Maximum throw about 3000 feet.

a fault of this kind is indicated by a pronounced difference in the strike and dip of strata on opposite sides of the break. Some hinge faults pass gradually into monoclinal folds (Fig. 237).

Faulting in Relation to Landslides. — Many landslides involve only a superficial cover of loose detritus (p. 33); but some of the largest slides have included enormous masses of bedrock that sheared off under their own great weight on steep mountain slopes or

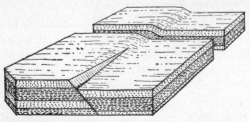

Fig. 237. — A hinge fault passing into a monoclinal fold. Front of block about 1 mile long.

in high canyon walls. The irregular fractures on which these displacements occur are faults of a special type.

The Magnitude of Faulting. — The scale of faulting varies within wide limits; displacement varies from a fraction of an inch up to thousands of feet, or even several miles. In the Plateau region of Arizona and Utah, several faults of great magnitude extend in a north-south direction, some of them crossing the Grand Canyon. Each of the largest fractures in this group can be followed 100 miles or more, and each has a throw measured in thousands of feet. The Great Basin region presents the phenomenon of faulting on a colossal scale. In the area between the Sierra Nevada on the west and the Wasatch Range on the east, the crust is divided into huge blocks by gigantic fractures; and differential displacement of these blocks, together with erosion, has resulted in mountainous topography (Fig. 278). A sunken tract due to downfaulting, or to uplift of adjacent areas, is called a *graben* (German for trough or ditch). Illustrations are the Jordan Valley and the Dead Sea basin in Palestine, the great rift valleys of Africa, and Death Valley in eastern California. An upstanding mass between two faults is a *horst* (Fig. 279).

Most of the great fractures mentioned above are normal faults. Detailed study of eroded mountain areas has disclosed reverse faults of enormous displacement, some of them with an exceptionally low angle of dip. Such faults, which occur only in regions where folding and crushing of the rocks have been exceptionally severe, are commonly known as *thrust* faults, or simply *thrusts*. Many of these are of such magnitude and importance that they have come to be considered as a special class of faults. The surface on which movement has occurred is spoken of as the thrust surface, or less accurately as the thrust plane.

Such thrusts have been discovered in the Alps, in northwestern Scotland, in Scandinavia, in the southern Appalachians, in the Rocky Mountains, and in many other mountain regions. The horizontal displacement of lower, older formations over younger rocks ranges from a few miles up to 25, 30, or even 40 miles for individual thrusts (Figs. 291–294). In many places erosion has partly destroyed the comparatively thin plate of the older rocks above the thrust, leaving isolated remnants resting on much younger foundations. An excellent example is Chief Mountain in Glacier National Park, Montana (Fig. 295). Such isolated masses that obviously are far removed from their natural position are called " mountains without roots."

The deciphering of these great thrusts is one of the triumphs of modern geologic research. It has led to rational interpretation of mountain structure that before seemed illogical and chaotic. An illustration of the practical value of such research was the discovery in Belgium of an important field of anthracite coal after it was recognized that the coal-

bearing formations lie concealed beneath older rocks
that were pushed over them
in a great flat thrust.

**Surface Expression of
Faults.** — Displacement of
the Earth's surface by a
normal or a reverse fault
gives rise to a cliff or scarp.
Within historic time, movements that caused severe
earthquakes have resulted
in new scarps from a few
feet to nearly 50 feet high
(Fig. 251). Many other
cliffs and mountain fronts,
some of them hundreds or
thousands of feet in height,
are recognized as fault
scarps, but it is extremely
improbable that any one
of these was formed by a
single displacement. There
is strong evidence that the
strain responsible for slipping on a fault is relieved
temporarily by abrupt displacement of a few feet or
tens of feet, and then accumulates for years or even
hundreds of years before
the movement is repeated.
Thus every high fault scarp
is a very old feature judged
by human standards, al-
though it may be youthful
from a geologic viewpoint.

Such a scarp made directly
by faulting is called simply
a fault scarp or an *initial*
fault scarp (Fig. 238).

FIG. 238

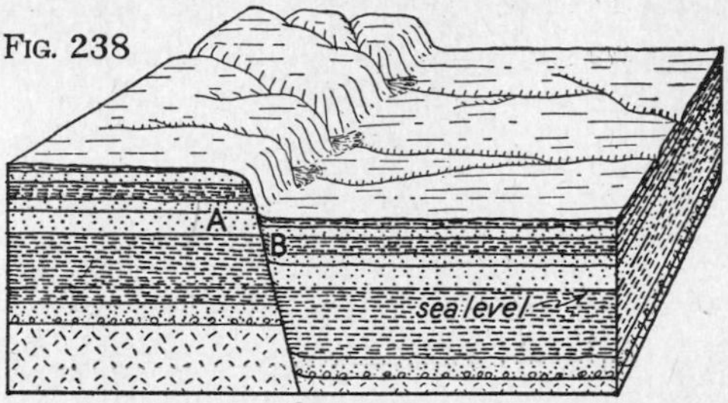

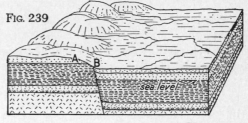

FIG. 239

FIG. 240

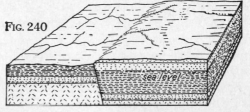

Figs. 238–240. — Possible development of a fault
scarp during one cycle of erosion.

Fig. 238. — Scarp made directly by faulting.
Only a little of the topmost stratum has been eroded
from the uplifted block, and streams are cutting deep
valleys into the high mass, spreading the débris on
the downthrown block.

Fig. 239. — The same fault shown in Fig. 238, at
a later stage in the cycle. A, and B, points at the
top and base of the scarp at this stage, were beneath
the surface when the initial scarp existed (Fig. 238).
Therefore the initial scarp has been entirely destroyed, and the scarp at this later stage is wholly
the work of erosion; it is a *fault-line scarp.*

Fig. 240. — A possible though not a common development in a late stage of the cycle. After the
sandstone layer at A (Fig. 239) is destroyed the weak
shales beneath are eroded rapidly. The sandstones
beneath B, on the downthrown block, make erosion
on that side more difficult. Aided by favorable
changes in drainage, these differences in the bedrock
may result in a fault-line scarp facing *toward* the
initial fault scarp.

Erosion begins to modify it as soon as it begins

to be formed, and the upper portion of every high scarp is considerably
dissected, both because that part has been subject to erosion since the
scarp was first initiated, and because erosion is most effective at high
altitudes (Fig. 280). After the faulting has ceased the entire scarp is
continuously lowered, and slowly retreats from the position of the fault.
As erosion progresses the scarp passes through the stages of youth, maturity, and old age, and finally, on peneplanation of the region, differences in elevation on opposite sides of the fault almost or entirely disappear.

A large fault displacement as a rule brings together on opposite sides
of the fault rocks that differ materially in composition and resistance.
As erosion proceeds the initial scarp is eventually destroyed, but so
long as the entire region has considerable altitude the position of the
fault is marked by a cliff or steep slope because weak rock on one side
is removed faster than resistant rock on the other (Fig. 239). A scarp
that is due entirely to differential erosion along a fault is called a *fault-
line scarp*, to distinguish it from the earlier scarp that resulted directly
from the faulting movement. Since resistant rocks at any particular
level are as likely to occur on the downthrow as on the upthrow side of
the fault, not uncommonly the block that originally stood the higher is
eroded far below the other, and the resulting fault-line scarp faces directly toward the position of the initial fault scarp (Fig. 240).

Some fault-line scarps are developed by regional uplift after peneplanation has removed the differences in elevation on opposite sides of
a fault (Figs. 241–243). There are excellent illustrations in central
Connecticut and Massachusetts, where scarps destroyed by the erosion
that formed the New England peneplane have been renewed since the
region was warped up during the Tertiary period. These examples
show the necessity of careful geological study in determining the exact
history of any fault.

In the southwestern United States, where large crustal movements
have occurred in late geologic time, and where climatic conditions favor
the development of excellent outcrops, there are many fine examples
of fault scarps as well as fault-line scarps. The east slope of the Sierra
Nevada and the west slope of the Wasatch Mountains are fault scarps
that are youthful in a geologic sense. At the base of each of these
ranges some of the movement has occurred so recently that scarps exist
almost uneroded in the soft fans of alluvial material brought down by the
streams. The last recorded movement along the east base of the Sierra
Nevada took place in 1872. These faults have grown by many successive displacements, and the upper part of each scarp has been greatly
eroded (cf. Fig. 280). The Plateau region, through which the Colo-

rado River cuts its way, is crossed by a series of great faults that are marked by prominent cliffs. These have been described as actual fault scarps; but most of them are fault-line scarps developed after peneplanation and renewed regional uplift.

Many old faults with vertical displacements amounting to thousands of feet are now practically unrecognizable in the surface forms. Obviously this relation in each case indicates erosion of great magnitude. Either there was a high fault scarp that slowly wasted away or the growth of the displacement was so slow that erosion almost kept up with it. This last suggestion is not unreasonable, for we have evidence of repeated movements on some faults after intervals of long geologic periods. If individual movements are small and widely separated in time, or if the rocks on the upthrow side of a fault are exceptionally weak, a prominent scarp has no chance to develop.

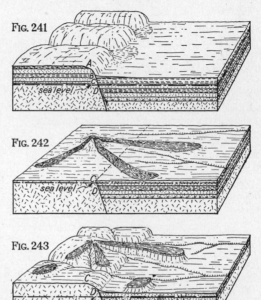

Figs. 241–243. — Development of a fault-line scarp during two cycles of erosion.

Fig. 241. — An initial fault scarp (A–B), modified by erosion but still growing by downward movement of the right-hand block.

Fig. 242. — The surface is reduced to a peneplane, through the point C, and lava flows spread across the position of the fault.

Fig. 243. — The entire region is uplifted uniformly, as indicated by arrows, and erosion forms a new scarp (C–D) by more rapid removal of the weak sediments on the downthrown block. Presence of the lava flows, crossing the fault unbroken, proves that this is a fault-line scarp, developed wholly by erosion and not by renewed movement on the fault.

CAUSE OF WARPING, FOLDING, AND FAULTING

The immediate cause of rock deformation is comparatively simple and generally agreed upon: it results from stresses set up in the outer shell of the Earth. Some rocks yield by warping or folding, but others are too massive or too brittle to permit yielding of this kind. The rate at which deformation occurs also determines in large degree the response of the rocks; if the forces act very slowly adjustment by bending is possible, but if stress is applied more rapidly relief occurs in the same rocks by forming new fractures or by slipping on old faults. Compressive stresses give rise to folds and also to reverse faults and thrusts. In regions of broad warping the rocks yield by torsion or twisting, which sets up tensional strains and produces normal faults. After fracturing, displacement occurs by gravitative settling and readjustment of the fault blocks. Thus over wide regions where the strata are not otherwise disturbed, as in parts of the Colorado Plateau, they are penetrated by steep fractures on which there have been great displacements.

The *ultimate cause* of faulting and folding evidently depends on those processes within the Earth which give rise to compressional or twisting forces and so set up stresses in the lithosphere. The forces themselves are hidden and can be inferred only from their effects. As the subject is obscure at best, and speculation must be guided by consideration of all available facts, it is best to postpone inquiry into the ultimate cause of crustal deformation until the structure and history of mountains have been discussed.

UNCONFORMITY, A RECORD OF ANCIENT DIASTROPHISM

Sedimentary deposits, especially those laid down on sea floors and later elevated above sea level, give a faithful record of the history of

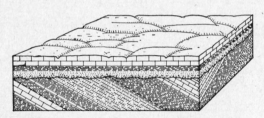

their times. In general the persistence of nearly uniform conditions, without any disturbance by crustal movements, results in continuous deposition of parallel strata with similar composition or with gradual change from one type of material to another, as from sandstone to shale. The strata in such a series are said to be *conformable* with each other. But if crustal

Fig. 244. — Angular unconformity between two series of marine strata. The lower series was deposited as a conformable sequence, then tilted and eroded; later submergence allowed deposition of the upper series, after which the area was lifted above sea level and the present drainage system was developed. The area represented is several miles square.

movement causes uplift and erosion of sedimentary beds, any later series of strata deposited above them is *unconformable* with them (Fig. 244). The *unconformity* of one group of rocks with another is evidence of a definite succession of events and therefore is a significant part of the geologic record.

The most conspicuous unconformities result when old eroded mountain regions, with their truncated folds and steeply tilted sections of sedimentary strata, are buried by later sediments. At practically every point the edges of the older beds form a considerable angle with layers in the later series, and therefore the term *angular unconformity* is appropriate (Fig. 244). Two or more angular unconformities in the same section indicate repeated severe crustal disturbances, each followed by long-continued erosion and a later period of quiet when sediments accumulated.

On the other hand, suppose a wide shallow-sea basin is warped up almost uniformly to make a land surface. Erosion sets in, and a considerable thickness of the marine strata is stripped away over the entire area. If the sea again invades the district, new strata are deposited above the old erosion surface, and a later upwarping, with consequent cutting of stream valleys, brings to view the older as well as the younger rocks (Fig. 245). Since the older strata suffered no appreciable tilting they are essentially parallel with the beds above them; but the two series are separated by the old buried erosion surface. The unconformity between the two

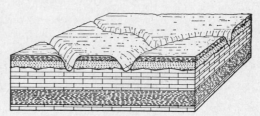

Fig. 245. — Disconformity between two series of formations. No tilting has occurred; but the lower series was uplifted uniformly and eroded before deposition of the upper strata. Compare Fig. 244.

groups of strata is important, because it represents crustal movement of wide extent and a long time interval during which no sedimentary record was being formed in the region, while part of the earlier record was being destroyed. However, this type of unconformity is not as conspicuous as an angular unconformity, which attracts attention at once by the divergence of beds above and below. In view of this striking difference, the special name *disconformity* is applied to an unconformity that is not characterized by any angular divergence between the two groups of strata.

It is difficult to recognize some disconformities, particularly if the same type of rock lies above and below. This is true in parts of the Mississippi Valley, where Paleozoic limestones deposited during several periods are almost as flat as the old sea floor on which they were formed. Geologists have learned to recognize and date the different formations by careful study of the fossils contained in them. In some sections exposed in quarries or in natural cliffs it can be stated confidently that a particular layer is many millions of years younger than the layer directly beneath it, although the two are parallel and superficially much alike. Conditions were exceptional during the Paleozoic era in what is now the Mississippi Valley. During long geologic periods shallow seas covered much of the region between the present Appalachians and Rocky Mountains.

Since land was far distant, only limy deposits accumulated on much of the sea floor. Slow warping movements made the sea now shallower, now deeper, and large tracts lay for a time above sea level, but so low that very little was eroded from the surface and no hill-and-valley topography could be formed. Other tracts were covered with water so shallow that the breaking of the waves on the bottom prevented any permanent deposition for long intervals of time. When enough deepening finally occurred to permit renewed sedimentation, the new strata were limestones, much like those directly beneath. In this way several important but inconspicuous disconformities were developed.

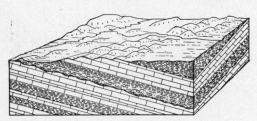

Fig. 246. — Disconformity between two series of strata, both series tilted together. A large part of the upper series was destroyed by stream erosion in developing the present surface. Compare Fig. 245.

Most disconformities can be traced without much difficulty. As a rule, the erosion surface on which the younger strata are laid down is decidedly irregular, and can be detected as it cuts across beds (Fig. 245). Moreover, the sediments deposited on the old surface usually are quite different in character from the rocks beneath, as explained in a later paragraph.

A distinguishing characteristic of disconformities is the parallelism of the younger and older strata; it is not essential that the beds shall be horizontal or undeformed. Commonly there has been disturbance, either slight or severe, at some time after the younger formation was deposited. Since both groups of beds are deformed together they remain parallel (Fig. 246).

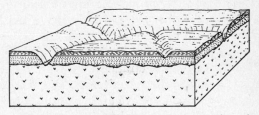

Fig. 247. — Unconformity made by erosion of granite bedrock and later deposition of sedimentary strata on the irregular surface.

Unconformities Involving Non-Sedimentary Rocks. — Although the conception of unconformity is inseparable from sedimentary processes, the old surface on which strata are unconformably laid may be developed on rocks of any kind. Granite and other massive igneous rocks, as well as metamorphic rocks of all kinds, have been bared by erosion in wide areas and later covered with sediments (Fig. 247). The contact is a surface of unconformity if the sediments were deposited on it. If the contact between rock masses of unlike character is due to faulting or to igneous intrusion, however, the term unconformity does not apply.

Common Features of Unconformities. — Since every unconformity involves some degree of erosion before deposition of the younger sedimentary series, the surface at the base of this series is more or less irregular. If the old land surface on which deposition began was hilly, the buried hills and valleys can be recognized provided the unconformity is well exposed. Generally the old lands were worn down to low relief before any permanent deposits were formed. If the unconformity represents invasion of the land by the sea, it is probable that submergence occurred very slowly and wave action near the advancing shoreline had opportunity to plane down the most prominent irregularities. If the sediments on the surface of unconformity are ordinary stream deposits, probably the old land had been reduced by streams to a peneplane, because most sediments laid down on a high, rugged land mass are swept away by continued erosion. Exceptions are the deposits in basins of interior drainage, which accumulate until they bury hills and mountain ranges (p. 79). Through changes in climate or important shifts in drainage some ancient basin deposits of this kind have become deeply dissected, and the extremely irregular contact between the sediments and the rugged old surface is exposed (Fig. 64). Tributaries of the Colorado River have exhumed old buried mountain topography of this sort in southern Nevada.

Usually the sediments deposited on a surface of unconformity are distinctly different in character from any sedimentary formations beneath. Whenever the sea invades the land every part of the submerged area is passed over by the advancing shore zone, with its characteristic deposits of pebbles and coarse sand (p. 232; Fig. 174). As a common result a *basal conglomerate*, composed in part of the beach materials, lies directly above the old land surface.

Whether the first sediments above an unconformity were deposited by the sea or by streams, some pebbles in the lowest layer had their source in the rocks on which the deposits rest. The presence in a conglomerate of pebbles obviously derived from granite beneath proves clearly that the granite is older than the overlying strata and therefore was not intruded into them.

Unconformities and Earth History. — A study of unconformities emphasizes the close relationship between crustal movements, erosion, and sedimentation. The lands are being worn down and sediments are accumulating continuously. But slowly the scenes shift. Folding or faulting in a geosynclinal basin, or upwarping at the edge of a continent, brings to light the strata built up during former ages. At once the forces of erosion attack the strata of shale, sandstone, and limestone, and in the act of destroying them reveal the record they contain. In the deeply incised stream valleys we see angular unconformities that testify to severe folding in remote geologic periods, or widespread disconformities that indicate ancient upwarping of large areas. As erosion bares these secrets the streams carry away the detritus and deposit it, perhaps on a land surface recently submerged. Thus construction in one place supplements destruction in another; the whole complex record shows the constant struggle between deep-seated forces that produce the major relief features, and processes at the surface that strive to keep the lands featureless and low.

READING REFERENCES

1. Field Geology; by Frederic H. Lahee. 3rd edition. 700 pages. McGraw-Hill Book Co., New York, 1930.

Gives excellent descriptions of structural features, with particular emphasis on types of structure that affect economic geological work.

2. Geologic Structures; by Bailey Willis and Robin Willis. 2nd edition. 496 pages. McGraw-Hill Book Company, New York, 1929.

3. Earth Movements in the Great Lakes Region; by G. K. Gilbert. 18th Annual Report, U. S. Geological Survey, Part II, pp. 601–647, 1896–97.

Gives the evidence for post-glacial tilting in the vicinity of the Great Lakes.

4. The Geology of the Netherlands East Indies; by H. A. Brouwer. 160 pages. Macmillan, New York, 1925.

Describes features that give striking evidence of deformation in late geologic time.

CHAPTER XIII

EARTHQUAKES

NATURE AND ORIGIN

Sensitive modern instruments distributed widely on all the continents show that the outer part of the Earth trembles almost constantly. Most of the tremors are not perceptible to our senses, although they are recorded instrumentally; many of them are caused by various activities at the Earth's surface, such as the ebb and flow of the tides, changes in atmospheric pressure, the rush of traffic on city streets, and the tumbling of streams over high falls. But numerous tremors, both powerful and weak, are the result of disturbances within the body of the Earth itself, and logically are called *earthquakes*.

Human Interest of Earthquakes. — The scientific value of earthquake study lies in the large amount of information it yields concerning the interior of the Earth. It is difficult, however, to consider earthquakes apart from their relation to human affairs. From the earliest recorded times the recurrent shaking of the ground, with consequent destruction on the surface, has been a cause of terror to man. Repeatedly, in numerous localities, populous communities have suffered great loss of life and property. Destructive earthquakes recorded during the brief span of human history are numbered by thousands. Geologic evidence indicates that violent shocks have been recurrent throughout the history of the Earth; and there is every reason to expect their frequent occurrence in the future.

The serious aspect of earthquakes from the human viewpoint is realized on review of some major catastrophes. On September 1, 1923, more than 140,000 lives were lost as a result of the Tokyo earthquake, and the estimated property loss was nearly $3,000,000,000. The shocks at Messina in 1908 and at Kansu, China, in 1920 were equally disastrous to life. According to report, more than a million and a half persons were killed in China by ten shocks between the eleventh and twentieth centuries; and Mallet, a profound student of earthquakes, estimated that for the whole Earth at least 13,000,000 lives were lost through destructive shocks in the course of 4000 years. Although activities of man himself, such as the waging of war and the operation of automobiles, result in a much higher death rate, nevertheless earth-

327

quakes are especially productive of fear, probably in part because they come without warning, and in part because their cause is more or less mysterious. Study of Earth shocks from a geologic standpoint has dispelled a part of the mystery. This study is *seismology* (from the Greek *seismos*, earthquake).

Causes of Earthquakes. — An earthquake is a trembling or undulatory motion in the elastic rock shell of the Earth, communicated to it by sudden jarring of some kind, just as a bell is set in vibration by a smart tap on its side. The jarring impulse evidently is the immediate cause of the earthquake; but what is the origin of such disturbances? Ancient philosophers tried to answer this question, but their speculations were without scientific basis. Aristotle taught that subterranean cavities are filled with air which in its struggles to escape causes the ground to shake. Lucretius, in his *De Rerum Natura*, made a shrewder guess in assuming roof-collapse in vast caverns as one of the primary causes. Probably some local shocks have originated in this way in karst regions like Dalmatia and parts of Kentucky (p. 101).

It is well established that some earthquakes are associated with volcanic activity. The violent outbursts of Krakatoa in 1883 (p. 254) and of Bandaisan (Japan) in 1888 were attended by shocks that were severe locally; but most earthquakes of this class are of low intensity and affect limited areas. Moreover many outbursts are not attended by any shocks, or at best are accompanied by only feeble tremblings, such as occurred during the eruption of Mont Pelée in 1902. For a long time it was thought that volcanic action was an important source of earthquakes, and this idea still appeals to popular fancy; but careful comparison of the two phenomena, especially in Japan, has shown that there is no necessary connection in occurrence between heavy earthquakes and volcanic eruptions. Instruments near Kilauea, in Hawaii, record frequent minor tremors — sometimes hundreds of them in a single month. Very few of these are accompanied by visible volcanic activity, although it is probable that shifting of magma at some depth is the principal cause of the local shocks.

Crustal Movements the Chief Cause. — There is strong evidence that most of the major earthquakes result from sudden yielding to strain in the Earth's crust, either by formation of a new fracture or by abrupt displacement along the walls of an already existent fault (p. 312). In many areas visited by disastrous shocks the surface of the ground has been broken along fault lines and the amount of displacement is clearly indicated. Commonly these movements take place along old fault zones which bear the marks of repeated displacement. In California a great fracture zone can be followed almost continuously, by means of its peculiar surface expression, from the southern part of the state northwestward for 600 miles. This feature, known as the San Andreas rift, passes near the city of San Francisco (Fig. 248). On April 18, 1906, abrupt movement along at least 270 miles of this fracture caused a destructive earthquake. The length of this break is somewhat exceptional among recorded earth movements; but similar breaks 25 to 50 miles long are not uncommon.

A careful study along the San Andreas rift, after the rupture in 1906, yielded valuable information on the nature and amount of the displacement. In general no scarp was made by the faulting, because the motion was almost entirely horizontal, parallel with the fault (Fig. 249). This fact was established beyond question by the offsetting of roads, fences, and other features that extended across the break. Some roads were cut cleanly across, and offset considerably more than their width (Fig. 250). The largest measured displacement was 21 feet. More commonly a part of the motion on a break of this kind

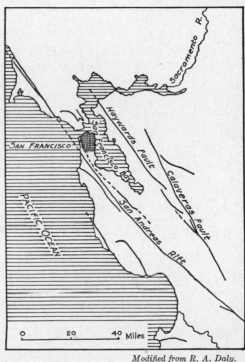

Modified from R. A. Daly.

Fig. 248. — San Andreas rift and other active faults in the vicinity of San Francisco, California.

is vertical and results in a steep scarp (Fig. 228). The great Yakutat Bay (Alaska) earthquake in 1899 resulted from an abrupt vertical displacement that lifted part of the coast nearly 50 feet and made new falls in some of the streams (Fig. 251).

If it is considered that the walls of a fault are pressed closely together, that movement is possible only by overcoming great frictional resistance, and that the displacement, once it occurs, takes place almost instantaneously, it is not surprising that powerful vibration is set up in the vicinity of the fault line. The exact nature of movement along the San Andreas rift was made the subject of special study, and it was concluded that mass-movement in the crust on opposite sides of the fault

G. K. Gilbert, U. S. Geol. Survey.

Fig. 249. — Trace of the fault concerned in the California earthquake of 1906. The thick mantle above the bedrock broke irregularly. As the movement along the fault was horizontal, no scarp was formed at this locality.

G. K. Gilbert, U. S. Geol. Survey.

Fig. 250. — Horizontal displacement of a road by movement on the San Andreas rift in 1906. Before the earthquake the two offset portions of the road were in a straight line. The fault extends from left to right, directly across the road.

was in slow progress for years before 1906. Deformation in the rock was by bending, until the strain could be borne no longer and relief occurred by *elastic rebound* along the old fracture (Fig. 252). According to this view the sudden movement of 1906 was confined to a comparatively narrow belt closely adjacent to the fault, and did not involve

W. W. Atwood, U. S. Geol. Survey.

Fig. 251. — New waterfall made by vertical displacement on a fault responsible for a great Alaskan earthquake.

the immediate shifting of great segments of the crust. The distorted rocks along the fault straightened with the abruptness of the springing of a steel trap; energy that had been accumulating for decades was released in an instant, striking the Earth a sharp blow that made it tremble. Vertical displacement on a fault is supposed to occur by similar elastic rebound after slow bending (Fig. 253).

It is not to be supposed that a visible fault appears in every area visited by an earthquake. Commonly the direct evidence of crustal movement is wanting, especially in connection with mild or moderate shocks. It is believed that actual displacement occurs very frequently at considerable depth and does not reach to the surface. This is a

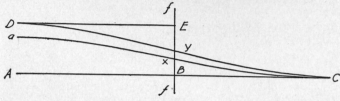

After A. C. Lawson.

Fig. 252. — Illustration of the elastic rebound theory of earthquakes. Sketch map of an area in the vicinity of the San Andreas rift (*f–f*). *ABC*, position of a line (say a fence) directly after the earthquake of 1868, when strain was relieved by movement on the fault; *axC*, position of the line several years later, when the rocks had been deformed by accumulating strain; *DyC*, position of the line immediately before the movement of 1906; *DE*, *BC*, the two separated portions of the line after slipping occurred on the fault, allowing *Dy* and *yC* to straighten. *C* is a stationary point outside the zone of movement.

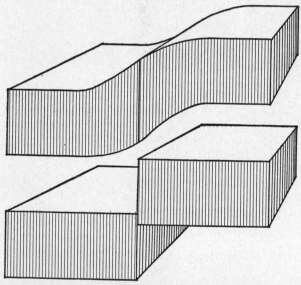

Fig. 253. — A segment of the crust showing elastic rebound from vertical strain, with the formation of a fault scarp. The upper block shows bending (greatly exaggerated) by accumulating strain before movement; the lower block represents the displacement after the elastic rocks have sprung into a position of no strain.

logical inference, since every break must be limited in extent, vertically as well as horizontally. Earthquakes of the first rank, however, are in a general way restricted to regions of active faulting, for which there is evidence at the surface. Many major shocks originate under the sea, and in some places soundings made after such an earthquake have demonstrated that the sea floor was displaced by faulting at the time of the shock.   Transoceanic cables have been broken by abrupt displacement of the floor athwart their courses.

Intensity of Earthquakes. — Earthquakes vary in strength from minute tremors to the irresistible shocks that cause major human disasters.   In order to compare the effects of different shocks, and the results of the same shock in different places, an arbitrary scale of intensity has been adopted; on this scale earthquakes are classified from I to X in increasing order of strength.

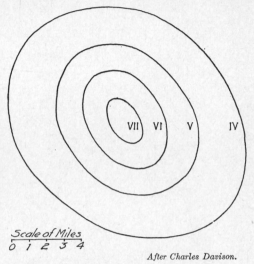

Scale of Miles
0 1 2 3 4

After Charles Davison.

Fig. 254. — Isoseismal map of an earthquake in England.

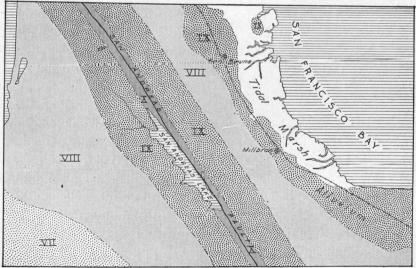

California Earthquake Commission.

Fig. 255. — Zones of intensity in the lower part of the San Francisco peninsula, for the earthquake of 1906.   Roman numerals indicate degrees of intensity in the belts concerned (see p. 333).   The highest intensity was restricted to a narrow belt on each side of the fault, and in general there was a gradual decrease on both sides; but the belt of alluvium near the Bay caused abnormal intensity.   Since there are no dwellings or other works of man on the tidal marsh, the intensity in that area is not known.

A shock of intensity I is hardly noticed even by an experienced observer, but is recorded by delicate instruments; one of intensity V is felt by nearly everyone awake, disturbs furniture in houses, and rings church bells; intensity as high as VIII is required to throw down chimneys and crack the walls of brick or stone buildings; intensity X causes widespread destruction of buildings and disturbance of the ground.

Fig. 256. — Seismic areas in the Western Hemisphere on S. L. Penfield's stereographic projection. (Compare Fig. 198.)

By the use of such a scale a region affected by an earthquake is divided into intensity zones, and the lines separating adjacent zones are called *isoseismals*. Ideally they inclose nearly circular or elliptical belts around the area of highest intensity (Fig. 254); but for an earthquake caused by slipping on a long fault, like the California earthquake of 1906, the isoseismals define narrow belts that are nearly straight for long distances (Fig. 255). Differences in the nature of the bedrock and also the irregular distribution of deep alluvium cause pronounced local irregularities in isoseismal maps (Fig. 255).

DISTRIBUTION

Seismic Belts. — Although earthquakes occur in all parts of the world, those that occur on land are concentrated in certain well-defined tracts, most of which lie in two great *seismic belts.* One of these follows the western coast of North and South America, the Aleutian Islands, and the island groups along the eastern coast of Asia such as Japan and the

Fig. 257. — Seismic areas in the Eastern Hemisphere on S. L. Penfield's stereographic projection. (Compare Fig. 197.)

Philippines, and thus borders the Pacific Ocean on the east, north, and west. The other includes the Mediterranean, the Alps, the Caucasus, and the Himalayas, and continues into the East Indies, where it intersects the first belt (Figs. 256 and 257). In a general way these zones coincide with the great volcanic belts (p. 273); and this fact might appear to support the idea that volcanoes are an important cause of earthquakes. However, since the belts correspond closely to young mountain systems and other marks of recent crustal movement, it is probable that earthquakes and volcanoes have a common cause in this disturbance of the crust. It is a notable fact that where the seismic belts lie directly along the continental borders, as on the coast of Chile and the eastern coast of Japan, the edge of the continental mass descends sharply, without any broad intervening shelf, to great depths. Some of these steep slopes descend into *foredeeps* (Fig. 2), which are great troughs that appear to be sinking while the bordering lands are rising. We conclude that these are zones of weakness in the Earth's crust where strains are being constantly relieved by movements, and in which therefore earthquakes are continually recurring.

It is commonly thought that certain regions are practically exempt from danger of earthquakes because no real disaster has happened in them since they have been settled and cities have sprung up within them. It is true that most of the Atlantic coasts, and large areas in continental interiors, are relatively free from earthquakes. The comparative stability around the Atlantic as compared with the Pacific is emphasized not only by the historical record, but by the existence of a wide continental shelf, which is in strong contrast with the deep water near the Pacific coasts. However, the experiences of the central Mississippi Valley in 1811 and of Charleston (South Carolina) in 1886 are a warning that no locality may be entirely exempt. Even in New England, which is not recognized as a seismic tract, there has been an average of one perceptible tremor a year since the settlement of the country. Probably none of these shocks has been of maximum intensity, although at least one, in 1755, was of intensity VIII.

Submarine Shocks. — The location of seismic belts near the margins of continents suggests that many earthquakes are of submarine origin. Their occurrence beneath the sea is shown directly by shocks communicated to vessels on the surface above, and by rupturing of submarine cables. Since the invention of sensitive instruments by which it is now possible to record distant earthquakes and determine their location, it has been learned that the majority of all earthquakes occur on the floor of the Pacific. The most conspicuous mark of a submarine earthquake is the huge wave that commonly is generated in the sea by disturbance of the floor. Such waves have long been known as "tidal waves," a misleading name since they have no connection with the tides. They are now generally known to seismologists by their Japanese name, *tsunamis*; they are also called seismic sea waves. Some are of immense size, measuring 100 or even 200 miles from crest to crest, and as much as 40 feet in height. They are so broad that in the open sea they are not ordinarily perceived; but on approaching a coast those of large size pile up in huge breakers and, sweeping far inland, cause enormous damage and loss of life.

Lisbon in 1755, Japan in 1703 and 1896, and Peru in 1868, suffered from great and disastrous tsunamis. The number of victims of a single inundation of this kind has been as great as 100,000. These vast waves are felt over whole oceans and move with tremendous speeds, ranging from 300 to 500 miles per hour. Some that originated near Japan have crossed the Pacific in about 12 hours. At such distances their height may be only a few inches; but they ebb and flow like small tides in periods of 15 to 30 minutes, and these variations are registered as undulatory lines on the record of a tidal gauge (Fig. 258).

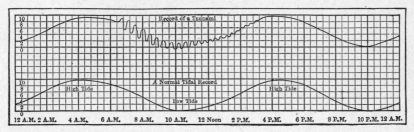

Fig. 258. — Records by a tidal gauge. The lower curve shows the normal succession of high and low tide; in the upper curve the rapid oscillations due to a tsunami are superposed on the tidal record. Vertical lines represent time spacing on the paper, driven horizontally by clockwork. Horizontal lines show heights in feet as recorded by the rising and falling pencil of the gauge.

SEISMOLOGY

Transmission of Earthquake Vibrations. — It is important that we distinguish clearly between cause and effect in earthquake phenomena. The displacements shown in Figs. 250 and 251 are not, as is commonly supposed, the *results* of earthquakes; they represent the *causes*. The effect of the sudden movement along a fault is to set up vibrations that move outward from that place, as circular waves spread out from the position at which a stone strikes the surface of a pond. Thus the earthquake is propagated as a series of waves in the highly elastic body of the Earth. In the passage of these waves the particles of bedrock usually are displaced only a fraction of an inch, even near the origin of the shock; but loose objects on the surface may be thrown several feet by the impulse. This effect is illustrated in miniature by placing a pebble or similar object on a board floor and striking the floor a sharp blow with a hammer; the pebble can be made to leap several inches although the floor in transmitting the impulse does not move perceptibly.

Oscillation of the ground during an earthquake reaches a maximum in deep alluvium that is saturated with water. At San Francisco the devastation was most acute on the low alluvial flat near the bay; well-constructed buildings on bedrock, even much nearer the fault, suffered less damage. At Messina, in 1908, there was an even more striking correlation between maximum destruction and alluvial ground (Fig. 259). The contrast in behavior of the deep alluvium and of bedrock may be illustrated by striking sharply a bowl in which there is jelly. The bowl is set vibrating with resulting sound, but actual motion in the walls of the vessel is imperceptible. However, the same impulse transmitted to the jelly sets up longer waves that are visible. Excessive destruction in wet alluvium is caused by this larger wave motion as compared with the behavior of solid rock. Some observers at Charles-

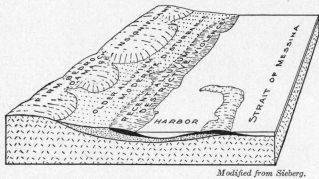

Modified from Sieberg.

Fig. 259. — Correspondence between belts of intensity and geologic formations at Messina, Italy, in 1908.

ton, South Carolina, during the destructive earthquake of 1886, reported that they saw the ground rise and sink with the swift passage of large swells.

If the origin of an earthquake were at a single point at some depth below the surface, the wave impulse would move out in all directions and each wave front would be spherical; the impulse would first reach the surface at a point vertically above the origin, and the surface area affected would grow from this point in an ever-enlarging circle. At one time this simple conception of earthquakes was commonly held. The supposed point of origin was called the *focus* or *centrum*, and the point directly above it on the surface the *epicenter*. On an ideal isoseismal map (p. 334) the epicenter is at the exact center, for according to the original conception the isoseismal lines should be exact circles, the intensity dying out uniformly away from the point directly above the focus. Usually, however, even where no indication of faulting is visible at the surface, the isoseismals are roughly elliptical, suggesting that the vibrations at the surface started along a line of some length instead of from a point. Not uncommonly, also, in a region visited at frequent intervals by earthquakes the different epicenters are situated along a line; such a line probably represents a fracture at some distance below the surface.

The terms focus and epicenter still have value in the study of earthquakes, although it should be understood that they are not points. The necessity for modifying the older views is evident when we consider the great length of the fracture on which slipping occurred to cause the San Francisco earthquake. Initial vibrations started along the entire surface of this fault, over a length of at least 270 miles and reaching from the surface to an unknown depth. Isoseismal belts for such an earthquake are extremely elongate.

The general position of the epicenter of a strong earthquake is indicated also by the directions in which objects on the ground are displaced by the shock. At the epicenter the force acts directly upward; in other positions the vibrations emerge obliquely and tend to throw objects away from the epicenter, although monuments and similar objects, from having their bases thrust outward, commonly fall *toward* the center of the disturbance. Therefore the positions of pillars and chimneys that have been thrown down by an earthquake furnish important information.

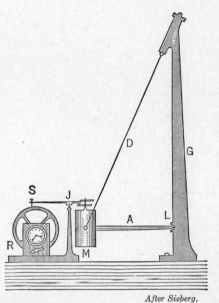

After Sieberg.

Fig. 260. — Diagrammatic representation of a seismograph. The upright post (G) and the recording device (R, J) are attached firmly to a pier mounted on bedrock. The heavy weight (above M) is connected with the post (G) only by a freely moving joint (L) and a flexible wire (D). Records are made by the stylus (S, J) on a revolving drum (R), which is driven by clockwork.

Seismographs and Seismograms. — *Seismographs* are precise and sensitive instruments that record all phases of an earthquake, even at a great distance, with the exact time of each phase. The general principle used in constructing a common type of such instrument is simple. A heavy mass of metal suspended like a pendulum has considerable inertia and so tends to remain at rest while the bedrock beneath it vibrates from the effects of an earthquake. A pencil or stylus is pivoted on a frame attached firmly to a pier mounted on bedrock (Fig. 260). One end of the pencil is attached by a free-moving joint to the heavy weight; the other end has a point resting on paper, which is mounted on a drum revolved slowly by clockwork. Ordinarily the pencil point remains at rest and traces a straight line on the moving paper; but when the bedrock is set in vibration by an earthquake the frame on which the pencil is pivoted moves from side to side, the heavy weight holds one end of the pencil stationary, and the point is carried back and forth, making a sinuous line. This line is the earthquake record, or *seismogram* (Fig. 261). Instead of a pencil some instruments have a small mirror that throws a beam of light upon a sheet of photographic paper; the seismogram is revealed only after the sensitized paper is

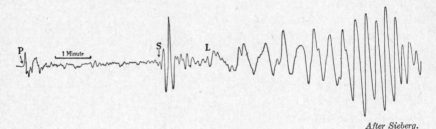

After Sieberg.

Fig. 261. — Record made at Pulkovo, Russia, of an earthquake in Asia Minor. *P* is the beginning of the primary waves; *S*, of the secondary waves; *L*, of the long waves, which make the most conspicuous part of the seismogram. The time elapsed between *P* and *S* was 3 minutes and 43 seconds, corresponding to a distance of 1400 miles between the station and the epicentral area.

developed. All modern instruments have a device that marks time intervals on the moving paper, so that each phase of the movement is timed closely, usually to the nearest second.

The recording of earthquake tremors thousands of miles from the epicenter testifies not only to the sensitiveness of the modern seismograph but also to the high elasticity of the Earth. Seismographs are now widely distributed on all continents, and every major earthquake is recorded in practically every civilized country in the world.

Interpretation of Seismograms. — The study of seismograms of distant earthquakes has led to the discovery that the main shock is preceded by smaller rapid vibrations known as the *preliminary tremors*. Thus a normal seismogram has the characters seen in Fig. 261. It has been determined that these preliminary tremors represent elastic impulses that come *through the Earth,* in the general direction of a chord from the seat of disturbance to the recording station; whereas the later large vibrations represent those waves that have traveled by a longer route around the circumference. The first preliminary tremors (*P* to *S*, Fig. 261) are caused by a compressional or longitudinal wave (commonly known as the *primary*), which travels several miles per second; the other preliminary set (S to L, Fig. 261) represents a transverse wave motion (the *secondary* wave), which travels at about half the speed of the primary. Therefore the time interval between the two sets of preliminary tremors is proportional to the distance traversed, and from this information the distance between the seat of the shock and the seismograph can be calculated accurately. If the distances from at least three separate stations are computed and circles are drawn on a

map with these distances as radii, the circles intersect in the epicentral area (Fig. 262). Most seismograms record a succession of vibrations following the first long waves. Some of these later phases represent recurrent after-shocks, and others are due to complex reflected and refracted wave motions in the Earth.

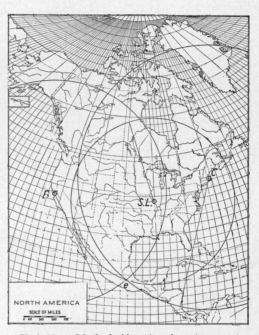

In the last few years, with the improvement of seismographs and the establishment of many new stations, it has been discovered that seismograms furnish important information about the inaccessible interior of the Earth. This aspect of seismology is discussed in Chapter XV.

Fig. 262. — Method of locating the epicenter of an earthquake from records at three stations. At Berkeley, California (B), St. Louis, Missouri ($S.L.$), and Cambridge, Massachusetts (C), the distance is found from the relation of P and S on the seismogram (Fig. 261). Using the distances as radii, circles drawn about the stations intersect in southern Mexico, at the epicenter, e.

Possibility of Predicting Earthquakes. — Will the science of seismology be so perfected that eventually we shall be able to predict accurately the occurrence of earthquakes in particular areas? This possibility has been suggested, but probably there will always be too many unknown and variable factors to permit this kind of forecasting with any certainty. The problem has been studied seriously for the San Andreas rift in California. Close attention was focused on this fault after the earthquake of 1906, and it is now evident that recurrent slipping has been in progress along the great fracture for a long time. In 1868 a displacement similar to that of 1906 caused a severe earthquake. During the intervening 38 years the area was free from heavy shocks; but presumably strain was accumulating by slow mass-movement, as suggested in Fig. 252, until slipping on the fault again brought relief. Careful surveys since 1906 demonstrate that points on both sides of the fault are slowly changing their positions, and therefore it is highly probable that strain is again building up, to be relieved by a future jarring displacement. Can the date of this event be fixed?

Any hope of solving such a problem must depend on precise surveys, made at frequent intervals of time, to determine the rate at which points in the region of the fault are being shifted by the growing strain. Aside from the large expense of making such measurements the problem involves many difficulties. Although we know the amount of displacement that occurred in 1906 along various parts of the fault, the few measurements made before that date give little information as to the exact positions occupied by critical points outside the fault zone before slipping took place; therefore we do not as yet have any dependable standard by which to decide how much deformation of the region is necessary before slipping must occur. We do not know the form of the fault surface underground; if it is somewhat irregular, possibly the movement of 1906 caused changes that will make necessary either more or less strain to cause additional slipping. There is no assurance that the forces causing the deformation now act in exactly the same direction as before 1906. Moreover, there are other active faults in the same general region, and possibly slipping along one or more of these will ease the strain near the San Andreas rift sufficiently to postpone movement on it for considerable time.

By analyzing all the information available, one seismologist estimates that another displacement along the San Andreas rift may be expected near the middle of the present century. However, he emphasizes the elements of uncertainty, which may either double or cut in half the average time interval between successive movements. Even such a conditional forecast as this has value, since it warns inhabitants of a threatened area to take every possible precaution in preparation for a shock that is sure to occur in the future.

In many other regions the problem of earthquake prediction is vastly more difficult than in California. The crustal movements responsible for the Tokyo earthquake of 1923 occurred chiefly under the sea, where no careful check by surveys is possible. Forecasting of shocks in such areas must depend on careful earthquake records over a long period of years, and perhaps on the recognition of minor warning tremors that may herald a major displacement on a fault.

Precautions Against Earthquakes

Man can not control the forces in the Earth's crust, but within limits he can protect himself against their destructive effects. Well-constructed buildings with steel frames stood the test remarkably well in Tokyo and in San Francisco. Masonry walls without reinforcement are badly damaged by severe shaking. Tough, resilient materials that yield to strain without breaking stand most successfully, and therefore frame dwellings survive a heavy shock much more successfully than those made of brick. It is important, however, to have all buildings as nearly fireproof as possible, since fires from broken electrical connections and from other sources are an incidental effect of every large earthquake. Commonly the water mains are broken when a severe shock affects a large city, and the uncontrolled fires do vastly more damage than the earthquake itself. City engineers in seismic areas are giving special attention to safeguarding water systems. The problem is particularly difficult wherever it is necessary for the mains to cross active faults.

Geologic Effects of Earthquakes

Although earthquakes are impressive in their display of power, they play a minor geologic rôle in comparison with running water and other agents whose work is continuous but as a rule not spectacular. One of the most conspicuous effects of earthquakes is the starting of landslides in mountains or hilly regions. Several large slides of this kind were formed near Tokyo in 1923; and in 1920 the great earthquake in Kansu, China, set in motion enormous quantities of loess, which buried villages and caused important changes in surface drainage.

Earthquake waves cause alternate compression and tension in the rock or alluvium through which they pass. The resulting disturbance causes changes in underground drainage; some old springs stop flowing, others have their volume increased, and new springs come into existence. Tensional impulses of the earthquake waves open deep fissures in soil or other mantle, and the impulses of compression force large quantities of water to the surface at some localities. Commonly the flow is concentrated at favorable points along a fissure, with the result that rows of small craters are formed by the sand and silt brought up by the water. Saturated sand in layers far below the surface is forced up to fill crevices, and the resulting " sand dikes " remain as a record of the disturbance. Small dikes of sandstone cutting across shale in old sedimentary rocks may have been formed by ancient earthquakes, although no doubt the pressure responsible for such features originates in various other ways also.

The effectiveness of disturbance in alluvium during an earthquake was illustrated in the region about Tokyo. Tile pipes used as lining for wells were forced out of the ground until they resembled chimneys several feet high. In one rice field where no obstructions existed the farmers found after the earthquake rows of wooden posts projecting three feet or more (Fig. 263); presumably they are piles used in a bridge

N. Yamasaki.

Fig. 263. — Wooden piles, probably hundreds of years old, thrust above the surface of a field during the Japanese earthquake of 1923.

built hundreds of years ago and buried to an unknown depth by flood-plain silt as the stream channel migrated to another position.

The most important geologic changes at the time of an earthquake are the vertical or horizontal movements of crustal blocks; but it must be emphasized again that such movements are the cause and not the effect of the shocks.

READING REFERENCES

1. Our Mobile Earth; by R. A. Daly. 342 pages. Charles Scribner's Sons, New York, 1926.

Chapters I and II give an excellent discussion of earthquakes and their cause. The style is vigorous and stimulating. Numerous excellent illustrations.

2. A Manual of Seismology; by Charles Davison. 249 pages. Cambridge University Press, 1921.

A clear presentation of principles and methods in earthquake study.

3. Report on the California Earthquake of April 18, 1906; by A. C. Lawson and others. 451 pages. Publication No. 87, Carnegie Institution of Washington, Vol. 1 and Atlas, 1908.

A full account of the San Francisco earthquake, with a description of the great San Andreas fault. Numerous excellent photographs and maps.

4. The Japanese Earthquake of 1923; by Charles Davison. 124 pages. Thomas Murby and Co., London, 1931.

Gives vivid descriptions of the earthquake, with a full scientific discussion.

CHAPTER XIV

METAMORPHISM

Metamorphism the Result of Adjustment to Environment. — In many places rocks occur that obviously are neither sedimentary nor igneous. They make up the third great group of rocks — the *metamorphic*. Metamorphic means *transformed*, and the term expresses the fact that such rocks are the results of the transformation of older rocks. This transformation, or metamorphism, consists in the development of new textures or of new minerals, or of both. The typical metamorphic rock is so distinctive in appearance that it would not be suspected to be an older rock in a new guise. In places, however, thoroughly metamorphic rocks pass by imperceptible gradations into those known positively to be of sedimentary or igneous origin. The discovery of gradations of this kind and the recognition of their significance gave the clue to the mode of origin of the group as a whole and led to its being called metamorphic.

Among the most surprising discoveries brought to light by the microscope was the fact that rocks are delicately adjusted to their environment. The minerals occurring together in a given rock represent the adjustment to the environment in which the rock was formed: they were in stable equilibrium under the conditions prevailing. Under changed conditions they cease to be stable. Adjustment to the new environment tends to occur and new minerals are formed. Metamorphism accordingly is the result of this tendency of rocks to adjust themselves to their environment. The factors determining equilibrium are temperature, pressure, and composition. Change in any one of these factors therefore tends to cause internal changes in the rocks, to promote metamorphism. Take for example a sedimentary rock. It was formed at the ordinary temperatures and pressures prevailing at the Earth's surface. If it becomes involved in crustal folding, it may become deeply depressed in the crust, miles below the surface. It is then in a greatly different environment, one in which temperatures and pressures are far higher. Many of the minerals are unstable under the changed conditions and react with others present to form new minerals that are stable. As a result a wholly new rock is formed.

Metamorphic rocks are formed not only from sedimentary and igneous rocks, as has long been recognized, but also as a result of the metamorphism of older metamorphic rocks.   The full implication of the great principle that metamorphic rocks are the products of adjustment to environment, which was formulated as long ago as 1889, is becoming apparent only today.   We are beginning to recognize that if a metamorphic rock, representing as it does an adjustment to one set of conditions, is brought into a new geologic environment, it will be metamorphosed again.   In fact, it may undergo as many metamorphisms as the number of times it is subjected to changes of environment.   In regions such as the Alps, where strong crustal revolutions have recurred, the same rocks have been repeatedly metamorphosed.

FACTORS OF METAMORPHISM

Temperature is one of the most powerful factors, if not the most powerful factor, in causing metamorphism.   Rise of temperature speeds up chemical reactions, and at higher temperatures reactions occur that can not take place at lower temperatures.   For every aggregate of minerals there is a minimum temperature that must be reached before reaction between them begins and new minerals can form.   The theoretical explanation is that the atoms must attain a certain amplitude of vibration before they can change places with others.

Temperature is also highly effective in increasing the plasticity of minerals, thereby increasing the deformability of the rocks in which they occur.

Pressure is another important factor in metamorphism.   Its rôle is at least threefold.   Ice can be used to illustrate some of the functions of pressure in metamorphism.   A block of ice dropped on a pavement breaks into innumerable fragments;   we say the ice is highly brittle.   But ice confined in a steel jacket, which is fitted with a piston, can be made to flow through an orifice in the jacket.   Ice thus subjected to a differential heavy pressure is no longer brittle but has become plastic.   The counterpart of this in nature is the flowing ice beneath the carapace of brittle ice composing the upper portion of a glacier.   In the same way rock salt, brittle at ordinary pressure, becomes plastic under differential heavy pressure, as experimentally determined.   This property of rock salt to flow plastically has recently been confirmed by the astounding discovery of salt "glaciers" in the rainless region of Persia.   Calcite, the principal mineral of limestone and marble, also has been made to flow plastically.   Brittle and plastic are relative terms, and it is regarded as probable that all minerals, under heavy enough differential pressure slowly applied, flow by plastic deformation.   Another function of pressure is to crush, mash, or " pulverize " minerals which, because of insufficient confining pressure or too rapid deformation, do not flow plastically.

If new minerals are being formed in a rock undergoing metamorphism, heavy pressure favors the development of those minerals which contain the most matter in the least space, in other words, heavy or dense minerals. Pressure thus tends to favor the formation of space-saving minerals. Metamorphic rocks formed under great pressure are therefore characterized by their high specific gravity.

Composition is the third variable factor in metamorphism. Inasmuch as metamorphic rocks are formed from igneous, sedimentary, and preëxisting metamorphic rocks, there must be from this cause alone an extraordinary diversity of metamorphic products.

KINDS OF METAMORPHISM

Contact Metamorphism. — The rocks bordering an intrusive igneous mass generally show notable changes from the normal condition they have at some distance from the igneous mass. These effects are produced chiefly by the heat supplied by the magma and the hot gases that issued from it when it solidified. The changes are of course strongest at the immediate contact with the igneous mass and fade out away from it; hence metamorphism of this kind is termed *contact metamorphism*; but the term igneous metamorphism has the advantage of emphasizing the agency that produces the changes. The most obvious form of contact metamorphism, probably the most impressive because coming more nearly within the ken of ordinary experience, is a coal bed that has been converted into a layer of coke by a sill injected just above or below it.

As an illustration of metamorphic phenomena, contact metamorphism is particularly enlightening. In the simpler cases we see the effects of one factor of metamorphism, heat, uncomplicated by the effects of other factors. Moreover, the transition from the highly metamorphic product to the raw material can as a rule be easily traced. We are thus able to ascertain which new minerals form at moderate temperatures and which require high temperatures and so we can provide ourselves with a scale for measuring the intensity of metamorphism.

Dynamic Metamorphism. — Metamorphism has occurred commonly, but by no means invariably, as an accompaniment of dislocations of the Earth's crust. As a result of folding, strata are thinned in the limbs of the folds and thickened in the arches, and this process under some conditions causes metamorphism.

Rocks adjacent to certain great thrust faults have been profoundly metamorphosed. As metamorphism of this kind is accompanied by tearing, stretching, and mashing of the original elements in the rock, such as deforming the round pebbles of a conglomerate into long pencils, all of which activities give vivid evidence of the work of enormously powerful forces in motion, this metamorphism is termed *dynamic metamorphism*.

Load Metamorphism. — Some metamorphic rocks appear to have been formed without the intervention either of igneous masses or of dynamic metamorphism. Here the cause of the metamorphism was apparently that the rocks were formerly deeply buried, having become depressed in the crust under a heavy load of overlying rocks. The increased temperature brought about by the deep subsidence has caused the development of new minerals and textures, and the heavy pressure due to the load favored the production of heavy minerals, such as garnet, which is a space-conserving mineral. As the Earth's own heat is the main factor here in transforming the rocks, the process is sometimes called geothermal metamorphism.

The best-established example of metamorphism of this kind is furnished by the German potassium-salt deposits. These salts were laid down in an evaporating arm of the sea in Permian time; they were of many kinds and of complex compositions, but they were stable under the conditions of moderate temperature that prevailed when the sea was evaporating. Later the basin in which they were deposited slowly subsided and they became covered by 20,000 feet of sedimentary beds. The temperature of the deeply buried salt beds rose to that determined by their depth in the crust. The rise of temperature was about 200° C. The complex assemblage of salts was no longer in adjustment with its environment: drastic rearrangement in the composition of the salts then took place and many new minerals were formed.

Coal is another substance peculiarly sensitive to load metamorphism. Its rank (p. 440) increases with depth; for every hundred feet of depth its fixed carbon content, which serves to measure its rank, increases 0.6 per cent.

Silicate rocks are far less sensitive to load metamorphism than coal and the minerals of the marine salt deposits. Nevertheless, certain formations of pre-Cambrian age are believed to have acquired their metamorphic state by load metamorphism. In places also the bottoms of synclines or synclinoria have become so deeply downfolded that the rocks thus deeply depressed in the crust have been subjected to load metamorphism.

There is this vital difference between the effect of dynamic metamorphism and that of load metamorphism: dynamic metamorphism deforms and obliterates the original textures and structures of rocks, whereas load metamorphism allows original structures to persist unscathed; for example, such sedimentary structures as cross-bedding and ripple-marking are beautifully preserved in some high-rank metamorphic rocks. Such preservation indicates that during the process conditions were static, not *dynamic*. There are other differences, such as that dynamic metamorphism tends to vary abruptly in intensity within short distances, whereas load metamorphism produces effects of uniform intensity over wide tracts; its effects, as we now see them exposed by erosion, are of regional extent.

We recognize, then, three kinds of metamorphism: contact, dynamic, and load. Nature is too complex to be bound by any hard and fast lines, however. Contact metamorphism has gone on in some regions concomitantly with crustal folding; for example, during the intrusion of a concordant batholith which, as we recall, is emplaced concomitantly with the folding of rocks it invades. However, we shall omit the description of these complex phenomena and devote our attention chiefly to the simpler forms of metamorphism.

Contact Metamorphism

The effects of contact metamorphism are essentially restricted to rocks into which igneous masses have been intruded. Every intrusive body — dike, sill, volcanic neck, laccolith, stock, and batholith — is bordered by rocks more or less strongly altered. Lava flows, however, at most slightly bake the soils or rocks on which they rest.

The most noticeable effect of igneous intrusion, especially in sedimentary rocks, is the baked and hardened condition of the rocks in the zone adjoining the intrusive igneous mass. Because the intensity of these changes diminishes and fades out with distance from the intrusive mass, the contact-metamorphic zone is sometimes called somewhat figuratively a contact *aureole*.

Width of the Contact-Metamorphic Zone. — The width of the contact zone depends on a number of factors: on the size of the igneous mass, on the susceptibility of the rocks in contact with the igneous mass, and on other conditions. The widest zones surround stocks and batholiths. Around some of them the contact zone attains a width of a mile or more, but generally it is a few hundreds of yards wide. Adjacent to small intrusive masses, such as narrow dikes and sills, it ranges from a few inches to a few feet.

The width of the contact zone around any one igneous mass may vary, for it is controlled by the configuration of the igneous body and by the attitude of the surrounding rocks. Thus in Fig. 264, which shows an igneous mass intrusive into a series of horizontal beds, the width of the contact zone as exposed at the surface is smallest on the side of the stock where the contact plunges steeply downward and is widest where the contact surface has the smallest inclination; the variable width of the contact zone on the Earth's surface is thus purely a geometric effect, for the thickness of the zone, measured perpendicularly to the contact surface, is everywhere the same. On the other hand the attitude of the surrounding beds — whether they dip toward or away from the intrusive mass — affects the actual width of the aureole, because heat is transmitted

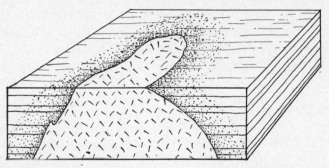

Fig. 264. — Stock, partly uncovered by erosion, intrusive into horizontal strata. Shows that the width of the contact aureole as measured on the Earth's surface depends on the dip of the contact surface. The scale of the diagram is roughly 3 miles to the inch.

more readily along the strike of the beds than across their strike, both by conduction and by emanations traveling through them. (Fig. 179.)

Contact Metamorphism of Rocks of Different Kinds. — The influence exerted by an igneous mass on its surroundings depends greatly on the nature of the rocks invaded. On pure sandstone the effect is rather small, though near the contact the sandstone is changed into quartzite — a compact rock so firmly cemented that it fractures across the grains, instead of around them as in the unaltered sandstone. Limestones are strikingly changed: many a dull, somber-colored aphanitic limestone is transformed to a sparkling snow-white marble visibly crystalline to the unaided eye. Manifestly the heat of the igneous mass has stimulated the growth of the calcite grains and has driven off the carbonaceous pigment. Shales show notable effects. The soft shales are greatly hardened, and near the contact they are converted into a rock known as *hornfels*, which to the unaided eye strongly resembles a black flint or a fine-grained igneous rock, such as basalt.

Coarse-grained igneous rocks, being the products of magmatic solidification and therefore having already been at high temperatures, are generally but little affected by later intrusions. A granite intruded by a younger granite remains unaffected. However, where volcanic rocks, such as basalts, have been invaded by plutonic rocks, extensive and drastic metamorphism has occurred. The conditions under which volcanic rocks form differ so markedly from those under which plutonic rocks form that when volcanic rocks are intruded by plutonic rocks far-reaching changes are necessary for adjustment to the new environment.

Highly interesting results are produced in limestones containing sandy or clayey impurities. They are turned into marbles carrying a great variety of newly formed minerals. These minerals are the results of reactions between the impurities and the calcite of the limestone, reactions that can take place only at high temperatures. Thus when a limestone containing silica as an impurity is heated above 500° C., the silica tends to drive out carbon dioxide according to the equation

$$CaCO_3 + SiO_2 = CaSiO_3 + CO_2$$

and the calcite is changed into calcium silicate, which forms the metamorphic mineral *wollastonite*. If the limestone contains dolomite, then the following reaction can occur:

$$CaMg(CO_3)_2 + 2\ SiO_2 = CaMg(SiO_3)_2 + 2\ CO_2$$

and a pyroxene is formed, and carbon dioxide liberated.

The pyroxene thus formed occurs in the inner, hotter portion of the aureole, whereas an analogous compound, a white amphibole (tremolite) is formed in the outer, cooler portion of the aureole; consequently these two minerals can be made to serve in a rough way as geologic thermometers in measuring the temperatures at which metamorphism is effected.

If other impurities occur in the limestone, such as clay furnishing alumina and iron oxides, many other new minerals can be formed.

Normal and Pneumatolytic Contact Metamorphism. — As a rule, the effects produced in the contact-metamorphic zones are chiefly due to the heat given off by the igneous mass: the surrounding rocks become highly heated and new minerals grow in them by recombination of the elements already present. Consequently the chemical composition of the resultant metamorphic rocks remains the same as that of the rocks from which they were derived. A marble, for example, has the same chemical composition as the limestone from which it was formed. Contact metamorphism of this kind in which the rocks remain unchanged in chemical composition is by far the most common type of alteration surrounding intrusive igneous masses; it forms continuous aureoles around stocks and batholiths, and, as these zones may be a mile or so wide, large volumes of metamorphic rock are produced. Because of its general prevalence it is termed *normal* contact metamorphism.

If, however, the igneous mass during its solidification gives off gases that carry iron, silicon, boron, and other elements, vastly different results are produced in limestones, because of the readiness with which limestones react with the gases released from the magma. Many new minerals are formed, as a rule beautifully crystallized. The resulting contact-metamorphic rock differs greatly in composition from the original rock: substances have been added in large amount by the gases that streamed from the magma. As a rule, the gases escape by way of fissures into the surrounding rocks, and the effects produced by the gases are localized along these channel-ways. Consequently, metamorphism of this kind does not produce a continuous aureole surrounding the igneous mass, such as is characteristic of normal contact metamorphism. As gases are the means by which the substances are transferred from magma to the surrounding limestone and cause the reactions in the limestone, contact metamorphism of this kind is termed *pneumatolytic* (Greek *pneuma*, wind, air). If the magmatic gases contain iron, copper, or tungsten in notable quantity, valuable ore deposits are formed in the limestones as incidental by-products of metamorphism of this kind. In working such deposits, an understanding of the laws of contact metamorphism becomes of prime importance.

Crystalline Schists

In addition to the rocks of contact-metamorphic origin, there is an immensely larger group of metamorphic rocks formed by the processes of dynamic and load metamorphism. We lack a good distinctive designation for this great group, and for want of a better name they are called the *crystalline schists*, in virtue of two characteristic features that most of them have: their obviously crystalline appearance and their *foliated* or *schistose* texture.

Foliation. — Most metamorphic rocks are visibly crystalline to the unaided eye, that is, the individual mineral grains that make up the rock can be discerned by the unaided eye; and these minerals are arranged in parallel orientation. This parallel arrangement of the minerals was termed by Charles Darwin *foliation* (from *folium*, a leaf); and rocks having it are known as *foliates*, a term that might well supplant " crystalline schists." A foliate tends to split more or less readily into flakes, leaves, or thin slabs parallel to the foliation. A coarsely foliated rock is called a *gneiss*, and one in which the foliation is well developed and closely spaced is termed a *schist* (Latin *schistus*, that which can be split).

There is no boundary between gneisses and schists: a complete transition from coarsely foliated to finely foliated rocks occurs in nature, and from schists this transition continues with decreasing grain size to the microcrystalline foliates called *phyllites*, and from phyllites it continues to *slates*, whose foliation is so perfect that they can be split into an indefinite number of thin plates.

Mode of Occurrence. — Crystalline schists are widely distributed over the Earth, and in places they are the only rocks exposed throughout large regions. Such regionally extended tracts of metamorphic rocks were formerly said to be due to *regional metamorphism*, but inasmuch as that term explains nothing it is becoming obsolete. Its chief merit is its noncommittal character; it leaves open the question whether the metamorphism is due to igneous, dynamic, or geothermal activity, or to combinations of these activities.

Crystalline schists are particularly abundant in the most ancient (pre-Cambrian) formations the world over. In the United States they occur throughout New England, in the Adirondacks, and in a belt extending from New York to Alabama. New York, Philadelphia, Baltimore, and Washington are built on crystalline schists. Metamorphic rocks of this kind are well shown in the inner gorge of the Grand Canyon of the Colorado, and in many other places.

Crystalline schists occur also in the cores of many mountain ranges, where they have become exposed by erosion. The structure of these mountain ranges, as is discussed in Chapter XVI, includes folded strata, and the degree of metamorphism of the rocks is proportional to the closeness and intricacy of the folding. In other ranges, however, strata just as closely and intricately folded have not been metamorphosed. Hence intricacy of folding does not of itself cause metamorphism. The depth at which the folding takes place within the crust and the speed with which it occurs are probably the controlling factors. A relatively rapid rate of folding would generate the heat necessary to bring about metamorphism.

Folding and metamorphism are so commonly related that, where we find rocks closely folded and highly metamorphic, we infer that highlands once existed but have been eroded away, or, in general, that metamorphic rocks are exposed to view only as a result of deep erosion. In conformity with this idea, crystalline schists are regarded as of *continental origin*, because they imply (if of sedimentary derivation) the following sequence of events: erosion of a land mass to supply sediment; the deposition of this sediment in a thick series of beds in a geosyncline; the folding of the beds to effect metamorphism, perhaps with the incidental making of a mountain range; and lastly, renewed erosion to expose the metamorphic rocks. Such a succession of events implies large-scale operations and can therefore occur only in the continents or continental shelves; consequently the occurrence of metamorphic rocks in place on Fiji, New Caledonia, South Georgia, and other islands, is held to prove that these islands are really detached fragments of the continents, which have been separated from the nearest continental mass by the subsidence of the former connecting land masses.

Mylonites. — In places where great slices of the crust have been shoved over the underlying rocks, as in the thrust faults described on p. 318, the rocks near the fault surfaces show signs of great mechanical disturbance. Along some of the great thrusts the rocks are reduced to

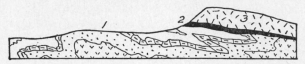

Fig. 265. — Zone of mylonite (*2*) formed by frictional drag as the result of the thrusting of the granite mass (*3*) over the underlying rocks (*1*).

unrecognizability. The constituent minerals are mashed, pulverized, and dragged out; as a result a streaky or banded, compact, flinty rock is produced, termed a *mylonite*, from the Greek *mylon*, a mill, expressive of the fact that the rock has been through the metamorphic mill. The terms mashing and pulverizing, although calling emphatic attention to the most striking feature of mylonitization, namely the production of an extremely large number of minute grains at the expense of the original grains in the rocks mylonitized, are somewhat misleading, because the mylonites do not lose their coherence or strength.

Rocks as strong as granite have been reduced to mylonites (Fig. 265); and were the transition from mylonite to undamaged granite not traceable in the field, the origin of the mylonite would remain enigmatic, so utterly different is the mylonite from the granite from which it is derived. Belts of granite mylonite as much as 3000 feet thick are reported to occur in Corsica.

Mylonites are the results of intense mechanical metamorphism: they are the finest examples of pure dynamic metamorphism, uncomplicated by the growth of new minerals. However, there are transitions from such purely mechanically deformed rocks to those in which some new minerals have developed, and finally to those in which all the minerals are of new growth and all evidence of the milling through which the rock went has disappeared. Such transitional varieties are supports to the theory that many foliates are of dynamo-metamorphic origin.

Slate. — Slates are foliates of such fine-grained texture that their constituent mineral grains can not be distinguished by the unaided eye.

Their most distinctive feature is their capacity to split or cleave into thin sheets. This property, the well-known *slaty cleavage*, reaches its acme in roofing slates, which cleave into almost indefinitely thin parallel sheets. Such remarkable cleavage is described as plane-parallel.

Slates are metamorphic rocks of the lowest rank. Some indeed — the clay slates — are argillaceous sediments that have merely assumed a slaty cleavage, whereas others — the mica slates — have not only acquired the slaty cleavage but have been reorganized by the growth of new minerals in them, most commonly white mica in ultra-fine scales. Thus the mica slates represent a stage of progressive metamorphism one step higher than that of the clay slates. On the one hand slates grade into shales and on the other they grade into phyllites. They can be regarded as metamorphic rocks arrested in the stage of incipient metamorphism.

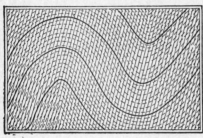

L. V. Pirsson.

Fig. 266. — Slaty cleavage (represented by the nearly vertical lines) cutting across the bedding of folded beds.

Slaty Cleavage. — The cleavage of folded strata that have been converted into slate is parallel to the axial planes of the folds (Fig. 266 and Fig. 267). As a result the cleavage cuts across the bedding of the slate in the arches and troughs of the folds and tends to become parallel to the bedding in the limbs of the folds. The closer the folds have been pressed together the closer the parallelism of bedding and cleavage becomes in the limbs of the folds.

The trend of the cleavage in a slate district maintains a constant direction. Unless keen discrimination is used, slaty cleavage can easily be mistaken for bedding; and if the cleavage is thus misinterpreted, the inferred geologic structure of the area in which the slate occurs will be in error.

The cause of the remarkable plane-parallel cleavage of slates is revealed by the microscope: it is the result of the parallel orientation of innumerable minute flakes of micaceous minerals. These flakes, consisting mainly of white mica and chlorite, have an excellent cleavage parallel to their flat directions; and the cleavage of the slate is therefore chiefly due to the marked capacity of these minerals to cleave.

Why these minerals have this strict parallel orientation in slates is another problem, and it can not yet be said to have been solved. From the facts that most slates occur in folded strata and that the fossils they happened to contain are distorted it is clear that pressure was a factor in developing the cleavage. Any flaky minerals present in the original sediment would tend to rotate so that their broad surfaces would be perpendicular to the pressure, and any new minerals that formed would grow perpendicular to the pressure. The direction of this pressure that caused the minerals to become oriented is probably that of the resultant of two pressures: the pressure that caused the folding and the vertical pressure due to the load under which the strata were being folded.

E. B. Harden

Fig. 267. — Slaty cleavage cutting across synclinally folded beds. Slatington, Pennsylvania.

Phyllites. — Phyllites are foliates that are intermediate between slates and schists. Those at the low-rank end of the sequence resemble slates, but their constituent mica is coarser, which gives them a glossy, silky luster. Some phyllites contain scattered through them prominent crystals, such as garnet, which are sure indices of the higher metamorphic rank of phyllites and clearly distinguish them from slates. The phyllites that form the higher-rank end of the series between slate and schist resemble schists but are finer in texture.

Schists. — Schists are the most abundant members of the great class of " crystalline schists." They are visibly crystalline to the unaided eye. Their foliation is thinly spaced, but it has lost the plane-parallel character of the foliation of the slates. The far greater grain-size of the minerals that make up the schists causes the foliation surfaces to be uneven and more or less rough. Foliation of this kind is called *schistosity*. Schists occur in great variety and are named according to their most distinctive constituent. Thus we have mica, hornblende, and chlorite schists, to name only some of the commonest varieties.

Mica schist is the most typical of the schists. Its essential minerals are quartz and mica, and the mica gives the schist its distinctive character. Different varieties of mica occur; the most common is a silvery white muscovite, which gives the rock a brilliantly spangled appearance, and the black mica — biotite — also is common. The micas are in irregular flakes with their cleavage planes oriented in the direction of the schistosity, and it is this parallel arrangement of the micas that

P. J. Holmquist.

Fig. 268. — Folded gneisses with intercalated layers of limestone (brilliantly white). Near Stockholm, Sweden.

produces the well-developed foliation of mica schist. Some mica schists contain prominent well-formed crystals of garnet, staurolite, and other minerals, which give the schists a texture simulating the porphyritic texture of igneous rocks.

Mica schists are rocks that have attained a high-rank metamorphic condition. The original material from which most of them were derived was an argillaceous sedimentary rock — a shale of some kind — and the transformation of the dull, amorphous substance of the shale to a brilliantly spangled mica schist is in a way as remarkable as the metamorphosis of a chrysalis into a beautiful butterfly.

Gneisses. — Gneisses are coarse-grained foliates. Many gneisses have a streaky or banded appearance, owing to the alternation of bands of unlike mineral composition. Some gneisses formed by the metamorphism of sedimentary rocks have inherited remarkably even regular banding or layers, as shown in Fig. 268.

Gneiss is one of the most common of metamorphic rocks, and its many varieties were formed under very diverse conditions: some under conditions of mild dynamic metamorphism in which the minerals were merely mechanically deformed, and others under conditions of most intense metamorphism, in which the mineral composition has been wholly reconstituted. Fig. 269 shows a gneiss derived from a granite by dynamic metamorphism. The granite was subjected to differential heavy pressure; the feldspars were partly crushed, the quartz was " pulverized," and the biotite dragged out into long streamers: the result is a gneiss of strongly marked characters. Many gneisses, however, are high-rank

Fig. 269. — Granite gneiss, the result of moderately strong dynamic metamorphism. Hoadley Point, Connecticut.

metamorphic rocks and are characterized by containing minerals formed at high temperatures and pressures, such as garnet and pyroxene.

Some granite gneisses are called *primary gneisses*, because their foliation was assumed while they were still only partly solidified magmas. If a granite magma is forced to flow after the biotite has begun to crystallize from it, the biotite takes on a uniform orientation, just as logs in a stream take on a common orientation. A batholith that became emplaced during crustal folding generally has a border of primary gneiss whose foliation faithfully follows all the sinuosities of the contact. Such primary gneisses resemble gneisses of metamorphic origin, but can readily be discriminated from them by field and microscopic work.

Quartzite. — Quartzite is a rock composed of quartz grains so firmly cemented that fracture takes place through the grains, instead of around them. Originally the rock was a sandstone, but has been changed to a quartzite (1) by filling the pore space of the original sandstone through the deposition of quartz from circulating ground water, or (2) by contact metamorphism, or (3) by load or dynamic metamorphism. Quartzites formed as the result of the deposition of a quartz cement by ground water are not regarded as metamorphic rocks.

Quartzites of load or dynamo-metamorphic origin are commonly interbedded with gneisses and mica schists. The original pore space in the sandstone has been eliminated mainly by compaction and rearrangement of the quartz already present in the rock. Although quartzites of this origin are intimately associated with foliated rocks, they themselves rarely show foliation.

Quartzites are generally compact hard rocks of light colors — white, gray, reddish, or buff — and are likely to be of vitreous appearance. Such vitreous quartzites are the most durable and resistant of all rocks; and wherever they occur in notable thickness they strongly influence the development of the topography by their resistance to weathering and erosion.

Marble. — Marble is the metamorphic equivalent of the sedimentary carbonate rocks, limestone and dolomite. During metamorphism the minute grains of which the limestone or dolomite is composed grow in size, with the result that they become visibly crystalline to the unaided eye. The resulting marble is harder and more compact through reduction of pore space, and it has purer colors. Some marbles take a good polish. Such visibly crystalline carbonate rocks are termed marbles in geologic usage, but in commercial practice any carbonate rock that will take a polish is called a marble and is given a trade name.

Most marbles are massive, showing no foliation even if they are subjected to great pressure. As rocks go, marble is highly plastic and flows under moderate differential pressure. If, for example, a dike or a bed of schist is inclosed in marble that is forced to flow under differential pressure, the dike or the bed, being brittle, ruptures and is torn apart, and the marble flows in between the dissevered fragments. Marble that has thus flowed is an impressive feature of many regions of metamorphic rocks.

Pure marble is white, and the mottling, banding, and colors shown by ornamental varieties are due to impurities: the red and yellow tones to oxides of iron, the grays and blacks to minor amounts of organic matter. Besides being produced by dynamic metamorphism, marble is also formed by contact metamorphism.

Retrogressive Metamorphism

Metamorphic rocks, such as the series beginning with slate and comprising phyllite, mica schist, and garnet gneiss, represent stages in progressive metamorphism. All these rocks are of identical chemical composition, but they are of greatly different mineral composition and physical appearance. Each succeeding rock in the series is the product of higher-rank metamorphism than the one that precedes it, chiefly as the result of adjustment to conditions of progressively higher temperature.

A rock that has become adjusted to the condition of highest metamorphic intensity may at some later time, however, be shifted into a new geologic environment, in which the conditions of stability are those of low-rank metamorphic intensity. A garnet gneiss, for example, may be reduced to a phyllite along the base of a great overthrust block of the Earth's crust. Outwardly the resulting phyllite resembles a phyllite formed by progressive metamorphism, but internally, as revealed by the microscope, it still retains evidence that it was once a high-rank metamorphic rock. The high-rank garnet gneiss has retrograded to the low-rank phyllite. By such *retrogressive metamorphism* many varieties of metamorphic rocks have been formed from other metamorphic rocks. By this process the already astonishing diversity of metamorphic rocks is greatly increased.

The concept of retrogressive metamorphism was first formulated to account for certain metamorphic phenomena seen in the Alps. Later research has shown that many schists and phyllites in the Alps and elsewhere thought to be of normal origin, *i.e.*, the results of progressive metamorphism, are in reality the products of retrogressive metamorphism. This new interpretation, as we can now see, is a logical extension of the fundamental principle of metamorphism that rocks tend to adjust themselves to their environment.

READING REFERENCES

1. The Principles of Petrology; by G. W. Tyrrell. 349 pages. E. P. Dutton and Company, New York, 1927.
Part III of this volume gives the only modern presentation in English of the difficult subject of metamorphism.
2. Metamorphic Geology; by C. K. Leith and W. J. Mead. 337 pages. Henry Holt and Company, New York, 1915.

CHAPTER XV

THE EARTH'S INTERIOR

Knowledge gained by study of the rocks at the Earth's surface impels man to speculate about the hidden interior. The materials and conditions that exist at great depth can never be known by direct observation. Openings in the crust, such as mines and deep wells, are extremely superficial in comparison with the long radius of the globe. We infer that some of the rocks now exposed in the cores of old mountains were at a depth of several miles before erosion laid them bare; but even so they were always a part of the " outer shell," and we can not be sure of their exact nature while they were under the relatively light load that has been removed in the course of long ages. If it were possible to make and maintain an opening to the center of the Earth, or to look down with a sort of super X-ray, what would be revealed? Does the composition of material change radically with depth, so that a large part of the interior bears little or no resemblance to the superficial rocks? What is the temperature at various levels? Is any large part of the interior in a liquid condition? How do the materials at great depths behave under the enormous overburden? These are profound questions. They are not prompted by idle curiosity merely; they represent the goal of scientific investigations whose attainment would make clear many of the phenomena seen at the Earth's surface.

Whenever direct evidence is not available, science turns to the indirect and circumstantial. It is possible, with aid of this sort, to draw certain inferences that are sound; but if we seek to advance farther into the unknown we must be content with hypothesis and speculation. Some suggestions can be accepted as probabilities, with the understanding that they may be found wanting after further investigation. It is well, at the outset, to state clearly the actual basis of fact and to outline the methods of attacking the problem. In this way we shall avoid misconceptions and be able to evaluate each suggestion on its merits.

INFORMATION AND METHODS

Size and Shape of the Earth. — The science of *geodesy*, which is concerned with exact measurement and mapping of the Earth's surface, has determined with precision the dimensions and the form of the globe.

This information, obtained by great labor through coöperation of scientific men in many countries, is of fundamental importance in problems relating to the Earth as a whole. It is known that the equatorial diameter exceeds the length of the polar axis by nearly 27 miles. As this figure is about $\frac{1}{297}$ of the diameter, it is stated that the *ellipticity* of the Earth is $\frac{1}{297}$. This departure of the globe from a true sphere is largely a response to rotation. Important inferences are drawn from this known distortion of the Earth, considered with relation to other facts.

Gravity and Density. — By precise physical experiments we determine the *constant of gravitation*; the method involves essentially the measuring of the force with which the Earth attracts a body of known mass. The result gives the total weight of the Earth, and since its size also is known, it is a simple matter to compute the average density. This value, arrived at by many experimenters, is 5.52; that is, an average sample of the Earth weighs five and a half times as much as an equal volume of water.

Direct determinations of density, using rocks of all kinds known at the surface, give an average value of 2.7. As this is less than half the density of the whole Earth, the interior must consist of much heavier material than the outer part. Other inferences are discussed in a later paragraph.

Relation between Density and Form. — In detail, the surface of the Earth is highly irregular. Continents stand well above deep-sea floors; plateaus, mountains, and deep troughs make irregularities of smaller order (p. 5). On a small globe made to true scale these surface features appear insignificant; but in actual dimensions some of them are large, and from a human viewpoint the irregularity is of the utmost importance since without it the sea would be world-wide.

Theoretically the surface of the Earth would be quite smooth if the material below the surface were uniform in its character. In reality we know that the rocks exposed to observation differ considerably in composition and in density. Basalt and other dark-colored igneous rocks are notably heavier than granite. By geologic investigation and by highly technical instrumental determinations a strong probability has been established that the rocks underlying the deep sea are in general denser than those composing the continental masses. Moreover it is concluded from careful geodetic study that the great mountain ranges of the Earth are composed of and underlain by material that is slightly deficient in density compared with the crust as a whole. These facts suggest that the larger surface irregularities are not haphazard, but have a fundamental cause; that large differences in surface elevation reflect differences in the density of the underlying rocks. Many important inferences and some theories are based on this relationship.   These matters are discussed in a later part of the chapter.

Behavior Toward the Moon and Sun. — The Moon and the Sun exert a constant pull on the Earth, and yielding of the oceanic waters to this pull gives rise to the tides.   By careful and ingenious experiments it has been determined that the body of the Earth also responds to the tidal force, but the yielding is very minute — about what would be expected if the Earth were composed of the strongest steel.

Another effect is produced by solar and lunar attraction on the equatorial bulge of the Earth, causing the globe to wabble slowly as it spins. Consequently the north pole of the heavens shifts slowly from year to year.   This effect, called precession, is known precisely, and the forces involved can be calculated closely.   The use of this information is discussed below.

Response of the Earth to Seismic Waves. — The most reliable information about the Earth's interior is furnished by study of earthquake waves (p. 340).   Vibrations that are transmitted through the body of the Earth and recorded by seismographs at varying distances from an earthquake focus reveal the elastic properties at different depths.   This is a most promising field of study, and undoubtedly many important revelations will be made through continued researches in seismology. At present the most significant facts resulting from the study are the following.

(1) The so-called *long* waves, which move around the Earth in the rocks directly beneath the surface (p. 340), travel at a higher speed through the deep-sea floors than through the continental masses.   For example, a seismographic record received in Japan of an earthquake in California shows a higher speed for the long waves than a record of the same shock received in New York.   We conclude that granite, the predominant kind of rock in the continental masses, does not form the deep-sea floors.[1]   This conclusion is also reached independently from geologic evidence, which suggests strongly that basalt and similar dark, heavy rocks predominate under the deep seas (p. 363).

(2) Both the primary and the secondary waves traveling through the Earth (p. 340) increase in speed with increasing depth of the path, down to a depth of about 1800 miles.   Thus in Fig. 270, the primary and secondary waves that reach stations *a* and *b* travel more rapidly than those received at *g* and *h*, which in turn move at a higher average speed than those that travel at a smaller depth.   The rate of increase is shown in the following partial table.

[1] The same kind of evidence suggests that the floors of the Atlantic and Pacific oceans differ somewhat in composition.

Distance of Receiving Station from Earthquake Focus, in Degrees	Velocity, in Miles per Second	
	Primary Wave	Secondary Wave
30°	5.4	3.0
60°	6.8	3.7
90°	7.9	4.3

The principal cause of more efficient transmission at greater depth is compression by gravity, which increases the rigidity and consequently the elasticity of the material. It is highly significant that the secondary or distortional wave is transmitted freely, since waves of this nature do not move through liquid but only through rigid substances. Thus one fact of seismology completely disproves the old notion that the Earth is molten except for a thin crust.

(3) At a depth of about 1800 miles (2900 km.) the behavior of the waves changes abruptly; the speed of the primary drops from about 8 miles to only 5 miles per second, and the secondary wave becomes very faint. Furthermore the primary wave penetrating to greater depth is refracted or bent, just as a ray of light is bent in passing from air into water (Fig. 270). As a result of these changes in the seismic waves, most stations located farther than 104° from the epicenter of an earthquake get no record of secondary vibrations; and in a belt of considerable width directly beyond the 104° limit the primary wave is lost, owing to refraction (Fig. 270). It is evident, therefore, that the Earth

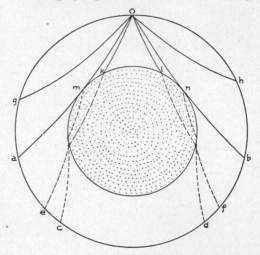

Fig. 270. — Section through the Earth, to illustrate behavior of earthquake waves, originating at O. Stations between O and a, and between O and b. receive a complete record. At stations beyond a and b (as e, c, d, f), record of the secondary wave is faint. Moreover the primary wave is refracted in its passage to these stations, as shown (Oke, Omc, Ond, Olf); as a result, a zone beyond a and another beyond b (ae and bf) receive no record of the primary wave. Waves traveling around the surface of the Earth reach all stations.

All of the waves travel by curved paths (as Og, Oh), since by going deeper, where the material is more elastic, they go through in less time than by traveling the shorter, shallower path along a chord.

For simplicity the shells outside the central core are not represented.

has a core, with a diameter of more than 4000 miles, which differs radically in composition or in state from the thick shell that surrounds it.

(4) There is strong evidence also that the thick shell itself is divided into two major parts. Although the velocity of the waves continues to increase down to 1800 miles, at a depth of 750 miles (1200 km.) there is an abrupt falling off in the rate of increase. It is probable, therefore, that the kind of material below the 750-mile level is different from that above.

(5) The central core and the change at a depth of 750 miles are detected by records of earthquakes at a great distance. " Near earthquakes " — that is, shocks that occur within a few hundred miles of the recording stations — furnish important information about the shallow zones of the Earth. In addition to the ordinary primary and secondary tremors the records of near earthquakes usually show an additional set of preliminary waves that have been refracted from a deeper zone of higher density (Fig. 271). In this evidence there is a

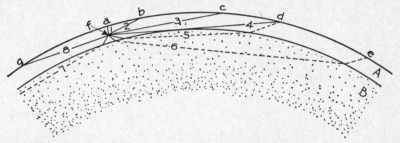

Fig. 271. — Explanation of the evidence indicating an outer shell (A) resting on a zone of denser rock (B). Waves radiating out from a shallow earthquake focus (f) follow the paths, 1, 2, 3, 4, 5, 6, etc., and reach recording stations. Station d receives the ordinary P and S waves over the route 4, and also a second pair of preliminary tremors over the route 5; this pair has been refracted down into a denser zone and refracted up again, as shown. Any station farther out than d, as e, receives only one pair of preliminary waves, which follow a refracted path (6).
Vertical scale greatly exaggerated.

definite indication that the rocks with which we are familiar at the surface form a comparatively thin shell, resting on rock of a distinctly heavier type. According to some calculations this shell is less than 10 miles thick; but values that have been obtained range up to 35 or 40 miles. These figures are not necessarily contradictory, since the shell probably varies considerably in thickness from place to place.[1]

Temperatures in the Earth. — Volcanoes and hot springs indicate high temperatures at depth locally, and direct measurements in deep

[1]Some records of near earthquakes suggest a second thin shell, of intermediate density. Possibly some of the calculations for thickness treat the two layers as one; but further evidence is required to establish the existence of the intermediate shell.

mines and wells suggest a universal increase in temperature downward. The rate of this increase varies between wide limits. In some places it is as high as 1° F. in 30 feet; in other places, as in the deep gold mines of the Transvaal, South Africa, it is only 1° F. in 250 feet. The average for all observations is about 1° F. in 60 feet. Thus in some wells that go to a depth of a mile and a half the difference in temperature between top and bottom is 125° F. or more. Mines that reach down several thousand feet are uncomfortably warm.

The determination in recent years that all known rocks contain appreciable amounts of radioactive elements, such as uranium and thorium, is of great importance (p. 278). It appears certain that these materials are not present in considerable quantities below a comparatively shallow outer zone of the Earth. Radioactive substances break down at a constant rate, and the disintegration liberates heat. Since rocks conduct heat away at an extremely slow rate, it can be calculated that the presence of uranium or thorium in minute traces, even at moderate depths, would result in permanent fusion. Granites contain higher percentages of radioactive substances than other known rocks, and hence it is argued that granites, which are the predominant rocks in the continental masses, are limited to shallow depth.

Behavior of Rocks under Pressure. — Since ordinary rocks are brittle they fracture and crush under high pressures in the laboratory unless special precautions are taken. When a rock specimen is confined on all sides and subjected to intense compression, its size decreases slightly; in other words rocks are somewhat compressible. If a marble core is fitted into a cylindrical opening in a strong steel jacket, and subjected to enormous pressure by means of steel pistons, in time the walls of the steel jacket are bulged outward. By cutting away the jacket it is found that the marble core has been shortened and thickened *but not crushed* (Fig. 272). Evidently it has *flowed* slowly, as a plastic substance. Since rocks deep in the Earth are confined under high pressure there is little doubt that under certain conditions these rocks are deformed by plastic flow (p. 347). Plasticity and rigidity are only relative terms.

INFERENCE AND HYPOTHESIS

Constitution of the Earth. — It is certain that the outer part of the Earth consists of material much lighter than the average of the Earth as a whole. Starting with this fact alone, however, several assumptions might be made as to the arrangement of light and heavy substances between the surface and the center. For example, one theory might be that light rocks, like granite, form a shell a few miles or tens of miles

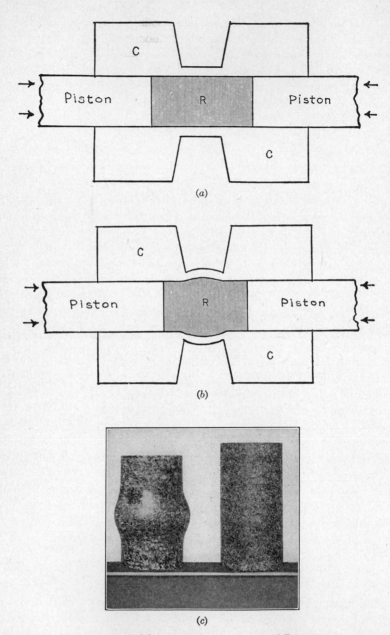

Fig. 272. — Rock flowage in laboratory test by Adams and Bancroft. (a) longitudinal section through steel cylinder (CC) with rock column (R) in place. Part of the steel wall was reduced to small thickness, as shown. (b) same after slow application of great pressure (up to more than 100,000 pounds per square inch) on the two pistons. (c) a rock column after and before the test.

thick, and that below this shell the Earth is composed of heavy substance with a uniform density of approximately 6. Again it might be assumed that from the outer zone of low density there is a gradual and progressive increase to a density of 9 or 10 at the center. By either of these arrangements the average density of 5.52 could result. Besides these two suggestions a number of other assumptions as to distribution of density might be made, all of them consistent with the known average density.

Fortunately there are other checks to guide us in attacking the problem. Any assumed distribution of the density must harmonize with the mathematical and mechanical knowledge to which reference has been made above (pp. 362 to 364) and also with the evidence from seismology. The small degree of flattening at the poles of the Earth suggests convincingly that a large percentage of the mass is concentrated in the central portion; and the same suggestion is evident from study of the precessional effect. These considerations therefore favor the inferences that density increases slowly downward in the Earth, and that the central core is composed of exceptionally heavy material.

Once this point is reached in the inquiry, another problem presents itself. Is the increase of density toward the center of the Earth due wholly to compression under enormous weight, or is there a concentration, toward the center, of metals that normally are heavy? Some students of the problem have argued that compression of ordinary rock material is a sufficient explanation. At a depth of 1 mile each square foot of rock bears a weight of 450 tons; and with each additional mile the pressure is increased by more than this amount, as the material grows progressively denser. Near the center, pressures amount to 2,000,000 or 3,000,000 tons per square foot. Without question such intense pressure has an effect in compressing the material. Since no pressures that are possible in laboratory experiments can even remotely simulate conditions deep within the Earth, we can not state positively how much compression can result. However, from various lines of evidence and reasoning it appears unlikely that ordinary rocks can be compressed sufficiently to give the high average density of the Earth. An especially significant fact is the abrupt drop, at a depth of 750 miles, in the rate at which the speed of earthquake waves increases downward (p. 366). If the entire Earth were made of ordinary rock, the speed of transmission of such waves should increase with depth at a nearly uniform rate, so long as the material remains rigid. Seismic waves testify that the Earth is rigid to a depth of 1800 miles, and therefore the material between the 750- and 1800-mile levels can not be ordinary rock. Hence it is logical to infer also that the more pronounced break indicated by seismic evidence at a depth of 1800 miles represents an abrupt change in composition. Therefore most scientists favor the view that the core of the Earth is metallic.

Which of the metals is most likely to exist in such abundance in the Earth? The most satisfactory answer to this question comes from consideration of the material that reaches us from outer space. The majority of known meteorites are composed of iron and nickel, and the others consist of dark-colored, heavy rock. Since these bodies probably were derived originally from the Sun, along with the material in the planets, it is argued that they suggest the composition of the Earth.

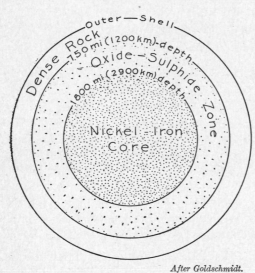

After Goldschmidt.

Fig. 273. — Section through the Earth showing the four principal zones and their inferred composition.

Accordingly it is commonly inferred that the central core, more than 4000 miles in diameter and therefore occupying more than $\frac{1}{8}$ the volume of the Earth, is composed of nickel-iron with an average density of about 8 (Fig. 273).

The sum of evidence indicates convincingly that the Earth has a "density stratification," with the heaviest material near the center and the lightest near the surface. This arrangement is the strongest reason for believing that the Earth passed through a molten stage in the early part of its history. During this stage, gravity caused most of the heavy metal to settle toward the center, and progressively lighter substances formed spherical shells between the core and the surface. A useful analogy is furnished by a smelter furnace in which metals are extracted from ore. When a large mass of ore is smelted the metal settles to the bottom of the container; directly above is a layer of sulphides and oxides which, although they are quite heavy, are distinctly lighter than the metal; and at the top is slag made of the molten rock. Reasoning from analogy it is inferred that the shell, 1050 miles thick, extending from a depth of 750 miles to the metallic core, is composed of sulphides and oxides with an average density of 5.6 (Fig. 273). This inference finds support in the presence of sulphides and oxides as common constituents of meteorites, and it explains satisfactorily the decline in the rate of increase of seismic-wave velocities below the 750-mile level.

The seismologic evidence indicates that rock extends continuously from the surface to a depth of 750 miles. Probably the greater part of this *lithosphere* consists of dark-colored rock of a type rarely seen at the surface; its density is 4 or slightly less. Above this zone is a shell, a few tens of miles thick, composed of the familiar rock types; basalt or gabbro at the bottom of the shell grades upward through diorite into the granite that forms the continental masses.

Fig. 273 shows diagrammatically this inferred constitution of the Earth. Probably the shells grade into each other, and so are not delimited as sharply as the drawing suggests. It should be kept in mind that the entire conception is a hypothesis, no part of which is subject to direct proof at present; it is merely an attempt to give a picture that is consistent with all known facts. However, the array of facts is becoming formidable, and therefore the hypothesis is infinitely more valuable than the uncontrolled guesses of the last century.

Temperatures at Depth. — The average change in temperature in the Earth for a given unit distance is known as the *geothermal gradient*. If the gradient determined in mines and bore holes should continue downward unchanged, the temperature at the center would exceed 350,000° F.; but for several reasons the average rate of change in the shallow zone can not be used with confidence for great depths. The length of the deepest opening used in estimating the gradient is less than $\frac{1}{2500}$ the Earth's radius; and the value obtained for this thin skin can not be accepted with any confidence for the whole body. Rocks such as granite are extremely poor conductors of heat. Therefore if the temperature at a depth of several miles should be high, say 1000° or 1500°, heat would flow out very slowly and the change in temperature for each 100 feet would be considerable. It is altogether likely that the heat conductivity improves with depth, both because high pressure compresses the rocks and because metallic substances, which are notably good conductors, probably grow more important in the deeper zones. Thus whatever the temperature of the deep interior, it is likely to be distributed more uniformly than in the outer shell of rocks. Therefore the gradient in the shallow zone probably is much larger than for any other part of the globe and can not be used to calculate the temperatures at great depth.

It is probable also that much of the heat conducted to the Earth's surface and lost by radiation does not come from great depth, but is generated in a shallow zone. The distribution in all known rocks of uranium and other radioactive elements has been mentioned (p. 367).

These elements disintegrate slowly but continuously, with evolution of heat. The possible significance of this process in connection with igneous activity has been discussed (p. 278).

Whatever may be the true value for the average temperature gradient, many lines of evidence suggest that temperatures in the interior are high. Probably they are above the melting-points for the materials under surface conditions; but since earthquake waves testify that no considerable part of the globe is molten in the outer 1800 miles of its radius, it is certain that heat is not great enough in this portion to cause general liquefaction under the great pressures that prevail. Locally this control by pressure may be overcome in one of two ways: by actual decrease of the pressure or by unusual concentration of heat. According to our conceptions, pressure can be relieved only at shallow or moderate depth, by local arching up of the superficial rocks or by deep fracturing. The most conceivable reason for exceptionally high temperature in the rocks is the presence of radioactive substances in unusual amount. Since these substances probably do not exist in appreciable quantities below a moderate depth (p. 367), it appears that conditions for liquefaction in the lithosphere are favorable only in a comparatively shallow outer zone. From local pockets of magma generated by any cause the surplus heat is dissipated in time, either by volcanic activity or through movement of the magma into higher and colder rocks. Thus the temperature finally is reduced below the critical point, and the rigid condition is resumed.

Until very recently the central core was thought to be fluid, because no record of the secondary waves could be detected at stations situated more than 104° from an earthquake focus (i.e., at stations beyond a and b, Fig. 270). However, sensitive modern instruments show that the secondary waves from violent earthquakes penetrate most if not all parts of the central core, indicating that the entire body of the Earth is rigid.

Isostasy, or Equilibrium in the Crust. — The Earth does not have the form of a cube or a pyramid or other angular figure, for a good mechanical reason. Rock is not indefinitely strong. Under great strain it adjusts itself to a condition of equilibrium as does any other material. If the Earth could by any means be forced momentarily into a greatly distorted shape, the laws of Nature would bring about restoration to a figure of equilibrium. This figure would be essentially a sphere if there were no rapid rotation; but the spinning on an axis makes the figure an oblate spheroid, with the degree of flattening determined by the rate of spinning.

How high can a mountain mass rise above the general surface, or how far can a " deep " lie below it? Certainly not to unlimited height or depth, for then the natural law would be violated. The strength of rock is sufficient to bear considerable strain, but there is a definite limit, as may be demonstrated by laboratory experiment. Is this limit ever exceeded in the outer part of the Earth? In geology we see the evidence that great masses of material are shifted from one part of the surface to another. Rocks are folded and crowded together by horizontal movements in mountain zones; continents and mountains are eroded, and the débris is piled along the continental margins; more than once vast quantities of water have been removed from the sea and heaped upon the continents in the form of thick ice sheets. These transfers of material tend to change the form of the spheroid, and set up great strains in the crust. Is there some mechanism for adjusting these strains?

This view of the subject is altogether deductive. There is also a more practical avenue of approach, through geodetic measurements and geologic evidence. The geodesists use two important methods of investigation. A plumb line suspended on a plain near a great mountain front

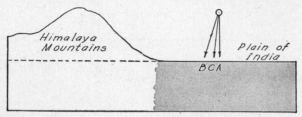

Fig. 274. — Effect of deficient density in a mountain mass. *OA* represents the true vertical; *OC* the actual position taken by a plumb line; *OB* the calculated position of the plumb line assuming rock of uniform density under mountains and plain. Angles and vertical scale much exaggerated. Shading indicates greater average density under the plain as compared with the rock beneath the mountain area.

is attracted laterally by the upstanding mass, and therefore does not point exactly toward the center of the Earth (Fig. 274). Knowing the volume of the mountain unit, and assuming that the rocks in and beneath the mountains have the average density of normal rocks at the surface, we can compute accurately the amount of lateral attraction to be expected. In actual experiments the deviation of the plumb line from the vertical is only a small fraction of the expected value; and therefore we reason that the rocks in or under the range are abnormally light. This conclusion is checked by precise measurements of gravity on the high and low areas, by the use of a delicate pendulum. The rate at which the pendulum vibrates is governed closely by the intensity of gravity, which varies at different localities with latitude, height above sea level, and other known factors. By considering these factors, geodesists can calculate closely what the value of gravity at any station should be; but for mountain stations it is found in general that the calculated values are too high. Again the result is explained by assuming that the excess *volume* of material represented by the mountains is offset by deficient *density* beneath. It is inferred, therefore, that the continental masses are approximately balanced against the deep-sea floors, and great mountain chains against adjacent low plains. The term *isostasy* (from the Greek meaning "equal standing") is used for this supposed condition.

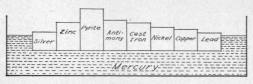

FIG. 275

A simple illustration of the principles involved in isostasy is given in Fig. 275. The different metals vary considerably in density. Therefore if blocks are taken with the same weight and cross-section, blocks of the light metals are considerably longer than those of heavy metals. All of these float in mercury, which is 13.6 times as dense as water. As the blocks have equal weight, they sink to the same depth, leaving the top surfaces at irregular heights. The longer blocks may be taken to represent mountains and plateaus; the shorter, low plains or basins. It is not to be un-

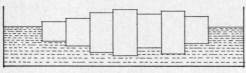

FIG. 276

Fig. 275. — Diagram to illustrate an irregular upper surface on floating blocks of differing density. The blocks are equal in cross section and in weight, and therefore sink to equal depth. This is an ideal illustration of one isostatic theory, which assumes that differences in altitude between major features of the Earth's surface are compensated by differences in density down to a certain level, below which the density is essentially uniform. (After W. Bowie.)

Fig. 276. — Copper blocks, equal in cross section but unequal in length, float in mercury. They sink to unequal depth, and also rise to unequal height. According to this conception of isostasy, a continent consists of a granite shell, essentially uniform in density but with variations in thickness. The thinner portions form low plains, whereas thicker parts project upward as plateaus and mountains.

derstood, of course, that the Earth's crust is divided into definite blocks, or that there is a liquid substratum at some depth. The illustration is highly artificial, and any attempt to press the comparison closely will result in misconception. It is intended merely to emphasize the principle of mass balance.

Fig. 275 may suggest that great differences in topography reflect large variations in kinds of rock at the surface. From geologic evidence, however, it appears that the commonest rocks everywhere in the continents are granites. Therefore it is possible that mountains represent merely a local thickening of the granitic crust. This conception is illustrated in Fig. 276, in which all the blocks are of copper, but of different lengths. Irregularities at the surface are reflected by similar inequalities reaching downward. This general arrangement applied to the Earth would satisfy the principles of isostasy as well as the conception in Fig. 275, and would accord better with geologic evidence.

Suppose now that a portion is cut from the top of one block (in either figure) and placed on another. Equilibrium is disturbed, and adjustment takes place by sinking of the loaded unit and rising of the other. In a liquid this adjustment is immediate and perfect. How can the principle apply in the Earth? We are satisfied that no continuous zone of liquid rock exists; but it is known that solid rock behaves as a plastic substance under high pressure. The laboratory proof has been mentioned (p. 367), and circumstantial evidence of rock flowage is seen in

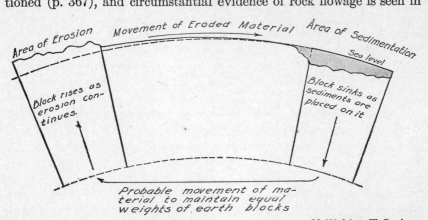

Modified from W. Bowie.

Fig. 277. — Diagram to explain the supposed mechanism by which balance is restored when load is shifted on the surface by erosion. The eroded area, at the left, continually loses weight, which is added to the low area at the right (shaded section represents sediments). In time this loaded part of the crust sinks, and forces deep-seated rock to move horizontally by slow plastic flowage. This material moves underneath the eroded "block" which rises to a position of proper balance. The plains area, across which eroded sediments are transported, suffers neither depression nor uplift. The representation is highly artificial, as there probably are no definite, freely moving "blocks" in the lithosphere.

metamorphic rocks exposed by deep erosion. It is inferred, then, that any overloaded part of the crust sinks, displacing the deep rocks by plastic flow and thus causing lighter parts of the crust to rise. The operation is much less perfect than in a liquid and of course requires a much longer time.

This inferred mechanism for preserving balance in the crust is illustrated by Fig. 277. A mountain mass is eroded deeply, and the débris is transported across an adjacent low plain, to be deposited in a marine basin. For a time the crust can bear the strain, but eventually the mountain segment becomes abnormally light through loss of mass;

the surrounding crust, and especially the part loaded by the sediments, forces deep-seated rocks to move laterally and buoy up the lightened segment. At first thought it may appear that this mechanism would make it impossible for erosion ever to wear highlands to a low level, as there would be constant rejuvenation. However, since the deep rocks are denser than those near the surface the amount of uplift can not equal the thickness of lighter rock removed; therefore mountains can finally be brought low, though only by long-continued erosion.

A striking confirmation of the isostatic theory is furnished by the areas in North America and Europe that were covered by great ice sheets during Pleistocene time. As the ice disappeared, the sea invaded much of the glaciated area, but was excluded by later uplift. Bones of whales and dolphins, and other evidences of this late submergence, are found in the region of Lake Champlain and Montreal several hundred feet above present sea level; and similar evidence is found in Scandinavia. The plain inference is that the mass of ice was an overload which depressed the land. After the load was removed some time was required for restoration of balance by slow plastic flow in the rocks at depth. Before adjustment began, the sea invaded the depressed area; and as balance was gradually restored by regional uplift the sea was expelled. Although it is thousands of years since the ice disappeared, probably the adjustment is not yet complete, as parts of Scandinavia are still rising at the rate of 2 or 3 feet in a century. Strong tilting of the Great Lakes basins in North America is ascribed to the postglacial uplift, which seems to have been greatest in southern and eastern Canada where presumably the glacial load was greatest. Frequent earthquakes of low intensity in the northeastern United States and southern Canada probably reflect slow uplift still in progress.

The general fact of isostasy appears to be established; but many uncertainties are connected with the subject. We do not know the depth at which plastic flow occurs during adjustment, though from several lines of reasoning it is argued that this depth is only a few tens of miles. The size of a load necessary to start the mechanism of adjustment is not known. These and other problems are likely to be solved by continued study.

CONCLUSION

The problems connected with the Earth's interior are fascinating but difficult. Their solution requires the coöperation of geology, physics, mathematics, and other branches of science. Perhaps some of them are quite insoluble; but a promising beginning has been made. It is well to keep in mind that some of the present views and conclusions

are tentative and may be changed by continued investigation. Speculations in this field are numerous, and these should be kept distinct
from legitimate inference and proved fact.

READING REFERENCES

1. The Earth; by Harold Jeffreys. 339 pages. Cambridge University Press,
2nd edition, 1929.
Includes chapters on seismology, isostasy, and the physical constitution of the
Earth.

2. Our Mobile Earth; by R. A. Daly. Scribner's, New York, 1926.
Chapter III (pp. 90–127) discusses evidence bearing on "The Earth's Interior."

3. On Some of the Greater Problems of Physical Geology; by Clarence E. Dutton.
Bulletin Phil. Soc. Wash., Vol. 11, 1889, pp. 51–64. Reprinted in Jour. Wash. Acad.
Sci., Vol. 15, 1925, pp. 359–369.
A classic paper, admirably written, in which the term *isostasy* was first proposed
and defined.

4. Lehrbuch der Geophysik; edited by B. Gutenberg. 993 pages. Gebrüder
Borntraeger, Berlin, 1929.
An excellent comprehensive treatment for those who read German.

CHAPTER XVI

THE ORIGIN AND HISTORY OF MOUNTAINS

Mountains are of great importance in geology, since they furnish a large part of the information on which the science is based. Dynamic processes, such as stream erosion and glaciation, are especially vigorous and their effects are strikingly evident in high ranges. The elevation of rock masses to great heights has resulted in dissection to unusual depths; and consequently a mountain region affords excellent opportunity for descriptive study of rock formations and for deciphering the history they record. But although mountains give aid in solving many problems relating to the Earth, they also present mysteries in themselves. Why have sea floors of remote periods become the lofty highlands of today? What generates the enormous forces that bend, break, and mash the rocks in mountain zones? These questions still await satisfactory answers; but the architectural features of great ranges at least offer hints as to their origin, and are worthy of study for their own sake.

MOUNTAIN UNITS

An isolated high land mass that rises above comparatively low surroundings is described simply as a *mountain*. Examples are Stone Mountain in Georgia, Mount Monadnock in New Hampshire, and Mount Etna in Sicily. No arbitrary lower limit is set to the height of features that are called mountains; in a low plains country the term is applied by the inhabitants to steep hills only 300 or 400 feet high, whereas in the Rocky Mountain region and in other rugged districts some relief features 2000 feet or more in height are known locally as hills. Thus there is some vagueness in the definition; but an essential characteristic of mountains, aside from great height, is comparatively limited width at the top. Near the mouth of the Grand Canyon, in northwestern Arizona, an observer looking eastward faces a steep, rugged escarpment 4000 feet high (Fig. 278). This precipitous rise in the land surface has a mountainous appearance; but if one climbs to the top he looks eastward for tens of miles across nearly level ground. Therefore the high escarpment is the edge of an extensive *plateau* and not a mountain front.

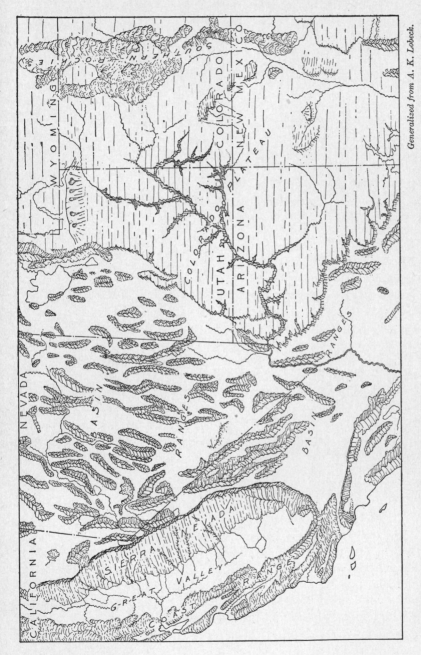

Generalized from A. K. Lobeck.

Fig. 278. — The North American cordillera in the southwestern United States. The units included at this latitude are, from east to west, the Southern Rocky Mountains, the Colorado Plateau, the Basin Range system, the Sierra Nevada, and the Coast Range.

Generally mountain masses do not stand alone but are parts of distinct units that vary in size and plan, from small irregular *groups*, like the La Sal Mountains of Utah and the Adirondack Mountains of northern New York, to the enormous belt that extends more or less regularly from Gibraltar eastward across Europe and Asia to the East Indies. Descriptions of the larger units or their parts employ somewhat loosely the terms *range, system,* and *chain.* As it is desirable to use descriptive terms with a definite meaning, the usage proposed many years ago by J. D. Dana is followed here.

A *mountain range* is either a single large, complex ridge, or a series of clearly related ridges that form a more or less continuous and compact unit. Excellent types are the Sierra Nevada in eastern California (Fig. 278) and the Front Range of Colorado. A group of ranges that obviously are similar in their general form, structure, and alignment, and presumably owe their origin to the same general causes, constitutes a *mountain system.* Thus the Basin Range system (Fig. 278) in Nevada and adjoining states consists of many distinct ranges that trend north or northwest and have similar structure and form; the Rocky Mountain system is a great assemblage of ranges, made at approximately the same time, extending from near the Mexican boundary northward through the United States and western Canada. The term *mountain chain* is used somewhat more loosely, to designate any elongate unit consisting of several groups or systems, regardless of similarity in form or age relationships. Thus all the mountains in the broad belt extending from Alabama to Newfoundland commonly are grouped together as the *Appalachian chain,* although the belt includes several distinct units diverse in plan, in structure, and in geologic date of origin.

But a still more comprehensive term is needed in referring to a series of chains, systems, and ranges that make a more or less compact belt of vast extent. For this purpose a Spanish word has been borrowed from the famous traveler Humboldt. All the mountain units in western North America, from the eastern border of the Rocky Mountains to the Pacific coast, are known as the North American *cordillera* (Fig. 278). Similarly the entire broad mountain belt that extends almost continuously from Alaska to Cape Horn is known as the American *cordilleras.* However, the same term has not been adopted universally for the major mountain belts of the Earth. In the literature the great mountain unit of southern Europe and Asia is designated variously as the *Mediterranean* (or *Eurasiatic*) *chains, zone,* or *belt.*

ORIGIN OF MOUNTAINS

Mountains owe their origin to various agencies, and differences in the structure and the plan of mountain units are due largely to this fact. The principal agencies involved may be stated as volcanic activity, movements of the crust, and differential erosion. Commonly two or more processes combine to produce complex results. However, the discussion will be clarified by a classification that recognizes the dominant agencies.

VOLCANIC MOUNTAINS

The most obvious process of mountain making is the accumulation of lavas and other volcanic products into heaps of mountainous size. Some of the loftiest peaks in the world, such as Chimborazo (20,517 feet) and Aconcagua (23,393 feet) in the Andes, and Kilimanjaro (19,321 feet) in Africa, have been built directly by volcanic action. Many such peaks, however, have their bases on high plateaus, and therefore the actual height due to volcanism is much less than the altitudes above sea level indicate. A large number of volcanic islands, like those of the Hawaiian group, are great volcanic piles, and some of them appear to be seated directly on the deep-sea floors (p. 252).

Some volcanic mountains, such as Vesuvius, are isolated cones rising above comparatively flat country. Other high cones occur in closely associated groups, like the San Francisco Mountains on the plateau south of the Grand Canyon in Arizona; elsewhere they are arranged in fairly regular rows, along great faults or other lines of weakness in the crust. Many volcanic peaks are superposed on mountains that resulted from other causes; this is conspicuously true in the Andes of South America. All mountain masses formed directly by igneous extrusion are sometimes called " mountains of accumulation." In areas of widespread volcanism the volcanic materials build also extensive plateaus, such as the Absaroka Plateau east of Yellowstone Park and the great Columbia Plateau of Washington and Oregon. After a time stream erosion carves such plateaus into high ridges and peaks, which are thus the joint product of accumulation and erosion. Erosion by streams or glaciers or both has modified all volcanic mountains to some extent, especially if volcanic activity has been extinct for a long time.

PLATEAU REMNANTS

High plateaus are dissected by stream erosion, and during a late stage in the process some of the more favored residuals have sufficient height, in relation to their surroundings, to be called mountains. Many of the larger buttes in the western United States are examples. The Catskill Mountains in New York are remnants of a former extensive high plateau, the greater part of which has been removed by fluvial erosion. A clear indication of this old plateau is given by the nearly horizontal sedimentary formations of which the Catskills are made; the thick strata now end abruptly at the steep borders of the mountains on all sides, and obviously their original extent must have been much greater. An early stage in a similar development is to be seen in the Grand Canyon of the Colorado, where great pyramidal erosion remnants rise from the depths of the chasm (Fig. 329). These masses are dwarfed by the high plateau surrounding them; but if they could be placed on a plain they would rise to mountain heights. It is not difficult to imagine that in a later geologic epoch the present youthful plateau will have been dissected thoroughly by the Colorado and its tributaries, and will be represented only by scattered high residuals separated by plains and valleys.

High plateau remnants are also called "mountains of erosion." However, deep differential erosion is made possible only by great uplift, and therefore residuals of mountainous size are the joint product of crustal movement and erosion. The forms and the distribution of the residuals are determined largely by the kinds and the structure of the rocks in the plateau. Horizontal sedimentary formations or homogeneous igneous rocks are dissected by dendritic stream patterns, and any remnants owe their preservation to chance location on divides or near the headwaters of major streams. In some plateaus, however, the rocks are steeply tilted strata whose edges were cut down to a nearly uniform level at a low elevation by previous erosion (Fig. 287). When such a peneplaned surface is warped up to form a plateau, the weak rocks, especially the shales and limestones, are attacked more effectively by weathering and streams than are the edges of resistant sandstone strata, which therefore are left standing in relief (Fig. 288). In this way the location and form of high erosional remnants are determined by the stumps of ancient mountains. This aspect of mountain history is discussed at more length on later pages.

MOUNTAINS WHOSE STRUCTURE REFLECTS CRUSTAL MOVEMENTS

Volcanic mountains and plateau remnants are important geologically, since they form groups of considerable size in the world today and probably have had wide distribution during past geologic periods. However, in most of the dominating mountain units now in existence the major relief has been determined either directly or indirectly by localized crustal movements that have caused more or less severe disturbance of the rocks.   In some of the young mountain systems much of the local relief was caused directly by these movements; in older belts, which have experienced deep erosion and perhaps more than one regional upwarping, the original disturbance of the rocks is important chiefly in guiding erosion.   But even if much of the present mountain relief is due chiefly to differential erosion, any characteristic structure produced by crustal movement has large importance in classifying mountain units.   According to the nature of the movements, as indicated in the resulting structure and form, mountains of this general type are divided into four classes.   (1) Faulting on a large scale results in relative uplift of rock masses, with or without tilting.   Ranges whose structure is produced chiefly by this process are *fault mountains*.   (2) Some vertical movements result in arching of the rocks into a general domal form, either nearly circular or somewhat elliptical in plan.   *Dome mountains* result from this process.   (3) More commonly the forces deforming the crust produce large anticlines and synclines, giving rise to the structure of *fold mountains*.   (4) In most of the great mountain belts we see the combined effects of two or more types of movement, particularly folding and faulting, with complications produced by igneous intrusion. The resulting mountains are of the *complex* type, but local sections may be classified according to the process that has played a dominant rôle.

Excellent examples of each mountain type exist; but Nature is complex, and consequently various combinations of the different types are most common.   The influence of erosion in varying degree is evident in all mountains, regardless of type.

Fault Mountains

Assume that a system of intersecting fractures, reaching to great depth, divides part of the Earth's crust into blocks or masses of very large dimensions.   Then conceivably mountains can be formed directly by movements of these blocks in several ways.   (*a*) If the region is initially a high plateau, some of the blocks may be depressed several thousand feet, leaving other blocks in their original elevated positions, to form mountain ranges.   (*b*) Regardless of original altitudes, some of the blocks may be elevated to mountain heights, by forces acting largely in the vertical direction, leaving adjacent blocks relatively depressed.   (*c*) All the blocks may move downward or upward, but each to a different degree so that in the end some stand much higher than others.   (*d*) Each of several blocks may be tilted or rotated, one edge being elevated and the opposite edge depressed.   Regardless of the nature of the movement, ranges that obviously are due to faulting are termed either *fault moun-*

tains or *block mountains* (Figs. 279, 280, 281).   Both normal and reverse
faults give rise to such mountains.

Fault blocks as we actually see them have been more or less modified
by erosion.   Débris worn from the high masses tends to bury those at

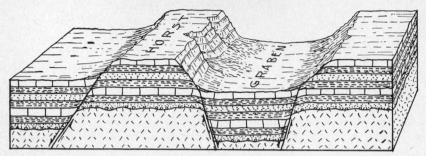

Fig. 279. — Mountain ranges formed by simple normal faulting.   The horsts form
the ranges, the grabens the intermontane basins (see p. 318).

low elevation (Figs. 279, 280).   In time this combination of erosion and
deposition nearly or quite obliterates the mountain relief, especially in
a region of interior drainage where nearly all the débris is caught in

A. Knopf, U. S. Geol. Survey.

Fig. 280. — East front of the Inyo Range, California.   The range is a great fault block;
the eastern scarp, about 8000 feet high, is greatly eroded at the top but much less modified
near the base.   Débris eroded from the mountain mass conceals the downthrown block
in the foreground.

basins between the mountains.   At a later date, as a result of broad
regional uplift accompanied by change of climate, or because of important changes in the drainage of adjoining regions, the waste may be

removed from the original intermontane troughs and the ranges given a
new lease of life. Obviously such resurrected ranges are the direct
result of differential erosion, and strictly they are plateau remnants.
However, the original faulting was the chief factor in guiding erosion
and continues to be reflected in the mountain forms. Accordingly the
original structure is given large emphasis, and it is common to use the
designation *fault mountains* or *block mountains* even for units that have
been greatly modified by erosion.

The Sierra Nevada of California is a tilted crust block 400 miles in
length and approximately 75 miles wide (Figs. 278, 281). Its eastern
edge has been uplifted 2 miles or more, to form an abrupt scarp facing
eastward. Roads from the east ascend this precipitous front with difficulty; but west of the crest they descend on a long, gentle slope — the

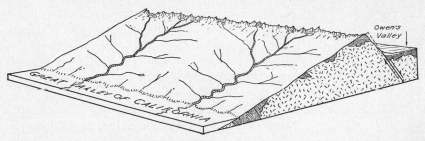

Fig. 281. — Generalized form and structure of the Sierra Nevada, California. The
remnants of folded rocks engulfed in granite record ancient crustal movements and enormous igneous intrusions, after which long-continued erosion formed a peneplane. In
late geologic time a movement of tilting uplift along the great fault formed the present
range. Pleistocene glaciation made the rugged peaks at the summit.

tilted upper surface of the block. In the Great Valley of California,
sediments thousands of feet deep have accumulated on the depressed
portion of the rotated mass. A great series of fault mountains lies in
Nevada and parts of neighboring states. Ranges in that region are so
similar in character that they are known collectively as the Basin Range
system (p. 318; Fig. 278). The great dislocations responsible for these
ranges and for the Sierra Nevada do not represent the first disturbance
of the region. In earlier periods the thick sedimentary rocks in Nevada
and eastern California were folded and thrust-faulted, and great igneous
masses were intruded into them. Mountains that existed soon after
those ancient events have long since disappeared, and in fairly recent
time the old deformed crust has been broken by great faults, to form the
present generation of mountains. Probably some of the ranges are
still growing, for within historic time, movements have occurred on several of the faults, giving rise to violent earthquakes. As a large part of

the region has no drainage to the sea, the mountains are partly buried by accumulations of their own débris.

Fault mountains in various stages of destruction are found in northern Africa, in Arabia, in central Asia, in Japan, and in many other parts of the world. The Triassic sandstones of Connecticut and Massachusetts are broken by great faults, and the resulting blocks have a strong tilt eastward; but the mountains that probably were formed by these dislocations disappeared through erosion long ago. Similar structural relics of ancient fault mountains, representing various geologic periods, are widely distributed in all continents.

Dome Mountains

Mountains whose structure reflects crustal uplift of distinctly domal character may be classed together, regardless of size or the exact cause of the uplift. The simplest and best understood are laccolithic domes, made by the bowing up of strata above thick, lens-shaped intrusions of liquid rock (p. 237). Ordinarily a dome of this kind that is high enough to be called a mountain has lost more or less of its original cover through erosion; and not uncommonly the resistant igneous mass, almost completely denuded, stands within circular or elliptical ridges formed by the upturned edges of the more resistant strata (Fig. 177, B). There are several excellent examples in the vicinity of the Black Hills. The Henry Mountains of Utah, classic examples of the type, are a large group of laccoliths in various stages of denudation. But not all mountains of this kind have ideally simple structure. The intruding magma in many laccoliths has ruptured the covering strata and lifted them irregularly, as in the Moccasin Mountains of Montana.

Dome mountains on a larger scale are illustrated by the Black Hills of South Dakota. In a casual journey through these mountains the traveler may gain an impression of disordered arrangement; but a good map or a block diagram of the entire unit reveals a beautiful symmetry of structure, involving an elliptical area about 100 miles in length by 50 in width (Fig. 282). In the middle and eastern portions the uplifted sedimentary formations have been stripped away, and there the crystalline basement rocks have been carved into ridges and peaks, including Harney Peak (7242 feet above sea level), the highest point east of the Rockies. Around the flanks of the uplift the upturned edges of sedimentary formations, yielding to erosion at different rates, make alternating high and low belts that encircle the uplands. Some of the heavy limestone members still cover the western half of the uplift, forming the " limestone plateau." A careful profile and section, in which the eroded formations are restored to their original positions, shows that the greatest erosion has occurred in the area of maximum uplift. The restored section indicates that the top of the dome was elevated 9000 feet above the flanks, although at present the greatest height above the surrounding plains is only about 4000 feet.

In contrast with a laccolith, the crystalline rocks exposed at the core of the Black Hills are much older than the domed sedimentary formations. Therefore the force by which the uplift came about was applied much deeper than any exposed part of the crust. If the cause of uplift

B. Newton, U. S. Geog. and Geol. Survey.

Fig. 282. — Diagram of the Black Hills uplift, South Dakota. View looking northward, along the longer axis of the elliptical dome. The valley encircling the dome is commonly known as "The Race Track." For underground structure of the dome see Fig. 328.

was the rise of igneous material, the molten mass was very large, quite symmetrical in form, and very deep-seated. The connection of some igneous activity with the movement is indicated by numerous laccoliths, which form small satellitic domes in the northern part of the Hills. Whatever may have been the part performed by magmas in causing the main uplift, it is very probable that the horizontal pressure responsible for the Rocky Mountain folds was an important factor also in shaping the Black Hills dome, since the long axis of the Hills is parallel with the Rocky Mountain front. According to this view the bulging up of the Black Hills was merely a local incident in forming the Rocky Mountain structure, and the laccoliths superposed on the larger dome represent still smaller incidents in the general process.

It is evident that the Black Hills uplift did not become an actual mountain group without the work of erosion, for if the youngest strata involved in the movement still extended unbroken across the summit, forming a broad, smooth dome, the area would be a small plateau rather than a mountain. It is essential, therefore, to keep in mind the limitations of any scheme of classifying mountains. The part played by erosion is of great importance in connection with every other process. However, the crustal deformation which controls the relief forms is important enough to merit recognition in a classification. The limit of size separating dome mountains from plateaus must be somewhat arbitrary; but as the Black Hills uplift is a definite unit of moderate size, with strongly defined boundaries, it seems proper to emphasize the structural form, provided the various steps in fashioning the highlands are kept clearly in mind.

Close study of the Black Hills reveals another important fact that emphasizes the complexity of mountain history. After the dome was partly formed it was eroded to low relief, and therefore the first generation of mountains was destroyed. Layers of sand and clay were deposited across most if not all of the area; then the dome was arched to greater height, and in the high part of the present Hills only a few small remnants of the sand and clay strata have escaped later erosion. Therefore the uplifting of the Black Hills was not a simple event that occupied a brief interval of time; the movement occurred slowly, with at least one long pause, and erosion prevented the dome from reaching its full height as a surface feature.

If the Black Hills should be worn down to a peneplane by future erosion, and a later warping movement should reëlevate the Great Plains region several thousand feet, subsequent erosion would be guided by the old structure and another generation of mountains similar to the present Hills eventually would be fashioned.

Fold and Complex Mountains

Mountains in which the rocks are strongly folded and broken are commonly described according to their internal structure, regardless of the later chapters in their history. Some old mountain units are strictly remnants of erosion; however, it is evident from their structure that a certain type of crustal deformation attended their early development, and their structural characteristics are used as the basis of their classification. For example, the Appalachians of eastern North America and the Cape ranges of South Africa have had long and varied careers. The original highlands were eroded through long ages, and almost or quite disappeared; and the present ridges have been brought into relief by differential erosion after later upwarping of the areas containing the old mountain "roots." Nevertheless, remnants of the original structure are clearly visible, and are recognized as important features of these mountain zones. It is well to keep these examples in mind throughout the discussion that follows. Deformed rocks are characteristic of all great mountain zones, but it is not to be taken for granted that the deformation gave rise to the present mountain elevations. Mountain *structure* and mountain *elevation* may not have any direct relation to each other. Nevertheless the structure continues as a dominant factor in determining relief because it guides differential erosion.

All the great mountain chains of the Earth include folded sedimentary rocks as a conspicuous part of their structure. These chains, therefore, are sometimes classed together as *fold* mountains, although faulting, igneous intrusion, and other important processes besides simple folding have played some part in their origin. Strictly speaking, every great system is more or less *complex* in its structure; but certain mountain units exhibit fairly regular plication of rock formations as their outstanding structural characteristic. The Jura Mountains in Switzerland and parts of the Appalachian Mountains are excellent examples. The Rocky Mountains and the Alps are characterized by enormous thrust faults in addition to folds, and consequently are illustrations of complex units. However, some parts of the Appalachians also are complicated by thrust faulting; and as there are all stages of gradation between the simpler sections of this chain and the almost incredible complexity of the Alps, it is clear that *fold* and *complex* mountains can not be separated as sharply contrasted structural types. Therefore it is desirable to include mountains of these two classes in a unit discussion, although the treatment logically emphasizes the simpler folding first, and then proceeds to more complex processes and results.

Considering the Earth as a whole, the finest displays of geologic phenomena are furnished by the mountains with folded and complex structure. There are to be found the greatest sections of upturned and dissected strata whose kinds, thickness, included fossils, and structure furnish the most effective key to past events. Commonly the making of such mountains has been accompanied by igneous activity, and the sections now exposed reveal both intrusive and extrusive masses of various types. Many of the most important ore deposits occur in these zones of disturbance, both recent and ancient. Some of the youngest complex ranges are the theatres in which many agents of erosion, as well as crustal movements and volcanism, play their most active rôles at the present time. For many reasons, therefore, the great mountain belts merit special consideration.

General Characteristics of Fold and Complex Mountains. — From examination of a globe or a world map it is apparent that the prominent mountain belts are elongated generally parallel with the continental margins. This relation is especially striking in the American cordilleras, the Appalachians, the Scandinavian chain, and the great Eurasiatic

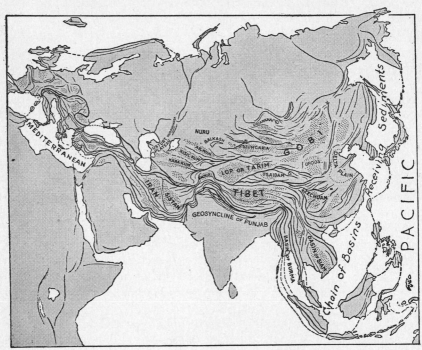

Modified from Berkey and Morris, Am. Mus. Nat. Hist.

Fig. 283. — Map of Asia, with parts of Europe and northeastern Africa. Trends of the principal mountain chains of Asia and southern Europe shown by black lines. The arcuate form of many units is striking. The trends are generally parallel with the south and east coasts of Asia. Note the series of great marine basins receiving modern sediments between the east coast and the island chains.

mountain zone (Fig. 283). Each major belt is composed of numerous ranges disposed somewhat irregularly but with the same general orientation. Some of the ranges are nearly straight in plan; but many are strongly curved into the form of great bows or arcs. The Alps, Carpathians, and Himalayas are striking examples of this *arcuate* type (Fig. 283).

Generally the exposed portion of each range is made up in part or wholly of distorted sedimentary formations. Commonly these strata, now on the flanks or even on the highest summits of the ranges, represent deposits in former seas, on deltas, and in swamps bordering the sea. Owing to the strong folding and faulting of these strata, followed by planation and dissection through erosion, the full thickness of the sedimentary cover is exposed in many places. In some mountain belts these thicknesses are astonishing; 4, 5, or even 6 miles are by no means exceptional values, and in some mountain areas the total sedimentary sections exceed 40,000 feet. It will occur to some readers that similar thicknesses may be common also outside of mountain zones, but are not known because not exposed by erosion. However, natural exposures and well records indicate clearly that sedimentary formations grow conspicuously thinner away from a folded mountain belt. Thus the strata in the Appalachians average 20,000 feet or more in thickness along the central axis of the folded tract; but at no great distance to the west the thickness is less than 10,000 feet, and in the Mississippi Valley it is only 4000 to 5000 feet (Fig. 285). On the east side of the Appalachians the sedimentary strata do not exist, and it will be shown presently that the deposits never extended far eastward from their present limit. Therefore the excessively thick sediments occupy a long and relatively narrow belt that corresponds closely in trend to the axis of the folded chain. This general relationship exists also in the Rockies, the Andes, the Mediterranean ranges, and other great mountain systems. It is a natural conclusion that the accumulation of abnormally thick sediments had a significant connection with the development of each of these mountain units.

The typical history of mountain systems with fold structure falls into three general divisions: the preliminary stages, when the site of the future mountain belt sinks slowly and receives a thick cover of sedimentary strata; stages of severe crustal movement, in which the folds and related structural features are formed and the initial uplift occurs; and subsequent stages, during which the mountains experience various modifications through erosion and repeated vertical movements. This subdivision of the history is useful, if it is understood that the periods are not sharply separated, and that some of the processes involved operate simultaneously. Thus some incidents of folding and thrusting occur long before the accumulation of sediments is complete; and inevitably the modifying influence of erosion dates from an early stage of uplift, while the orogenic or mountain-making processes are active. The growth and decline of every range is the result of a slow, complicated interplay of forces that act either continuously or recurrently during a very long geologic interval. Recognition of general stages in the history serves to clarify a brief discussion; but these stages overlap and merge irregularly into one another.

Preliminary Stages: Development of Geosynclines. — Sedimentary strata in the great ranges consist of conglomerates and sandstones interbedded with shales and limestones. It is clear that thick deposits containing coarse sediments must have been laid down near the margin of a land that suffered prolonged erosion. The great thickness of deposits may suggest that sedimentation began in an excessively deep basin. However, there is unquestionable evidence that most of the sediments involved in mountain folds were laid down in shallow water or at only moderate depths. Accumulation of such deposits to a total thickness of several miles indicates that slow subsidence of the sea floor was continuous or recurrent while deposition was in progress. Moreover, as enormous volumes of sediments were delivered into the subsiding basin during long periods, the wasting land must have risen continuously or recurrently adjacent to the area of sedimentation. In any case, the preliminary structure that determines the location of a future fold system appears to be a sinking trough into which the waste from near-by land accumulates in unusual thickness. An elongated subsiding tract of this nature is known as a *geosyncline* (p. 308; Figs. 284, 285). A modern example on a large scale may be the great chain of shallow seas parallel with the east coast of Asia, into which the Hwang-ho and other great rivers of the continent, as well as shorter streams from the western slopes of the Japanese and other islands, are pouring floods of sediment (Fig. 283).

In the Appalachians various features of the strata indicate that conditions within the old geosynclinal trough fluctuated repeatedly. Sandstones and shales with abundant ripple marks and mud cracks are interbedded with thick limestones that contain marine fossils. Such relations imply a laterally shifting shoreline and considerable variation in depth of water. In fact at some periods the sea gave place to great delta plains or to enormous swamps in which materials for coal beds accumulated. These changes depended on the relative rates of subsidence and sedimentation. If sinking of the trough halted for a considerable time, accumulating sediments made the sea shallow or even displaced the sea water entirely over wide areas. With renewal of subsidence the water came back. If the adjacent land was elevated rapidly for a time, erosion may have been stimulated sufficiently to keep the seaway full even though subsidence of the trough was continuous.

From study of the sedimentary sections in the Appalachians it is clear that the coarser sediments are on the east, giving way westward to marine shales and limestones (Fig. 285). Therefore the land from which the

sediments were eroded lay to the east of the geosyncline.   A narrow
belt of ancient rocks near the present coast presumably represents the
western edge of the former land; but it must have extended far eastward,
over the area of the present continental shelf, in order to have volume
adequate to explain the vast quantities of sediments it supplied.   The
name " Appalachia " is applied to this ancient land of unknown extent
(Fig. 284).   The sea that lay west of it, covering much of the present
Mississippi Valley region, was shallow and fluctuating.

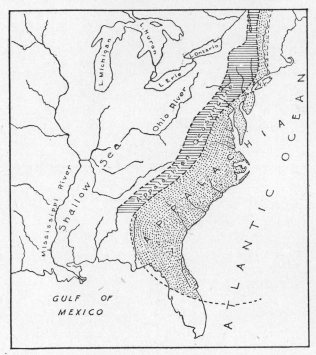

Fig. 284. — Map showing general location of the Appalachian geosyncline and of the
old land Appalachia.

Similar histories have preceded the making of other great ranges.
The Rocky Mountains grew up from a great geosyncline that stretched
from the Gulf of Mexico to the Arctic, with highlands to the west; an
old land that furnished sediments to the Alpine geosyncline lay to the
north of the Alps; strata folded in the Caucasus were derived from
lands to the south while seas stretched northward over Russia.   Thus
it may be accepted as a general principle that on one side of the mountain zone lies an area of much older rocks, the source of the deformed
clastic deposits.   The time occupied in the accumulation of sediments
in the geosyncline extends over long geologic periods.

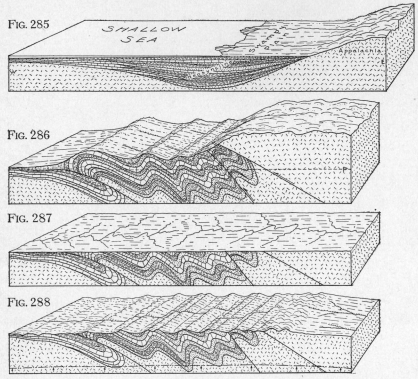

Figs. 285–288. — Four stages in the evolution of the present Appalachians. Views looking north.

Fig. 285. — The geosyncline and the edge of the old land Appalachia, composed of granite and metamorphic rocks.

Fig. 286. — Folding and thrust-faulting of the rocks in the geosyncline. The form and height of the surface are entirely hypothetical; it is not known how much uplift resulted directly from the folding or to what extent erosion kept pace with the uplift. After several geologic periods had elapsed the region was worn to a peneplane, indicated by the broken line at P. The thickness of rock above this line suggests the vast work of erosion in reducing the original mountains.

Fig. 287. — General appearance of the peneplaned Appalachian region near the close of the Mesozoic era. The eastern part of the region was submerged and received a veneer of coastal-plain sediments; possibly this veneer covered most of the folded belt, and has been removed by erosion.

Fig. 288. — During the Tertiary period the region was warped up, as indicated by arrows at the bottom of the block; belts of weak sedimentary rock were eroded, leaving the present ridges composed of resistant strata. (The broken line corresponds to the base of the block in Fig. 287.)

Stages of Severe Crustal Movement. — It is clearly evident, from the structural features found in any one of the great mountain belts, that crushing of the old geosyncline and its burden of sediments was performed by forces acting in a lateral direction, parallel with the Earth's surface. Thus in zones of most intensive folding, the folds not only are

closed so that their limbs are parallel, but they are even more severely compressed, with mashing of the beds and the production of very complicated structures. This is illustrated by sections in the Appalachians and in the Alps (Figs. 286, 296). Considering the scale of these sections it is impossible to imagine the formation of such structures except by lateral compression of great severity.

Ordinarily some strong folding movements occur while development of the geosyncline is in progress. In eastern Pennsylvania and in the Hudson Valley we find that the strata first deposited in the Appalachian geosyncline were thrown into steep folds, and now lie with strong angular unconformity beneath formations that were laid down later. The greatest disturbance, however, occurred after the youngest of the geosynclinal sediments were deposited (Fig. 286). Likewise on the floor of the sea in which the Alpine formations accumulated there were repeated disturbances that folded and broke the strata, and we see the result in numerous unconformities. As the folding continued the entire belt finally emerged from the sea, and the most powerful crushing and thrusting by lateral compression occurred after nearly all the sedimentary strata had been formed.

Thus the folds that characterize the structure of great mountain systems are a record of horizontal compressive forces which begin to operate early in the history of geosynclines but reach their culmination only after the accumulated sedimentary formations have attained great thickness.

Thrust Faulting. — It is obvious that such extreme folding of rocks could not take place without rupturing and displacement of the strata. We find, accordingly, that faulting is especially common in mountain ranges. As we pass from consideration of the simpler fold ranges to those of more complex types, the faulting becomes more pronounced until finally it culminates in thrust faults of great magnitude (Figs. 289–294). An excellent example is the great Lewis thrust in Glacier National Park, Montana (Fig. 295). The flat attitude of the thrusts and their trends parallel with the axes of the ranges indicate that the thrusts were made by horizontal compression, just as were the folds. In fact many of the folds, after being overturned, have broken and passed into thrusts; thus the origin of the two types of structure from the same forces is clearly established.

Cleavage. — It has been pointed out (p. 356) that cleavage in metamorphic rocks, such as slates, is the result of great pressure. Many of the rocks of the great mountain belts have been turned into schists, slates, and other metamorphic types, depending on their original composition and other factors. This alteration is most evident where the deeper

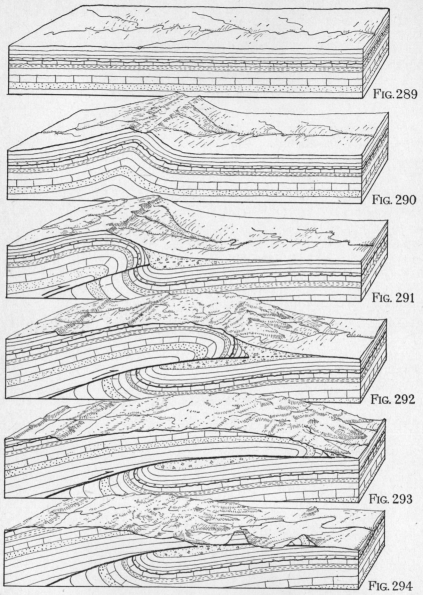

Figs. 289–294. — Development of a great thrust fault. Length of block about 50 miles.

Fig. 289. — Undisturbed strata before the movement has begun.

Fig. 290. — Horizontal compression has formed a fold, overturned to the east.

Fig. 291. — The fold has developed into a thrust fault. Débris eroded from the rising structure has accumulated in the synclinal depression at the base of the range.

Fig. 292. — The mass is pushed out over the land surface, and overrides some of its own alluvial débris.

Fig. 293. — The thrust reaches its maximum extent.

Fig. 294. — After movement has ceased erosion has full sway. The thrust mass is cut down and back. Note the isolated remnants of the older rocks. (Compare Fig. 295.)

portions of the folded belt are exposed by erosion.   Close study of these metamorphic rocks reveals that the cleavage planes usually stand at high angles and strike generally parallel with the axes of the folds.   Thus the cleavage together with the folds and thrusts testifies to a compressive force that acted horizontally.

Amount of Compression. — The magnitude of the forces and of the masses is indicated by the amount of compression which investigation shows has actually occurred in some of the great folded belts.   It is estimated that in the Appalachians the original width of the geosyncline was decreased 40 or 50 miles, and in some sections still more, by the mash-

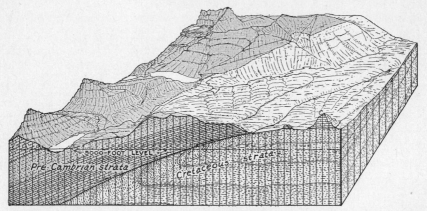

Fig. 295. — Part of the great Lewis thrust, in Glacier National Park, Montana.   The old rocks pushed up and forward in the thrust are indicated, both at the surface and beneath, by the darker color.   The thrust has been cut back farthest where the largest stream has eroded its valley.   Chief Mountain (*C*) and another small remnant are "mountains without roots"; they show that the thrust reached farther eastward than at present, but probably do not record its maximum extent.   (Compare Fig. 294.)
View looking northwest.   Front of block about 10 miles long.

ing and crumpling of the mass.   If the folded strata in Pennsylvania, which now resemble a crumpled blanket, could be smoothed out toward the southeast, their extent would be increased sufficiently to cover the state of New Jersey.   In the Rocky Mountains also the structure represents shortening by tens of miles, and the amount of compression in the Alps is much greater.

Influence of Resistant Elements. — The geosyncline is a zone of weakness, as indicated by its sinking during long ages; the sedimentary formations that accumulate in it are relatively weak also, since their stratification makes them susceptible to folding by compression.   By contrast the old land mass along whose margin the sediments have been deposited is a strong, resistant element in the architecture of the outer shell of the Earth.   This mass rises as the geosyncline sinks, and long-continued erosion exposes the granite and other massive rocks that exist at lower levels. When later compression becomes sufficiently strong, the weak sediments are crumpled by pressure against the strong adjoining mass. Rocks in the resistant element are mashed and fractured to some extent, but there are no stratified formations in it to yield by folding. Irregularities in the margin of the old land appear to have an influence on the trend of the mountain folds, causing prominent bends or arcs. Therefore the general plan of fold ranges seems to be determined in an important degree by the situation of the old lands, which act as resisting buttresses at the time the folds are formed. Thus the Appalachians from southern New York to Alabama imitate roughly, in their sinuous trend, the former western coast of the old land Appalachia. It is suggested also that the curving trend of the Alps has been determined in large measure by old land masses, parts of which are now visible in central France, the Vosges, and the Black Forest.

Variations of Fold Structure. — It is to be expected that the results of folding should differ considerably in character between separate ranges, or between distant parts of the same range. Differences in thickness of sediments, in proportions between strong and weak formations, in the form of old rigid masses that transmitted the thrust, and in severity of the lateral forces, are reflected in the individuality of mountain folds. The Jura Mountains, a small member of the Alpine system, have irregular folds, many of them broken and crumpled. These folds were produced far out in front of the Alps proper, in a relatively thin sheet of strata, as an incidental effect of the forces that deformed the greater Alpine zone (p. 400; Fig. 297). The Appalachians present a wider variety of fold structures. In the slate and anthracite regions of eastern Pennsylvania the folds are closely compressed, many of them to the isoclinal stage (p. 307, Fig. 221), and the axial planes are strongly overturned toward the northwest. Farther west in the state the folds tend to be open and upright; and the deformation dies out westward. Going to the south, through Virginia and Tennessee and into Alabama, we find that many of the folds were ruptured by the severe compression and developed into thrust faults (Figs. 289–294). This kind of complexity is especially pronounced in the Alps, which merit special description.

Thrust Faults and Recumbent Folds of the Alps. — Alpine structure is characterized by great folds that have been pushed over to a horizontal attitude, and by flat thrusts that are related to these overturned folds. These features are developed on an unprecedented scale, with the result that the Alps consist of a series of great rock sheets, driven one over another so that they overlap like the shingles on a roof. The Germans call the individual sheets *Decken*; the French refer to them as *nappes*.

Because of their location, the Alps have received more intensive study than any other mountains. Accordingly, in spite of astonishing complexity, their structure and history are fairly well known. Like the Appalachians, they resulted from deformation of thick marine deposits; but a large part of the Alpine sediments bears evidence of deposition in deep water, far from any shore. Land lay to the north, in the present position of central Europe, where mountains of nearly the same date as the Appalachians were being eroded. Orogenic movement began in Mesozoic time, with pressure from the direction of Africa. The soft

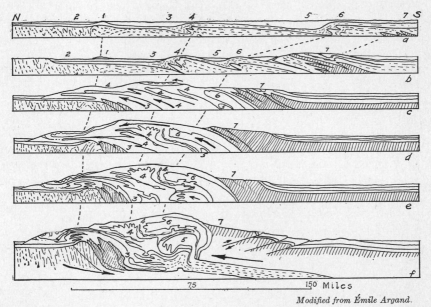

Modified from Émile Argand.

Fig. 296. — Development of the structure of the Alps. Sections show successive stages from the beginning of folding and thrusting (upper section) to the final intricate structure (lower section). Corresponding numbers, together with dotted lines, indicate the large horizontal movement required for the development of the folds and thrusts.

sediments on the sea floor were bowed up slowly, until chains of islands appeared above sea level. During early Tertiary time the compression accelerated powerfully, and an enormous rock sheet was driven northward over the geosyncline. Beneath this sheet the plastic sediments suffered extreme distortion. With recurrent thrusting during the Tertiary period other sheets were driven forward, and all were severely folded (Fig. 296). Erosion cut valleys and " windows " (German, *Fenster*) through the sheets, exposing the entire series; and in parts of the Alpine area nearly the whole of one or more sheets has been swept away, leaving remnants of old rocks to form isolated peaks standing on younger rocks that were overridden and covered during the thrusting movement. Like Chief Mountain, Montana (Fig. 295), isolated peaks that have this anomalous relation are " mountains without roots." The Matterhorn (Fig. 115) and the Mythen are famous examples. Some of these masses are 50 miles or more north of their original positions. Heim, the great Swiss master of Alpine structure, tells us that the Alpine zone as a whole was made narrower by considerably over 100 miles owing to the thrusting and folding. Locally, as in the Simplon Tunnel section, the original width was reduced as much as 90 per cent.

Depth of Folding. — How deep is the segment of the crust affected by folding, thrusting, and mashing in mountain zones? There is of course much uncertainty about this matter, but for some localities a partial answer can be given. In the Alps, erosion has cut through the folded and uplifted cover of strata in several places, exposing the older rocks on which the sediments were deposited. Mont Blanc and the Aar *massif* are parts of the floor of the former geosyncline, now lifted to a high level and completely denuded. These areas were not in the deepest parts of the old basin; yet they were covered with sediments many thousands of feet thick, and the crustal movements reached much deeper than the present surface, since the old rocks are sliced with thrusts and otherwise deformed. The Appalachians have not been elevated sufficiently to permit erosion to expose the floor in the deepest part of the old trough; but thrust faults have brought some of the lowest sedimentary formations to the level of the present surface. Similar evidence from the Rocky Mountains and from the older mountain zones of Scotland and Scandinavia leaves no doubt that deformation by horizontal compression extends at least several miles in depth, affecting the " basement " rocks beneath the thickest sedimentary sections; but how much deeper the effects may reach is not known.

After Buxtorf.

Fig. 297. — Structure of the Jura Mountains. Horizontal thrust from the southeast (right) caused the plate of stratified rocks to fold by slipping over the older rocks beneath, which therefore were not affected by the movement.

On the other hand it is certain that some folding ends at comparatively shallow depth. The folds of the Jura Mountains, northwest of the Alps, are closely compressed (Fig. 297); but the sedimentary formations involved in the folding have a total thickness of less than a mile, and the older rocks beneath were not affected by the deformation. Near the bottom of the sedimentary section there is a weak formation of shale. When the Alpine zone was being crushed by powerful thrusts from the south the deformed rocks, crowded toward the north, transmitted part of the pressure to the flat-lying strata beyond. The weak shale at the base of the section served as a sort of lubricating zone, permitting the overlying strata to wrinkle into close folds by sliding over the " basement " rocks. To duplicate the effect in miniature, lay a thin block of tissue paper on a table with the far edge of the block against a book, and push against the near edge; the paper yields by wrinkling into folds, at the same time sliding on the table. Shallow folds of the Jura type appear to be developed incidentally in connection with more important and deeper-seated crustal movements.

Mountain Elevation. — There is a natural tendency to assume that mountains rise to greater heights continuously with folding and thrusting, as a logical result of crowding excess material into a narrow zone. For a long time, indeed, this conclusion was taken for granted, and attempts were made to compute the original height of eroded ranges by restoring the folds from study of the eroded limbs. As the steps in mountain history become clearer, however, it is found that much of the actual elevation occurred at a distinctly later time than the folding and thrusting. After the Rocky Mountain deformation in early Tertiary time, the folded and faulted area was eroded to a nearly even surface at a low altitude; and the present great heights in the Rockies are due to vertical movements in the late Tertiary. Similarly, after much of the thrusting and folding was complete, the Alps had only moderate height, and the sea washed the flanks of the range both on the north and on the south. In very recent geologic time a vertical movement of the entire mountain belt carried the Alpine summits to great height. The Andes and the Himalayas have had a similar history.

If the principle of isostasy is kept in mind, it does not seem strange that horizontal pressure acting alone fails to force the folded zones to great height. An overload results from horizontal transfer and piling up of the rocks, and the mountain area continues to subside under the increasing weight, in order to maintain approximate balance with adjacent parts of the crust. Therefore even the enormous amount of material heaped together in the Alpine zone did not result at once in high mountains. Presumably there was slow flowage outward from the deformed area, in a deep plastic zone, to prevent an extreme overload. The cause of the later broad uplift is a matter for speculation. It is suggested that the cold rocks of the upper crust, carried to a deeper and hotter zone by the continued heaping up and sinking, slowly changed their state owing to heating and expanded. Such increase in volume would not change the total weight of the mountain mass, and therefore the surface would rise without disturbing isostatic balance. In a qualitative way this explanation is satisfactory; but the problem involves many factors that are unknown at present and therefore can not be solved quantitatively.

Rôle of Igneous Agencies. — Although the making of mountain structures by compression appears to be independent of direct igneous action, and some ranges contain little or no visible igneous rock, nevertheless an upwelling of magma to produce both intrusive and extrusive bodies

P. B. King.

Fig. 298. — The granitic core of a mountain range, exposed by prolonged erosion. The granite batholith cuts across folded and metamorphosed sediments.

has been a common incident in mountain making. The effect of this action is to modify the structure due to folding and faulting, and by the addition of large massive bodies to increase the rigidity and strength of the mountain zone. Probably the most effective way in which this happens is by the intrusion of great batholiths, usually composed of granite, into the lower portions of ranges. A granite intrusion of this nature that has become exposed by deep erosion is spoken of as the " granite core " of a range (Fig. 298). Intrusion of the heated magma, combined with the folding and mashing of the strata, causes profound metamorphic effects over wide areas. Invading masses of this character are an especially conspicuous feature of the Coast Range in western Canada, where granitic rocks are exposed in a continuous belt 1100 miles long. Batholiths are important also in the Sierra Nevada, the Green and White mountains of New England, the Caucasus, and the mountains of Scotland and Norway.

Intrusions of molten magmas not only make great batholiths at the cores of ranges, but pressing upward along belts of weakness caused by folding and faulting, they form sills, laccoliths, dikes, and other bodies (Chap. X). In some mountain zones the magmas break through to the surface and form lava flows or give rise to violent volcanic action. During the formation of the Rocky Mountains, Wyoming and Montana were the scene of great volcanic activity, the dying phases of which are still evident in Yellowstone Park (p. 282). Folding and faulting of strata, combined with intrusion and extrusion of magmas, has resulted in geologic structure of wonderful complexity, now revealed to us by deep dissection.

Subsequent Stages of Mountain History. — Although mountains may be classified according to the crustal movements involved in their formation, it is not to these processes alone that any mountains in their present form are due. Hand in hand with uplift goes the work of erosion, that mighty chisel of Nature, which carves the elevated masses into the forms familiar to us. The sculpturing proceeds throughout the period of orogenic activity, and continues so long as the highlands exist. During the subsequent stages the history of a range consists chiefly of progressive changes due to erosion, by which the mountains reach maturity and old age.

So long as the orogenic forces are at work, a mountain range grows in so far as its structure is concerned. Whether it actually rises in height or not depends on the adjustment between (1) vertical movements that tend to make it rise, and (2) the work of erosion which tends to cut it down. Always during the formative period this struggle goes on, and the height of the range at any time is a resultant of these two forces. When the orogenic movements cease erosion has full sway, and ultimately, provided no renewal takes place, the range must disappear. In this process various stages are to be distinguished. When the range is at its maximum elevation the erosive agencies are most severe; to the work of running water on steep slopes is added very commonly the effect of frost, snow, and ice. It may happen also that at this time the rock material exposed to erosion consists chiefly of the later beds laid down in the geosyncline, which have experienced less consolidation than the deeper, older ones, and are thus less resistant to erosive attack. If igneous extrusions have contributed to swell the volume of the range, it will be the more easily eroded tuffs and lavas that are first attacked.

Hence, in general, the youthful range is dissected rapidly and takes on a rugged form characterized by deep valleys and sharp peaks. As erosive processes continue their work the high relief decreases and the serrate summits give place to smoothly rounded forms. The progress of degradation goes more slowly as the slopes lessen and as the resistant metamorphic and intrusive igneous rocks of the inner core are reached. After an enormous lapse of time the mountain forms may be obliterated; but even then some clue to their former existence will be furnished by the upturned and dislocated nature of the eroded strata (Fig. 299), by the widespread metamorphism of the rocks, by the slaty cleavage and faults that cut them, and by the presence of large granitic intrusive masses. We can not determine the former elevations, for, as LeConte has said, " We find only the bones of the extinct mountains "; but these remains indicate the trends and extent of the ancient ranges. Thus from the attitude of the rocks of southern New England, which is now only a hilly country, we are led to infer that it was once a mountainous region, with ranges trending generally north and south.

Crustal movements in the mountain zone do not cease entirely, however, at the time the ranges reach their maximum height. As erosion

N. H. Darton, U. S. Geol. Survey.

Fig. 299. — East front of the Laramie Mountains, Wyoming. Erosion has reduced these mountains to low elevation; but even if they are eroded to a plain the upturned strata of limestone, sandstone, and shale will mark the position and the trend of the old range.

proceeds, its work is partly offset and the mountain forms are complicated by recurrent upwarping of the region. The old Appalachians have been bowed up repeatedly, even in late geologic time. After their birth during the Permian period they experienced long-continued erosion; and although uplifts probably occurred, the entire folded tract finally was reduced to a peneplane. During the Tertiary period the region was warped up strongly and dissected, and therefore the present mountain ridges are strictly plateau remnants. The latest pulses of uplift are recorded by high terraces along the streams.

DATING OF MOVEMENTS IN A MOUNTAIN ZONE

To fix the geologic period in which the sedimentary formations of a geosyncline were deformed it is necessary to determine the age not only of the youngest strata involved in the disturbance but also of the oldest strata that escaped deformation (Fig. 300).   The closeness of dating by this method depends upon the length of the interval between deposition of the two sets of formations.   Thus if the youngest deformed rocks are of late Triassic age and the oldest undisturbed formation was deposited early in the Tertiary, the movement may have occurred either in the Jurassic or in the Cretaceous period.   The Appalachian folding is dated rather closely, since Permian rocks are affected and Triassic rocks are not.

In some mountains the rocks have been disturbed in several periods, and therefore the method just explained can be used to date only the latest movement.   However, the earlier disturbances generally are

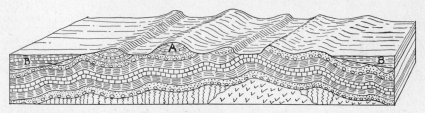

Fig. 300. — Cross-section of a range with fold structure, showing evidence of the date at which deformation occurred.   A, youngest surviving strata that were involved in the folding; the deformation occurred after they were deposited.   B, strata deposited after the deformation.   Length of section about 50 miles.

recorded by unconformities (p. 322).   If a surface of unconformity cuts across strongly folded rocks, and the formations above the unconformity also are deformed, there were at least two important movements.   The several pulses of violent disturbance that affected the Alpine zone are differentiated by evidence of this kind.

Mountain-making movements of any kind are dated by following the same general principles.   The latest episode of uplift on faults can not be older than the youngest rocks affected by the faulting.

THE ULTIMATE CAUSE OF CRUSTAL MOVEMENTS

When it was believed that the Earth consisted of a relatively thin crust resting on a hot liquid interior, it seemed easy to explain deformation of the crust by assuming that there was steady contraction of the Earth's mass from loss of heat.   Since this contraction would be greatest in the hot interior, the cold outer crust would be folded up as it gradually sank upon the shrinking core, very much as the skin wrinkles upon an apple that contracts from drying.   This view in its original simple form can no longer be held, because it is known that no large part of the Earth is liquid, at least in the outer half of its radius.

Nevertheless a view commonly held to account for crustal deformation assumes contraction by loss of heat. This is a survival of the idea mentioned above, but changed to accord more nearly with later knowledge. It assumes that the Earth is rigid but very hot within, and that progressive loss of heat causes slow shrinkage below a comparatively shallow depth. An English scientist has shown that this mechanism would account for a large proportion of the observed buckling that has occurred in the outer shell, provided we make certain reasonable assumptions as to the temperatures in the interior. Another form of the contraction hypothesis discards the idea of cooling, but assumes that the enormous pressures deep in the Earth cause matter to increase in density and decrease in volume. The net effect would be the same as if cooling occurred, as the outer shell, unchanged in volume, would collapse on the shrinking core with consequent folding and thrusting.

It has been suggested also that vertical adjustments in the outer crust to maintain isostatic equilibrium (p. 372) may be a sufficient cause of deformation. This suggestion does not find support in the evidences of enormous lateral pressure and displacement. In some mountain belts, individual rock sheets have been thrust horizontally for distances of 25 miles or more; and every large folded geosyncline represents lateral movement through tens of miles. It is difficult to conceive of a mechanism whereby slow vertical movements of the crust could be responsible for horizontal forces of such magnitude. However, isostasy probably is an important factor in some stages of mountain development. As erosion removes great quantities of material from a mountain belt the loss of load necessitates uplift to preserve balance in the crust, and thus the repeated rising of old mountain belts receives a logical explanation. Therefore isostasy is a factor to be reckoned with in mountain making but it can not be a primary cause.

Within the last few years some geologists have suggested that whole continents shift horizontally through long distances. It is claimed, for example, that Africa moved northward against the old Mediterranean geosyncline and crushed it to form the Alps and neighboring mountains; that the great folded chains of Asia were caused by southward shifting of that continent; and that the American cordilleras are the result of slow, long-continued westward drifting of North and South America. It is urged that no other explanation will suffice in view of the stupendous shortening recorded by mountain folds and thrusts. But even if we should admit the moving of continental masses, the fundamental problem of orogeny would remain unsolved so long as the ultimate forces and conditions to cause such movement are wholly unknown.

It must be admitted, therefore, that the cause of compressive deformation in the Earth's crust is one of the great mysteries of science and can be discussed only in a speculative way. The lack of definite knowledge on the subject is emphasized by the great diversity and contradictory character of attempted explanations. It is a fascinating problem, but lengthy discussion of its various aspects has no place in this volume. The facts and relationships of mountain structure present a large field of study in themselves, aside from the problem of ultimate forces.

Fault mountains that are due chiefly to thrust faulting present problems similar to those encountered in mountains with fold structure, since the fundamental cause is enormous lateral compression. Some steep faults that bound mountain blocks appear to be related to irregular shifting of magmas at depth, during the formation of intrusive or extrusive igneous bodies; and others are explained by vertical movements to restore or maintain isostatic balance with shift of load. Still others are formed in or near belts of severe folding, by irregular local twisting of the crust during the period of compression; and as fault mountains made in this way are merely incidental effects of the larger deformation, they become a part of the greater problem. Many dome mountains certainly owe their formation to igneous intrusion, and therefore the problem of their ultimate cause is closely linked with the problems of igneous activity. Some of the larger domes appear to be closely related in origin to great folded units, and therefore involve similar uncertainties as to origin.

Summary of Mountain History

Mountains may be classified generally according to types of structure, which reflect different forces that acted on the mountain zones. The visible structure may be due to simple dislocation and tilting of blocks, to simple doming of rocks, to folding with or without faulting, to large thrust movements, or to various combinations of these diverse processes. Connected with any type of movement there are commonly injections and extrusions of igneous material, which complicate the final structure of the mountain mass. Nearly all mountain-building movements take place in a series of pulses or phases distributed over a very long time; this is especially true of the chains that have complex structure. The cause of the great lateral pressure to which the belts of folding and thrusting bear eloquent testimony is an unsolved problem. We only know that long belts of weakness in the crust indicate their presence first by continued subsidence as geosynclines, and finally by yielding to forces that make the structures characteristic of the great mountains.

Actual elevation to mountain heights commonly follows the period of folding and appears to be largely independent of it. Repeated uplifts greatly prolong the efforts of erosion to destroy the great ranges.   Many chains owe their present existence to differential erosion following broad upwarping of old folded and faulted belts.   The continuous struggle between internal and external forces has left its clearest record in the diverse land forms of mountain regions.

READING REFERENCES

1. Mountains: Their Origin, Growth, and Decay; by James Geikie.   285 pages. D. Van Nostrand Co., New York, 1914.

Not up-to-date on all points, but has good descriptions, well written.

2. The Structure of the Alps; by Léon W. Collet.   272 pages.   Edward Arnold & Co., London, 1927.

An excellent guide book for the study of Alpine geology in the field.

CHAPTER XVII

LAND FORMS

GENESIS OF LAND FORMS

We have learned something of the various kinds of rocks that constitute the Earth's crust; we have examined the several processes that operate on the face of the Earth, and we have studied the intermittent movements of the crust that result from forces within the Earth. Having in mind these three factors, each of which exercises its own control over erosion and deposition, we are prepared to inquire into the shapes into which the land is sculptured. These shapes are termed *land forms*, and their study is important, not only because of their intrinsic interest, but because an understanding of a group of these forms greatly helps to reconstruct the later history of the part of the Earth in which they occur. Land forms are therefore a valuable means to an end, and should be studied as such.

Relation of Land Forms to Erosion and Deposition. — The wave-cut cliff is a feature so distinctive that even where we find it standing high above present sea level we confidently ascribe it to wave-sculpture and draw the further inference that it was carved either by a lake now extinct or by the sea later affected by a change of level. Similarly the undercut walls and slipoff slopes of a stream valley are so characteristic of fluvial sculpture that, even where we find these two features facing each other across a valley with no stream between them, we are sure that a stream formerly existed in the valley and that it carved the valley sides. Again, the discovery of a mountain crest partly consumed by the growth of cirques and notched here and there with cols leads us to the firm conclusion that the crest was formerly sculptured by valley glaciers even though none now exist there.

The wave-cut cliff, the slipoff slope, the undercut wall, the cirque, and the col, distinctive units in the surface of the land, are typical land forms. Each of these features is characteristic of the work of a specific group of processes: marine, fluvial, and glacial. Similarly the domes of the Yosemite (p. 21) are the work of weathering, the deflation hollows of the Gobi Desert and other arid regions (p. 158) are the work of the wind, the sinks (p. 90) common in limestone regions are the work of subsurface water, and the fillings of lake basins (p. 113) are the work of lakes.

It will be noted that all but the last of the forms mentioned are *erosional* in origin. The same groups of processes, however, also build up *depositional* land forms. The (marine) beach and bars, and (fluvial) fan, the (glacial) end-moraine, and the (eolian) dune are examples. Land forms, then, are determined by the processes that created them, and the processes are erosional or depositional or both.

Relation of Land Forms to Rock Composition and Structure. — Processes, however, are not the only factor involved in the making of land forms. A wave-cut cliff, an undercut valley wall, and a cirque carved from very resistant rocks are bolder, steeper, and more rugged than the same types of forms carved from very weak rocks. Each is still recognizable; each still records the process that sculptured it; but each clearly records the influence of an additional factor: the general composition of the rocks from which it was carved. Furthermore, land forms also commonly reflect the structure of the component rocks. For example, the steplike character of the walls of the Grand Canyon (p. 74; Fig. 4) shows at once that the rocks are essentially horizontal. Similarly the appearance of the ridges in Fig. 304, which are fluvially sculptured land forms, shows at once that they are being carved from folded rocks.

Igneous activity and movements of the Earth's crust exercise the chief control over the composition and structure of many rock masses from which land forms are carved. A volcanic cone, for example, evolves through a definite succession of land forms as it undergoes erosion by streams (p. 270). Fault-blocks likewise suffer a well-defined series of changes as erosion destroys their initial fault scarps and eventually creates fault-line scarps (p. 319).

Relation of Land Forms to the Cycle. — It is clear therefore that rock composition and structure combine with erosion and deposition to control land forms. Yet some additional factor must be involved. The land forms between the streams in Fig. 52 are very different in appearance from those in Fig. 51 in spite of the fact that the processes at work and the rocks being worked upon are identical in both figures. The only difference between the two, indeed, is one of age, the land mass shown in Fig. 52 being farther advanced in the cycle than the one shown in Fig. 51. Age or position in the cycle, therefore, in addition to the rocks and the process in operation, is an important factor in the shaping of land forms.

Value of Land-Form Study. — Every land-form unit therefore contributes to the temporary aspect of a continuously changing landscape, for it is evolved from different features that preceded it and it is certain to be altered into still different features by the processes that ceaselessly shape it. The practical value in the study of land forms lies in the fact that, since the character of any one unit usually betrays not only the rock composing it and the processes that sculptured it but also its position in the cycle, we can work backward from it and thus reconstruct landscapes that have long since disappeared. In this way we can bring to light chapters in the history of the Earth that would be legible by no other means.

The folding and uplift of strata discussed in the preceding chapter are accompanied and followed by erosion, usually with streams the chief agent. During the fluvial cycle of erosion of fold mountains, a number of characteristic land forms are evolved, which are common in many parts of the world and are easily recognizable when their origin is understood. It is therefore very important to examine the fluvial cycle on folded strata in contrast with the fluvial cycle on homogeneous rocks.

THE FLUVIAL CYCLE ON FOLDED STRATA

In a humid climate the erosion of an area of folded strata is based on the same principles that control erosion of homogeneous rocks (p. 67). Differences in detail, however, are introduced because of the unequal yielding to erosion of alternating weak and resistant rocks. Many variations are possible, but the following account, illustrated by Figs. 301–305, represents a typical cycle under these conditions.

Initial Stage. — Let the scene be set with a land mass in old age (essentially a peneplane) developed on a series of horizontal sedimentary rocks, alternately resistant and weak (Fig. 301). The area is drained eastward by a main stream that reaches the sea over a well-developed floodplain. The tributaries, because the rock is horizontal, form a dendritic pattern (p. 53).

Stage of Early Youth; Antecedent Streams and Synclinal Valleys. — This section of the crust then begins to be compressed, and as it gradually yields, it is very slowly bowed into a series of gentle folds (Fig. 302), of which one plunges northward. The main stream, its gradient increased by uplift attending the folding, is just able to cut downward through the slowly rising folds. A stream that is strong enough thus to maintain its former course in spite of uplifts across its path is said to be *antecedent*. Some of the streams that cross ranges of hills in the Los Angeles region in southern California are said to be antecedent to anticlines that form the ranges, and certain streams in central Washington are probably antecedent to anticlines lying across their courses. Here,

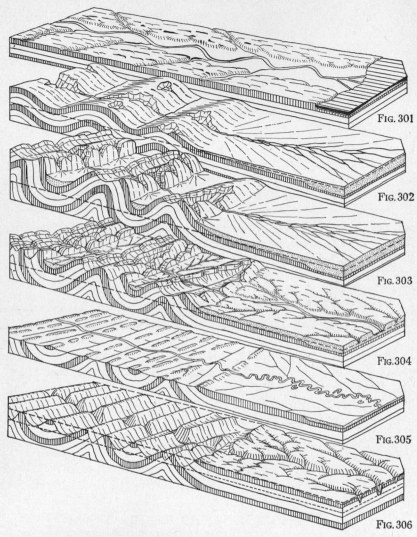

Figs. 301–306. — Fluvial cycle on folded strata in a humid climate.   Each block is
    oriented so that its right end faces east and its long upper edge faces north.

Fig. 301. — Initial stage, showing a land mass inherited from an earlier cycle.

Fig. 302. — Stage of early youth, showing the beginning of folding and the development
of an antecedent main stream with consequent tributaries forming a trellis pattern.

Fig. 303. — Stage of later youth, showing valley filling, extensive breaching of the anticlines, and the development of anticlinal valleys bordered by hogbacks.

Fig. 304. — Stage of maturity, showing dissection of the earlier valley filling, decrease in
relief, and the development of rounded ridges within the anticlines.

Fig. 305. — Stage of old age, showing the weak rocks reduced nearly to baselevel, leaving only monadnocks of resistant rock for the streams to cut.   Essentially a peneplane.

Fig. 306. — Stage of maturity in a second cycle instituted by regional uplift and rejuvenation.   (See p. 423.)   Also compare Figs. 321, 322.

however, the tributaries smaller and weaker than their main, do not fare so well; they are blocked off by the anticlines and are extinguished. But new drainage lines are provided by the synclinal troughs. Concentration of drainage takes place in each of these, and pairs of tributaries are thus developed at right angles to the main stream, as consequents upon the folded surface. In this way the dendritic stream pattern is extinguished and a right-angled, *trellis* pattern takes its place, with the chief tributaries occupying the synclinal tributary valleys. At the same time, rapid runoff down the slopes of the anticlines forms steep consequent tributaries of the second order, which rapidly excavate deep gorges. Directly these tributaries cut through the surface bed of resistant rock, and penetrate the weak bed below, they begin to

J. Barrell.

Fig. 307. — Lehigh Water Gap at Slatington, Pennsylvania. Cut by the Lehigh River through a ridge of resistant sandstone left standing above a weak-rock lowland. The flat top of the ridge is part of an uplifted former peneplane.

cut the weak rock, undermining the resistant rock and quickly widening their valleys. This process is characteristic of the early stages of the cycle, in that the weak rocks are attacked as widely as possible, while the resistant rocks, escaping direct attack, fall by undermining. The main stream crosses the anticlinal arches through *water gaps* of its own cutting, and its greatly increased load is deposited farther downstream. That the stream system is confronted by a long period of cutting is indicated by the volume of rock above the new baselevel (indicated by a dashed line, Fig. 302).

Stage of Later Youth; Hogbacks and Canoe-shaped Valleys. — The folding has now reached its climax (Fig. 303), and the anticlines grow no higher. The crests thereby attain their maximum elevation above baselevel (dashed line, Fig. 303). But because much erosion has taken place since the uplift began, the actual mountains can never be as high as might be inferred at a later time by projecting upward the stumps of the anticlinal limbs. Steepening of the anticlinal slopes (compare Fig. 303 with Fig. 302) has resulted in such greatly increased erosion by the tributaries of the second order that the streams in the synclinal valleys, whose gradients have not been steepened much since folding began, are not able to carry away the waste contributed to them. The synclinal valleys are therefore partly silted up with waste in the form of fans. The long ridges formed by the steeply dipping resistant bed are termed *hogbacks*. They are common in the Colorado Rockies (Fig.

M. R. Campbell, U. S. Geol. Survey.

Fig. 308. — Hogback of resistant sandstone at Morrison, Colorado. The sandstone bed is a part of the much eroded eastern limb of a great anticline from which the Colorado Rockies have been sculptured.

308), the Big Horn Mountains, the Black Hills (p. 431), and many other anticlinal mountain masses. Whereas the anticline in the center (Fig. 303) has been breached along its entire crest, the anticline to the east is only partially breached, and that where its axis is highest. Since this is a plunging fold, its axis descends to the north, and hence the tributaries of the second order have lower gradients. This being the case, their cutting power is far less than that of their steeper neighbors, and the resistant bed that caps the anticline is therefore much less readily cut through. This brings about the excavation of a *canoe-shaped valley*, the prow of the canoe pointing down the plunge of the anticlinal axis and the sides of the canoe formed by the hogbacks developed on the anticlinal limbs. The canoe gradually widens as the hogbacks are undermined. The whole structural skeleton is now dissected out in greatest relief, but the stream system has much cutting to accomplish before it can remove all the rock above baselevel and carry it into the sea.

Stage of Maturity. — The weak strata continue to receive the most vigorous direct attack by the streams, and the resistant strata fall block by block as they are sapped and undermined, widening the canoe-shaped valleys (Fig. 304). Erosion of the weak strata in the middle anticline has now completely laid bare the rounded back of the lower resistant bed, which like the higher resistant bed is breached to form an inner canoe-shaped valley. Figs. 303 and 304 show the appearance and development of other such rounded ridges in the hearts of the anticlines.

The whole land surface by this time has been reduced appreciably toward baselevel (dashed line, Fig. 304; compare Fig. 303). In fact the heights have been lowered sufficiently to decrease greatly the supply of waste to the tributaries. The latter, freed from a part of their load, are able again to devote a part of their energy to downcutting, and they begin to dissect their previous deposits in the synclinal valleys and in the region east of the anticlines, sculpturing them into pronounced terraces. The main stream has now come so close to baselevel that it can cut down but little farther. It swings laterally, develops meanders and broadens its valley by extensive lateral cutting. In this it is slowly followed by the tributaries in the synclines.

Stage of Old Age. — The increasing effectiveness of lateral cutting by the whole stream system during late maturity and old age results in the cutting away of the remaining highlands. The reason is simply that all the weak rock has already been worn down essentially to baselevel, leaving nothing but resistant rock for the streams to cut (Fig. 305; note that the dashed line has disappeared because the old-age surface practically coincides with it). Because of the great resistance of the only rock left above baselevel, and because the gradients are low, the process of cutting is almost infinitely slow. Fig. 305 depicts a peneplain with elongate monadnocks formed by outcropping edges of the resistant beds, together with one rounded ridge in the plunging anticline. The structure is essentially beveled, weak and resistant rocks alike (Fig. 310). The cycle is virtually ended; from now on the streams can work only to destroy the monadnocks, with scarcely appreciable results.

Adjustment of Streams to Structure. — Figs. 301–305 show that although the initial tributaries develop as consequents in the synclinal troughs they steadily decrease in importance until in old age (Fig. 305) they are almost completely extinguished. As the resistant rocks that form the crests of the anticlines are breached, tributaries develop in the underlying weak rocks, and extend their valleys headward from the main stream along the exposed belts of weak rock. Streams establishing themselves by growing headward along belts of weak rock in this manner are termed *subsequent streams*. As the cycle progresses, the subsequents rapidly eroding their weak-rock valleys gain over the consequents which have to cope with the resistant rocks in the synclinal troughs, so that before the end they have acquired the lion's share of the local runoff. From this the principle may be set up that *stream*

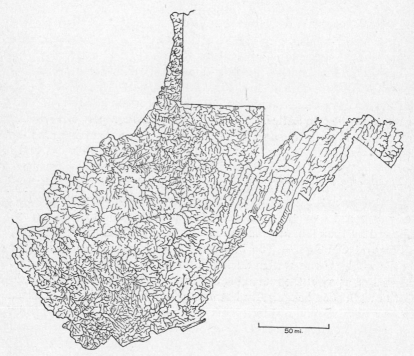

Fig. 309. — Stream patterns in West Virginia. In the central and western regions the rocks are nearly horizontal and the pattern is dendritic. In the east the rocks are strongly folded along NE-SW axes and the resulting pattern forms a trellis, the long straight streams being subsequents which have cut their valleys headward in belts of weak rock. Note how thoroughly the region is drained (mature dissection in a humid climate), and compare Fig. 59.

systems adjust their courses so as to flow as much as possible on weak rock and as little as possible on resistant rock. Drainage developed in folded strata rarely reaches an adjusted condition before late maturity or old age. The more or less complete adjustment of the larger streams in the folded Appalachians is illustrated in Fig. 309. From the trend of the trellis stream-pattern the strike of the folds can be readily inferred.

Significance of Uniform Beveling of Weak and Resistant Rocks. — The significant fact emerging from the description of such a cycle is that, if left undisturbed, streams, aided by the processes of chemical weathering, wear down a land mass to *a peneplane in which both weak and resistant rocks are evenly beveled* (Fig. 310). Remnants of such peneplanes exist in many parts of the world, each one cutting cleanly across rocks of various kinds and thereby testifying to the fact that it was formed at baselevel, the only level at which streams aided by weathering can cut down both weak and resistant rocks to a common plane.

Such peneplanes would be much more numerous if the Earth's crust were stable, allowing land masses to stand still throughout an entire

W. C. Mendenhall, U. S. Geol. Survey.

Fig. 310. — Beveling of strata of unequal resistance by a peneplane surface near Blue Canyon, Arizona. After uplift a terrace was formed at a lower level, also beveling the strata.

cycle of erosion. What happens in the majority of cases is that movement of the crust occurs long before the cycle is completed, either depressing the land, drowning the mouths of the valleys, and raising the baselevel, or causing the land to rise higher above the sea, increasing gradients and rates of erosion, and thereby starting the cycle over again. It is because of frequently repeated crustal uplifts of the land, forcing the streams to renew downcutting, that the continents have not long since been reduced to great low-lying peneplanes. Changes of level of land masses are therefore highly significant events in the history of the Earth. For this reason we must examine their effects on stream-sculptured land forms, so that by recognizing the sculptured forms in

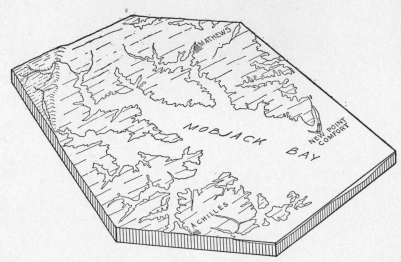

Fig. 311. — Mobjack Bay, an arm of Chesapeake Bay in the vicinity of Mathews, Virginia, showing its origin as a drowned stream system. Greatest length of block, 20 miles.

American Geographical Society.

Fig. 312. — Lambs Creek, another arm of Chesapeake Bay, Virginia, showing its drowned character. Vertical view from the air. (W. T. Lee, "The Face of the Earth as Seen from the Air.")

any region we can work back to the changes that produced them and thereby add still further to our knowledge of the Earth's past history.

Effects of Change of Level of a Land Mass

Downward Movement; Drowning

Downwarping of the crust beneath part of a stream's course sometimes causes a local decrease in gradient generally followed by extensive deposition. The effects of downward movements are most plainly visible, however, near the mouths of streams, which, if depressed below lake or sea level, become drowned (p. 185). The mouths of most of the large streams of the Atlantic coast of the United States are drowned; the Hudson is drowned as far upstream as Albany, and Chesapeake Bay represents the drowned lower courses of the Susquehanna and the Potomac combined (Figs. 311, 312). The bay is broad and shallow because it is cut in weak rocks. The mouths of streams in southwestern Britain and northwestern France likewise are drowned over wide areas. Extensive drowning results in a highly irregular shoreline (p. 186).

Uplift and Rejuvenation; the Second Cycle

Upwarping of the crust is likely to increase the cutting power of the streams affected, by increasing their gradients. A stream given an increased gradient is said to be *rejuvenated*. The effect of rejuvenation upon its valley is far more noticeable if the stream is already old or

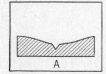 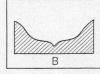 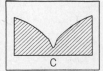 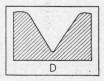

Fig. 313. — Transverse profiles of valleys showing that the effect of rejuvenation depends on the stage at which it occurs.
A, old stream rejuvenated: effect very strongly marked. *B*, mature stream rejuvenated: effect strongly marked; former valley floor cut into terraces. *C*, young stream rejuvenated: effect barely perceptible in the spurs along the valley sides. *D*, very young stream rejuvenated: effect not registered. Compare Fig. 314.

mature than if it is still in its youth (Fig. 313). This follows from the fact that renewed downcutting normally excavates a new V-shaped valley in the floor of the former one, and that if the existing valley is already V-shaped its transverse profile is scarcely altered. A keen eye can sometimes detect the evidence of uplift in a valley still youthful (Figs. 313*C*; 314).

If the evidences of uplift are distinct and widespread, the cycle of erosion is said to be ended (even though it is not completed) and a following or *second* cycle is instituted. Thus the valleys shown in Fig. 313*A*, *B*, and *C*, are now in a second cycle initiated by an uplift which has carried the land to a new position higher above baselevel.

C. R. Longwell, U. S. Geol. Survey.

Fig. 314. — East end of Boulder Canyon, southern Nevada. Note abrupt changes in slope of valley walls, suggesting at least two rejuvenations. Compare Fig. 313.

Incised Meanders. — If a meandering stream (p. 54) is affected by uplift so rapid that the rate of lateral cutting by the stream can not keep pace with it, the stream is rejuvenated in the meandering course it followed immediately prior to rejuvenation. The meander loops

H. H. Vinson.

Fig. 315. — Valley of the San Juan River 30 miles below Bluff, Utah. The stream has been rejuvenated, incising the meanders to a depth of 1200 feet. Note the outcrops of horizontal resistant strata.

are gradually excavated into a continuous winding gorge whose bends are separated by partition-like, steep-walled projecting spurs (Fig. 315). These winding gorges are *incised meanders,* and are usually an indication that relative uplift has taken place in the region where they occur.[1]

The meanders can not remain deeply and narrowly incised for long. The process of sweep (p. 56) begins to operate as soon as the incision begins. Lateral cutting is most rapid against those walls that face up the valley, while the stream tends to slip away from the walls that face down the valley. By this process the valley is gradually widened and the projecting spurs are destroyed.

On every continent there are more large streams with incised meanders than with normal meanders. This is a striking fact, and it furnishes one more proof of the instability of the Earth's crust by recording the repeated uplifting of land masses, with rejuvenation of their streams, and the institution of new cycles of erosion in the place of partially completed former cycles.

Stream Terraces. — Many stream valleys, particularly in their middle reaches, are bordered by bench-like flats (Fig. 316) the tops of which are

A. C. Waters.

Fig. 316. — Terraces of alluvium along the Columbia River near Chelan, Washington. Two distinct levels are visible, below which the stream has cut a deep channel. Note the fans built at the mouths of gullies in the terraces.

higher than even the flood stages of the present streams. Not uncommonly there are several benches in series, rising away from the stream like two long flights of steps facing each other. Usually they are small remnants, but in some valleys they are continuous for long distances. Because of their bench-like character and fluvial origin these forms are termed *stream terraces*. Some consist entirely of alluvium; others, resulting from deeper incision, consist of alluvium-veneered bedrock. Manifestly their surfaces are remnants of former valley floors into which the streams have cut trenches.

Some terraces occur in pairs, each pair at a nearly uniform height above the stream (Fig. 317). For each pair of terraces there must have been a sharp uplift of the land[1] and rejuvenation of the stream, setting up a

[1] Sudden decrease of stream load or increase of stream volume might accomplish essentially the same result.

new cycle and causing first renewed downcutting and then widening of the valley. Thus in Fig. 317 a peneplaned surface *a* must have been rejuvenated with downcutting and valley widening near baselevel *b*. A second uplift resulted in a new cycle marked by cutting of the

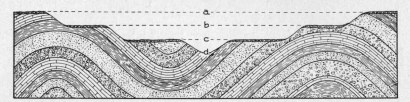

Fig. 317. — Paired terraces caused by successive rejuvenations. (After Wright, Virginia Geol. Survey.) Terraces *a*, *b*, and *c* are remnants of former valley floors elevated by three successive uplifts, the latest of which caused the excavation of the trench *d*. Width of cross-section, about one mile.

plane *c*, which after a third uplift was dissected into terraces by downcutting of the trench *d*. Obviously none of these four cycles was completed and no peneplanes were formed, for if so, the higher terraces would have been destroyed. Each terrace is veneered with a thin layer of alluvium deposited during the periods between the uplifts.

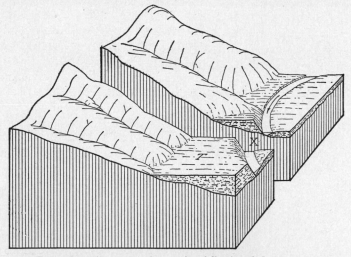

Fig. 318. — Formation of a terrace by erosion following deflection of a stream at *X*, where it impinges against a bedrock spur. The stream swings away from the spur, and as it cuts downward leaves the protected alluvium as a terrace, *T*.

On the other hand, some valleys contain terraces that are not paired, *i.e.*, that do not " match up " at a common height on both sides of the valley. Ordinarily such terraces occur along a stream that is swinging from side to side of its valley as it slowly lowers the valley floor. At various points the stream encounters the bedrock that constitutes the valley walls. Deflected by these resistant obstacles, it swings away and is thus prevented from undercutting the floodplain deposits that lie vertically above and immediately downstream from each outcrop of bedrock. The floodplain remnants remain as terraces (Fig. 318), gradually increasing in height as the stream continues to cut downward. But because the stream, lowering its bed, impinges first on one side of its valley and then on the other, no two terraces left on opposite sides of the valley will lie at exactly the same level, because the stream will have lowered its channel slightly between the time it deserts one valley wall and the time it encounters the other. As a result, the terraces do not occur in pairs at uniform heights on both sides of the valley (Fig. 319).

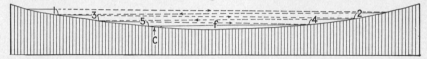

Fig. 319. — Non-paired terraces, left by a downcutting stream that is swinging from side to side of its valley, encountering bedrock, as in Fig. 318, at various points. Dashed lines indicate the path followed by the swinging stream. The terraces are numbered in the order in which they were cut. The present floodplain, *f*, is trenched by the channel *c*.

Many non-paired terraces have been formed by streams rejuvenated so gently that they are able to swing widely as they cut downward; others may have been cut by streams which, having reached grade in an uninterrupted cycle (p. 48), slowly continued to lower their valley floors.

The Uplifted Peneplane. — In some cases rejuvenation does not occur until the earlier cycle has reached the peneplane stage. The completion of the ideal cycle outlined on pages 411–415 and depicted in Figs. 301–305 is followed (Fig. 306) by uplift and rejuvenation, during which the peneplaned surface (upper dashed line) is lifted high above baselevel (lower dashed line). This permits the stream system to renew the work of excavation which it had completed under the old conditions. Reëxcavation is complicated by the fact that, although the surface itself has been smoothed out during the earlier cycle, the structure below the surface remains. The folded strata of unequal resistance are still there, having disappeared as relief features through the beveling effect of peneplanation, but they need only a second uplift of the land to bring them again into prominence. No new deformation of the rocks is required. A simple broad uplift such as has occurred repeatedly throughout the Earth's history accomplishes the result. The sluggish streams are rejuvenated; they begin to cut actively. The weak rocks are again etched away from the resistant rocks, which are left standing as prominent ridges. The tops of these ridges which were beveled flat during the earlier cycle are worn down so slowly that during all the early part of the second cycle they preserve the level of the former peneplane from which the intervening weak rocks have been cut away (Fig. 320). These *peneplane remnants* on the upper surfaces of the ridges can be formed only by uplift and the beginning of a second cycle following the completion of an earlier one. Thus the highest ridges of the present Appalachians are remnants of a former peneplane. Their

Dept. of Lands and Forests, Quebec.

Fig. 320. — Peneplaned mass uplifted 900 feet above sea level and dissected to a stage of maturity in the second cycle. The tops of the spurs and ridges are peneplane remnants beveling several different kinds of rocks, all of them strongly folded. Restigouche River near Campbellton, New Brunswick.

flat beveled tops betray the fact that they once stood at or close to baselevel and that they were later left in relief by erosion following a great uplift.

In Fig. 306 the weak rocks in the two synclines are temporarily preserved as ridges because they are protected by narrow caps of resistant rock. These caps must disappear in time, however, by being undermined, and the synclinal ridges will then be quickly destroyed. The completion of the second cycle will see a new peneplane (developed in the plane of the lower dashed line) much like that of Fig. 305. There will be two chief differences, however: (1) Monadnocks will be fewer because of the complete removal of the upper resistant layer from the two synclines. (2) The remaining monadnocks will be farther apart because the hard layers will be intersected farther down their limbs by the plane of the new baselevel. These ridges, apparently fixed in position, are in reality slowly migrating as they are eroded down the dip of the resistant strata of which they are composed.

Superposed Streams. — Adjustment to structure is not as common or as complete as might be supposed. Many large streams cut across the strike of weak and resistant rocks without any regard to their structure. Such a discordant relationship, we have seen, may be brought about by crustal warping or folding across the path of a previously existing stream, in which case the stream is *antecedent*. In Figs. 302–304 the antecedent character of the main stream is clearly shown by remnants of the folded surface still preserved in the tops of some of the anticlines. In Fig. 306, however, every vestige of the original folded surface has been destroyed, and there is therefore no way of proving the antecedent origin of the stream. But it is clear that the tops of the ridges represent remnants of a peneplane, and that the main stream, formerly flowing on the peneplane, was let down or *superposed* upon its present bed through uplift of the peneplaned land mass. The stream is then said to be *superposed from a peneplane*. Although we can usually be sure of the history of the stream since the peneplane was formed, ordinarily we have no means of knowing how the stream originally came to be discordant with the structure.

Streams can be superposed in another way. Suppose that the seaward part of a peneplane developed on folded strata of unequal resistance (Fig. 305) is depressed below sea level. During the resulting submergence, marine deposits are laid down almost horizontally upon the drowned peneplane, forming an angular unconformity (p. 322). When the monotonous marine plain is later uplifted, consequent streams develop on the gently sloping surface, exhibiting a dendritic drainage pattern (Fig. 321). In time the streams cut down through the unconformity into the different rock and complex structure below. In so doing they become *superposed from an unconformable cover* upon the underlying rocks, to which they are entirely unadjusted since their courses are inherited from the consequent courses assumed on the overlying horizontal strata (Fig. 322). Small remnants of the overlying cover remain throughout part of the cycle as caps on the ridges. As long as they remain, they testify to the manner in which the streams acquired their discordant courses.

Streams might be thus " let down from above " from glacial, volcanic, eolian, and alluvial deposits as well as from marine deposits. In any case, gradual adjustment will take place as the cycle progresses.

From the foregoing discussion we must conclude that a stream which through long distances cuts across the structure of folded rocks, and which therefore cuts water gaps in inclined resistant strata, must be either antecedent or superposed. If antecedent to the structure, the stream must have been in existence *before* the folding occurred, and have maintained its course in spite of the obstacle that rose across its path. If superposed upon the structure, the stream must have been let down either from a peneplane or from a cover of unconformable strata on to the discordant structure below. Neither consequent streams nor subsequent streams could occupy such markedly unadjusted positions without first going through one or other of these processes. And finally, since antecedent streams and more especially superposed streams are both numerous and widely distributed, we find in them still another evidence of the instability of the crust, and of the complexity of sculpture of the lands to which crustal movements give rise.

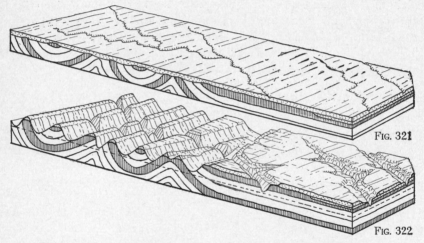

FIG. 321

FIG. 322

Figs. 321–322. — Superposition of a stream from an unconformable cover.

Fig. 321. — The peneplaned land mass of Fig. 305 has been submerged, covered unconformably with horizontal sedimentary strata, and reëlevated, and consequent streams have begun a new cycle on the uplifted surface.

Fig. 322. — Later stage, after the streams of Fig. 321 have cut down through the unconformity into the discordant rocks beneath. The horizontal strata have been eroded away except along the tops of the resistant ridges.

Wind Gaps; Capture by Subsequent Streams. — A water gap (Fig. 307) abandoned by its through-flowing stream becomes a *wind gap* (Fig. 323). Most wind gaps are the result of capture of the gap-cutting streams by more powerful subsequent streams.[1] This process is well illustrated by the case of Snickers Gap, a prominent notch in the Blue Ridge of Virginia 15 miles south of Harpers Ferry. The floor of this notch hangs 700 feet above the Shenandoah River at the west base of the ridge. A small stream, Beaverdam Creek, heads near Snickersville at the east base, and flows eastward away from the ridge. The notch is

[1] Wind gaps must be carefully distinguished from somewhat similar notches made by erosion along joints, faults, and other structures.

large, and must have been cut by a large stream. Its reconstructed history is this: During a cycle earlier than the one now in progress, when the land around the base of the Blue Ridge stood as high as the notch of Snickers Gap, this notch was occupied by a transverse stream,

J. Barrell.

Fig. 323. — Wind Gap in Kittatinny Mountain, the resistant ridge of sandstone shown in Fig. 7, at Pen Argyl, Pennsylvania. The gaps shown in Fig. 307 and Fig. 323 are related to each other in the manner shown in Fig. 326.

the ancestral Beaverdam Creek (Fig. 324). But the much larger transverse ancestral Potomac, which crossed the ridge 15 miles farther north, was able to cut its gap downward much more rapidly into the hard, ridge-forming rocks. The Shenandoah, a subsequent tributary to the Poto-

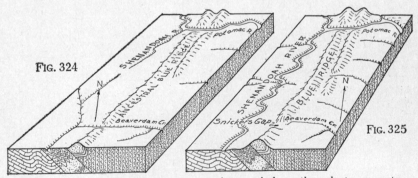

Figs. 324–325. — Evolution of a water gap into a wind gap through stream capture.

Fig. 324. — Former drainage across the Blue Ridge in northern Virginia.

Fig. 325. — Present drainage resulting from the beheading of Beaverdam Creek by the subsequent Shenandoah.

mac flowing north through an easily eroded limestone area west of the ridge, had no difficulty in keeping pace with its master stream, and with the resulting favorable gradient, lengthened its valley headward toward the south, cut through the divide that separated it from Beaverdam Creek, and "beheaded" the latter by diverting its upper course toward the Potomac (Fig. 325). The gap was forthwith abandoned, and the beheaded and weakened creek found itself confined to the area east of the Blue Ridge.   As the Shenandoah and the small streams east of the ridge continued to cut downward, the ridge was left standing in greater relief, with the abandoned gap high and dry.

Some wind gaps may have been formed by relatively weak streams which, affected by upwarps athwart their courses, were able to maintain their courses only for a time, having been later forced to abandon them and to flow along the trends of the upwarps.

COMPLEX HISTORY OF LAND FORMS

Thus far we have examined land forms sculptured by some one process only, in simple rocks of simple structure during one or at most two cycles. In many regions land forms have a more complex origin, but still they can be understood by applying to their study the same principles used in interpreting simpler forms.   We can best understand these complex features by seeing actual examples, and can begin with those characteristic of the Appalachians.

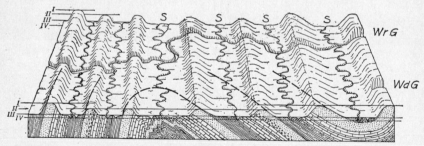

Fig. 326. — Ideal segment of a part of the northern folded Appalachian region.   The main stream is superposed, trenching seven ridges of resistant rock through seven water gaps (*WrG*).   A former stream course, long since abandoned, is indicated by a wind gap (*WdG*).   The present tributaries are subsequents (*SS*).   Four successive baselevels (*I, II, III, IV*) are indicated by four accordant series of summit levels or valley floors, thus indicating four regional uplifts relative to sea level, representing four successive cycles.   Compare Fig. 306.

History of the Appalachians

The Appalachians as we see them today consist chiefly of long parallel ridges formed by the outcrops of very resistant rocks such as sandstones and conglomerates in a strongly folded sedimentary series (Fig. 326). Most of the ridges, though narrow, have remarkably level summits, broken here and there by water gaps (*WrG*) and wind gaps (*WdG*). Even a casual observer might notice that groups of these ridges reach a common level (*II*, Fig. 326), and if he examined them more closely he could see that certain of them reach a notably uniform higher level

(*I*, Fig. 326). If our observer gave some attention to the lowlands (*III*, Fig. 326) between the ridges he would discover what appear to be broad terraces or old valley floors deeply dissected by small streams into a network of low hills. The small streams drain into larger meandering subsequent streams (*SSS*, Fig. 326), flowing along the strike of the strata, and all the meanders are incised. The subsequents in turn are tributary, in the northern and central Appalachians, to great streams that flow eastward indiscriminately across hard-rock ridges and weak-rock valleys. These streams are the Delaware, the Susquehanna, and the Potomac.

With these facts in mind, how much can we reconstruct of the Appalachians' history? *First,* a period of strong deformation, as revealed by the great folds whose eroded stumps appear in the ridges. Erosion must have begun during the first uplift, and have continued throughout at least one long cycle, resulting at length in a peneplane. This we know because the hard rocks in the folded series have been beveled down to a common level, as in the ridges *I* and in many others like them. Of course these rocks did not exist as ridges during the peneplane stage, but were merely parts of a low, gently undulating surface near sea level. *Second,* slow bodily uplift of the whole region, beginning a second cycle by rejuvenating the streams, most of which, being already adjusted and therefore in weak-rock courses, excavated the weak rocks again, leaving the resistant strata once more projecting as ridges. Near the close of this second cycle the entire surface was again reduced to a second peneplane at level *II*, upon which the ridges composed of the most resistant rocks (*I*) were not reduced, but persisted as long narrow monadnocks. *Third,* another slow upwarping, beginning a third cycle, during which the hard rocks beveled by peneplane *II* reappeared as ridges while the weak rocks were reduced to a new peneplaned surface *III*. The gap (*WdG*) must have been converted from a water gap into a wind gap early in this third cycle, because its floor lies at the level represented by the peneplane remnants *II*. Abandonment of the gap probably occurred through capture of the gap-cutting stream by a weak-rock subsequent (*S*; see also Figs. 324, 325). The new surface (*III*) was a very incomplete peneplane because of the great quantity of hard rock (all the *I* and *II* ridges) remaining unreduced. *Fourth,* another uplift, rejuvenating the streams and causing them to incise their meanders and with the aid of their tributaries to dissect their former valley floors (*III*) into the present network of small hills.

These appear to be the chief events in the history of the Appalachians, readily reconstructed through a study of their land forms. The main transverse streams (one of which is shown in Fig. 326) have been super-

posed from the highest peneplane (*I*), but their history prior to the time
of that peneplane is uncertain. Authorities are not as yet agreed as to
the date at which each peneplane was formed, but the whole sequence of
events from the folding of the strata down to the present may have
required 200 million years.

History of the Paris Basin

In northern France lies a shallow synclinal basin composed of alternating weak and resistant layers of marine sedimentary rock. The outcropping edges of the resistant strata give the whole basin the appearance

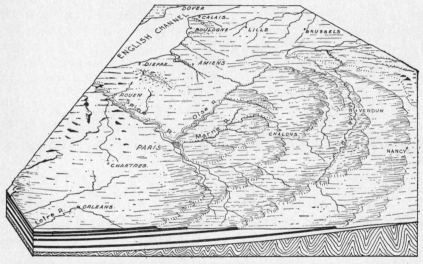

Fig. 327. — The Paris Basin, developed in a shallow syncline. Each of the outcropping
resistant strata forms a prominent cuesta. The River Seine is shown with its (subsequent)
adjusted tributaries. Length of front of block 200 miles.

of a low stack of dishes, each dish smaller than the one underneath it
(Fig. 327). Paris stands on the uppermost dish, which derives its
title of *Île de France* from the fact that its rim was once believed to
be a wave-cut cliff marking the shore of a former island.

Like the far higher and more resistant ridges of the Appalachians
(Fig. 326) the beveled rims of the dishes are remnants of a former
peneplane. The drainage pattern, also like that of the Appalachians,
consists of main streams (the Seine system) out of adjustment with
the symmetrical structure, and tributary streams some of which are
adjusted to the weak-rock belts beyond the edges of the resistant
strata.

The chief events in the history of the Paris Basin can be reconstructed from this evidence. After the sedimentary rocks were laid down in a former shallow sea, they were gently warped into a broad syncline and lifted above sea level. The resulting fluvial erosion at length reduced the entire area to a peneplane, evenly beveling weak and resistant rocks alike. On this peneplaned surface the major streams followed the unadjusted courses they have at present, although how they acquired these courses is not certain.

The peneplane was then uplifted, and the streams were rejuvenated and superposed from the peneplane. Rejuvenation resulted in the headward growth of a new generation of valleys along the weak-rock belts, forming a trellis drainage pattern. The excavation of these valleys left the resistant rocks standing in relief as asymmetrical ridges between them. A ridge of this kind formed by gently dipping resistant strata is a *cuesta*. Cuestas differ from hogbacks (p. 414) only in that they are formed by gently dipping instead of steeply dipping strata.

The growth of subsequent streams has resulted in partial adjustment of the streams to the structure; but the major streams still pursue the unadjusted courses they inherited from the peneplane recorded by the beveled tops of the cuestas.

The concentric arrangement of cuestas brought about by the basin-like structure gives the capital of France a unique series of natural fortifications. Furthermore, because of variations in the dip and character of the strata, cuestas are more strongly developed on the east side of the basin than on the west. This arrangement was of the highest importance to the Allied armies on the western front during the Great War, since it presented a series of difficult natural obstacles to the German advance.

History of the Black Hills

The Black Hills in southwestern South Dakota (Figs. 282, 328) form a great mass 100 miles long and 50 miles wide. The highest peaks rise 4000 feet above the surrounding territory. The center consists of a core of ancient metamorphic and igneous rocks locally cut by much younger igneous intrusions. Belts of sedimentary rocks chiefly of marine origin cut by the same intrusions are arranged symmetrically around it, dipping away from the central mass and neatly framing it. The frame of sedimentary rocks is made more distinct by the fact that the upturned edges of the more resistant strata form hogbacks and cuestas whose scarps face the central mass. The lowlands between the cuestas are drained by subsequent streams, which in turn are tributary to larger streams that radiate outward in all directions, cutting water gaps through the cuestas. The hogbacks and all but the highest ridges and divides on the central mass are beveled by an erosion surface resembling an imperfect peneplane.   Here and there remnants of a once continuous veneer of stream-deposited conglomerate, sandstone, and shale lie unconformably upon it.

These details enable us to reconstruct the history of the Black Hills. In shallow seas that once covered the entire area, the marine sedimentary strata were built up on the surface of the ancient rocks.   The whole mass was then arched into a great dome.   The arching was accompanied by intrusions of magma, some of which formed small laccoliths, doming the sedimentary rocks here and there.

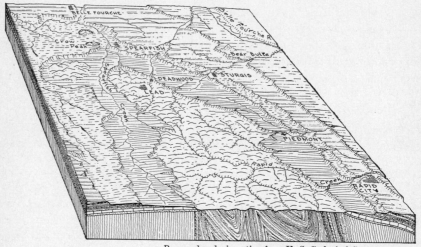

Base and geologic section from U. S. Geological Survey maps.

Fig. 328. — Northern end of the Black Hills, developed on a large dome breached and surrounded by cuestas along the outcropping edges of the resistant sedimentary strata. Bear Butte, Crow Peak, and the adjacent circular masses are laccoliths.   Length of front of block, 50 miles.   Geologic structure beneath the sedimentary caps generalized because details are not known.   (Compare Fig. 282.)

Streams developed on the dome, flowing off down the slopes and forming a pattern like the spokes of a wheel.   The dome was breached (Fig. 303).   Subsequent tributaries developed and cut their valleys headward along the strike of the weak layers of sedimentary rocks, leaving the resistant layers standing out as hogbacks and cuestas, each of which migrated steadily outward down the dip of the strata as erosion continued, thus laying bare more widely the central core.

The cycle initiated by the doming resulted at length in the reduction of the area to an incomplete peneplane truncating the dome, and leaving a central group of monadnocks composed of the ancient basement rocks.   Streams then deposited alluvium, shifting their courses from time to time and gradually building up an alluvial veneer that covered the surface.

A second uplift rejuvenated these streams, and as they cut down once more they became superposed from the unconformable cover on to the more complex structure below. The streams are still eroding in the cycle initiated by this uplift,[1] and have thus far only partially adjusted themselves to the structure on which they found themselves superposed. Bits of the old incomplete peneplane are still preserved at the tops of many of the divides, some of them still capped by ragged remnants of its unconformable cover.

The history of the Rocky Mountains in Colorado and Wyoming is similar in many respects to the history of the Black Hills. The evolution of the Rockies has been complicated, however, by the introduction in the higher ranges of a cycle of valley glaciation (p. 139) now in its waning stage. Glacial sculpture has imparted a sawtooth skyline to the high Rockies which is lacking in the non-glaciated Black Hills. There is evidence that the evolution of both the Rockies and the Black Hills from their folding to their present condition has required 60 million years.

Dissected Plateaus; the Grand Canyon Region

The land forms of the Grand Canyon region, although sculptured from structures much simpler than those of the Appalachians, the Paris Basin, and the Black Hills, are more impressive because of their great size. The initial land mass which is being carved up is a great plateau country that extends over much of Utah, Arizona, New Mexico, and western Colorado. The underlying rocks consist of both marine and non-marine sedimentary strata that have been lifted thousands of feet with very little deformation, so that they are still nearly horizontal. Here and there the flat-lying beds are interrupted by faults and flexures of minor significance compared with the plateau mass as a whole.

The surface of the plateau in the vicinity of the Grand Canyon is a well-developed plane that bevels the minor irregularities in the strata. It is an extensive peneplane recording the final product of a former cycle of erosion. Into this peneplaned surface the Colorado has incised its canyon (Fig. 4), with a course not adjusted to the structure represented by the flexures and faults. Evidently the stream must have followed this course on the peneplane, from which it was superposed as the surface was uplifted to form the plateau. The cause of the discordant course upon the peneplane is not certainly known. The uplift of the peneplane to a height of 6000 to 8000 feet above sea level instituted the

[1] Disregarding later minor uplifts recorded by stream terraces.

present "canyon cycle" of erosion, during which the rejuvenated Colorado has cut a gash locally more than a mile deep. In spite of this tremendous depth of excavation, the canyon cycle has not yet progressed beyond the stage of youth. Its tributaries have not worked far headward from the main stream, and have succeeded in making but little impression on the vast plateau surface. Near the river, where dissection is greatest, it is true that divides between the tributaries have been reduced to narrow spurs, and that some of these spurs have been carved up into huge strings of pyramids by tributaries of the second order (Fig. 329). Many of the pyramids are of moun-

Drawn by W. H. Holmes.

Fig. 329. — Part of the Grand Canyon seen from Point Sublime, showing dissection of the plateau surface into narrow ridges and spurs.

tainous size and would certainly be described as mountains if their origin as detached remnants of the near-by plateau were not so obvious.

The excavation of the canyon following the uplift of the peneplaned mass may not have required much more than a million years. After a far greater time has elapsed, however, the tributaries will have cut their valleys so far headward as to cut the plateau into a network of ridges and residual remnants, destroying the identity of the plateau and converting it into an intricate maze of buttes and spurs of mountainous size.

This process gives us a key to the origin of many masses commonly described as mountains, such as the Catskill Mountains, the Allegheny

Mountains, and the mountains of central Idaho. In the first two the rocks are essentially horizontal strata, whereas the rocks of the Idaho mountains are chiefly massive granite. In all three regions, however, the summits lie in a common plane. It is evident that such masses as these are merely dissected plateaus (p. 381).

History of the Great Lakes Region

The Appalachians, the Paris Basin, the Black Hills, and the plateaus of the Grand Canyon region show us that two or more cycles of erosion have had a hand in the modeling of many of the land forms of today. In each of the four regions described, the cycles were brought to an end by uplift and rejuvenation, permitting the same process, fluvial erosion, to operate on them anew. The Great Lakes region, on the contrary, has had a different history. The region as a whole is a great plain whose surface consists largely of glacial deposits left by the recent invasion of broad ice sheets (p. 151). The plain is interrupted by the basins of the several Great Lakes. The glacial material, although very thick in some places, is so thin elsewhere that it fails to mask the topography of the bedrock beneath it.

From a study of this topography, supplemented by data gained from the records of thousands of well-borings, we can reconstruct the landscape as it was before the ice sheets crept down from the north and covered it. The elongate basins now occupied by the lakes were then large stream valleys belonging to one or more well-developed systems fed by an intricate network of tributaries. Probably these former valleys were converted into lake basins by a combination of glacial erosion, local warping of the crust, and the heaping up of glacial deposits to form dams. The topography, in a stage of late youth or early maturity, may have resembled that of central Kentucky and Tennessee today. If glaciation had not occurred this region would have continued to evolve through the cycle on which it had begun. But the advent of the ice sheets introduced a second (glacial) cycle of erosion, and their subsequent wastage left the surface so profoundly altered that a third (fluvial) cycle was instituted. The principal valleys of the former stream system were filled with glacial deposits and many of them were entirely obliterated. The runoff was forced to follow courses consequent upon the newly made surface, substituting a new drainage pattern for the old.

The Great Lakes region therefore affords an example of a three-cycle development of a group of land forms in which the second and third cycles were introduced not by uplift and rejuvenation but by *change of process.* The glacial (second) cycle has left an impress upon the present (third) cycle that can not be obliterated for a long time to come, because even though the glacial deposits should be completely removed by erosion, the streams developed on their surface would inevitably be superposed on the underlying bedrock, with which they would be out of adjustment. The former presence of the unconformable cover could therefore be inferred even though it had been entirely stripped away.

Conclusion

The foregoing discussion brings out the fact that land forms are the response of the surface of the land to various processes acting for various lengths of time upon various kinds of rocks having various structures. Alter one of these factors and the land forms respond at once. The process factor depends chiefly on climate. Thus a change from a moist climate to a dry climate may cause the development of interior drainage and increase the efficacy of the wind as an agent of erosion, whereas a change from a temperate climate to a cold climate may freeze the water into perennial ice and bring on a cycle of glaciation.

Composition and structure of the rocks likewise are of vital importance to the land forms modeled by any of the erosional processes. For example, the landscape fluvially sculptured from a mass of weak rocks elevated only slightly above the sea can never evolve beyond rolling monotony even in maturity when relief is greatest, because gradients are necessarily low at the outset. On the other hand, resistant rocks lifted high above sea level will be cut by valleys with steep gradients and steep sidewalls, which yield very slowly to the changes wrought by erosion during the progress of the cycle.

Thus it appears that the seemingly unending variety of landscape is controlled in reality by comparatively few factors, and that variations in these factors result in the differences in scenery that lend enjoyment to travel and add to the value of human existence.

READING REFERENCES

1. Geomorphology of New Zealand; by C. A. Cotton. 462 pages. Dominion Museum, Wellington, N. Z., 1926.

A systematic treatise on land forms, arranged chiefly according to processes, with examples drawn from the landscape of New Zealand.

2. Earth Sculpture; by James Geikie. 320 pages. John Murray, London, 1898.

A treatise on land forms containing much good material although based on a somewhat empirical classification.

3. The Scientific Study of Scenery; by J. E. Marr. Chaps. 8, 9, 10. Methuen & Co., London, sixth edition, 1920.

Very readable but by no means complete.

4. Battlefields of the World War; by Douglas W. Johnson. 648 pages. American Geographical Society, New York, 1921.

A most interesting account of the war on both western and southeastern fronts, laying special stress on the influence of land forms on the character and conduct of the fighting.

5. The Seine, the Meuse, and the Moselle; by W. M. Davis. Geographical Essays, Boston, pp. 587–616, 1909.

The interrelated histories of three neighboring streams.

6. The Rivers and Valleys of Pennsylvania; by W. M. Davis. Geographical Essays, Boston, pp. 413–484, 1909.

A complicated but valuable discussion, emphasizing many of the details of fluvial sculpture in folded strata.

CHAPTER XVIII

MINERAL RESOURCES

Relation of Mineral Resources to Geology

One of the striking features of modern civilization is its dependence on mineral products. The mineral industry is second in importance only to agriculture. During the first quarter of the present century more of the world's mineral resources was mined than in all previous history. As a result our mineral resources are being consumed at an unprecedented rate. Practically, this enormous draft on our mineral resources means that the known supplies are being rapidly exhausted and that in order to maintain production the discovery of new supplies must keep pace with exhaustion. The easily found mineral deposits have already been discovered, so that more ingenuity and more work are necessary to find new deposits. Therefore the cost of discovering new deposits is steadily rising. It is the counsel of prudence, then, to enlist all possible aids to minimize the financial risks of exploration. The application of the principles of geology to the search for valuable mineral deposits is one of the main functions of economic geology. Powerful auxiliaries to aid in this search have recently been developed, notably the seismograph for " seismic prospecting," the torsion balance, and other geophysical instruments. We call these instruments auxiliaries advisedly, for the results obtained by their use must be interpreted in the light of the geology of the area examined before they can become practically useful.

More important even than the aid given by applied geology in finding new deposits is its power to guide intelligently the development and exploitation of the deposits already found.

An economically valuable mineral deposit represents a concentrated accumulation of substance that originally was thinly scattered through one of the envelopes of the Earth. A coal bed is made up of carbon that has been concentrated by the photosynthetic power of plants from the carbon dioxide thinly diffused throughout the atmosphere; an oil pool is an accumulation of petroleum generated from carbonaceous matter thinly scattered through certain sedimentary strata; an iron-ore deposit is an amassment of iron that was disseminated through the Earth's crust.

The problem of the origin of valuable mineral deposits is in essence then the problem of how the scattered material became concentrated. It is mainly from this point of view that the following presentation is written. It will appear that all the major geologic processes — igneous action, sedimentation, metamorphism, weathering, and erosion — have under certain circumstances brought about the valuable concentrations of minerals.

COAL

Coal is the chief mineral fuel. The per capita consumption in the United States, having risen from 2.5 tons per year in 1890, has recently shown a tendency to become stabilized at 5 tons per year. Although coal is a far more prosaic resource than gold or the industrial metals, it vastly outdistances them in value. The Pittsburgh coal bed is the most valuable single mineral deposit in the world. In Pennsylvania alone it has already yielded $6,500,000,000. More than 3500 million tons of coal have been mined from it in Pennsylvania, West Virginia, Ohio, and Maryland, and it still contains several times that amount.

Occurrence and Nature of Coals. — Coals are compact masses of carbonized (coalified) plant débris. Peat, the embryonic form of coal, has already been described (p. 116). From peat to anthracite there exists a complete series of gradational varieties of coals, and it was this gradation that led to the conclusion that all coals, no matter how structureless and amorphous in appearance, consist of carbonized plant remains. This conclusion has now been fully confirmed by the results of modern microscopic study, which have shown that coals are not amorphous but consist of plant débris in various stages of alteration. Fragments of wood, bark, leaves, roots, spores, seedcoats, lumps of resin, etc., have been recognized. Even in such highly coalified material as anthracite the plant ingredients can be made visible, and unexpectedly enough, are found to be so well preserved that many of them can be specifically identified. Coals occur in beds which are inclosed as a rule between sandstones and shales. Their association with strata of this kind harmonizes with the other evidence that they accumulated in freshwater swamps. Limestones are rare, either immediately above or below a coal bed, and where they do occur they indicate that the swamp was near the sea and at sea level and therefore likely to be subjected at intervals to marine inundation.

Most beds of coal are underlain by a layer of clay, the underclay, which, because it contains the roots of plants, is interpreted as a fossil soil. Stumps of large trees, with their root systems in place, occur in abundance in some coal fields. These features lend support to the prevailing idea that the coal beds were formed from plant matter that grew in place.

Chemical Composition of Coals. — It is customary to ascertain the composition of coals in determining their value as fuels, and in the ordinary analysis the following constituents are reported:

(1) Fixed carbon, the carbon that is left after the gas has been driven off; (2) volatile matter, mainly combustible hydrocarbons (" gas ") but including some inert gases, such as carbon dioxide; (3) moisture; (4) ash; and (5) sulphur.

The fuel value of a coal depends on the fixed carbon and volatile combustible matter, whereas the moisture, ash, and sulphur are undesirable ingredients.

Classification of Coals by Ranks. — Coals can be classified according to ranks by a combination of their fixed carbon content and their physical properties. There is a continuous gradation from low-rank to high-rank coals; the divisions adopted must therefore be arbitrary. The lowest-rank coals are the *lignites,* as they are called in reference to their obviously woody appearance, or *brown coals,* in reference to their color. These immature coals when taken from the mine may appear to be perfectly dry, yet they contain 30 to 40 per cent of moisture. On exposure they lose most of this water; they slack and crumble to pieces and become dangerously subject to spontaneous ignition. The medium-rank coals are the *bituminous.* They do not slack on exposure and generally have a prismatic jointing perpendicular to their banding. In a more detailed classification the coals intermediate between lignite and bituminous are termed *subbituminous:* their black color and non-woody structure distinguishes them from the lignites, and their tendency to slack distinguishes them from the bituminous coals. The highest-rank coal is *anthracite,* distinguished physically from the bituminous varieties by its conchoidal fracture and absence of cross-jointing. Moisture and volatile matter are extremely low, and nearly all the carbon is fixed carbon.

The increase in the rank of a coal, then, is marked by the progressive increase in the fixed-carbon content and the decrease of volatile matter.

Relation of Rank of Coal to the Geologic History of the Coal. — Coals have formed in all the geologic periods since the establishment of a flora on the lands. Most of them have formed in coastal swamps. The nature of the environment in which they were formed is inferred from the botanical character of the coal-forming flora and from the character of the inclosing sedimentary strata.

There are two stages in the transformation of plant matter into coal — a biochemical and a geochemical. The biochemical stage consists of a bacterial fermentation (p. 116), which after a longer or shorter interval becomes arrested by the toxic products formed during the bacterial activity. The various substances of which the plants are composed — a dozen or so — are destroyed in a definite order: the most sensitive — the protoplasm — disappearing first, and the most resistant — the waxes and resins — last. Accordingly, the duration and intensity of the biochemical stage determine the proportions of the ingredient material of the coal. The composition thus acquired influences somewhat the future history of the coal.

The subsequent changes are termed geochemical, because the chemical changes in the coals are determined by geologic activities. The most influential factor is folding of the strata, which raises the rank of the coal by eliminating the moisture and volatile combustible matter. Nowhere is this better shown than in the Appalachian belt. In Ohio the coal-bearing strata are horizontal, but as we go eastward across the coal belt they become more and more closely folded. Concurrently there is a rise of more than 40 per cent in the fixed-carbon content of the coal. The anthracite fields of Pennsylvania, which furnish 99.9 per cent of this country's supply of anthracite, are in the highly folded portion of the Appalachian coal field, and in them the coal has been nearly completely devolatilized.

One-third of the unmined coal reserves of the United States is in the Fort Union lignite field of the northern Great Plains and adjacent portions of the Rocky Mountains. In the Dakotas and eastern Montana this coal is of very low rank, containing as much as 40 per cent of moisture when mined; and though it occurs in beds 4 to 40 feet thick, it can hardly compete in its own territory with coal imported from Illinois. Westward toward the Rocky Mountains the lignite rises in rank, and near the mountains, where the effects of mountain-making forces were more pronounced, the lignite has been transformed into a valuable fuel.

Coal, then, is sensitive to metamorphism; it is in fact the most sensitive substance in the Earth's crust and gives indications of metamorphism long before the associated rock strata show any signs of alteration. By means of chemical analyses the changes in the coals due to this metamorphism can be determined accurately; and as many analyses of coals are available in most coal fields, it is possible to show on a map the regional variations in the intensity of metamorphism.

Oil and Gas

Oil, or petroleum as it is more formally called, consists of various hydrocarbons — gaseous, liquid, and solid — in mutual solution. As there are many of these hydrocarbons (compounds of carbon with hydrogen) and as they are mixed in various proportions, the oils differ markedly in the various oil fields. A distinction is commonly made between *light oils*, those much lighter than water, and *heavy oils*, which are near water in specific gravity. The light oils have a high content of gasoline, whereas the heavy oils are low in gasoline. As the gasoline content largely determines the commercial value, the light oils command a considerably higher price per barrel than the heavy oils.

Requisite Conditions for the Occurrence of Oil. — Four conditions must be fulfilled in order that oil can accumulate in the rocks. First a *source rock* must be present containing the necessary carbonaceous matter from which the oil can be formed. Apparently it is necessary that this carbonaceous matter should consist of plant remains of a special kind high in hydrogen, such as spores, which thus supply the hydrocarbons of which petroleum is composed. As a result of experience it appears that marine bituminous shales are the most common source rocks; limestones are rarely source rocks. Why rocks of freshwater origin should not give rise to valuable accumulations of oil has not yet been ascertained, but the fact of their unfavorable nature is of great practical interest, for it excludes from consideration areas underlain by such strata as most unlikely to contain valuable accumulations of oil.

The second requisite is a *reservoir rock* in which the oil can accumulate. Most commonly the reservoir rock consists of sandstone, whose pores are large enough to allow the oil to move freely through it. Less commonly limestone and dolomite serve as reservoir rocks. In sandstones the average pore space is 15 per cent, and the range is from 5 to 40 per cent; in other words, a sandstone of maximum porosity can hold eight times as much oil as one of minimum porosity.

The third requisite is a favorable structural arrangement of the strata, which is the condition that determines the place where the oil collects in the reservoir rock. The most simple form of such a favorable geologic structure is an anticline. It was the first structure that was recognized as controlling the accumulation of oil, but now nearly twenty kinds of structural traps are known to occur in the world's oil fields.

The fourth requisite is an impervious layer, generally shale or clay, which overlies the reservoir stratum, and which with the structural arrangement forms a structural trap in which the oil is held.

All four conditions are fundamental for the occurrence of oil; without any one of them commercial accumulations of oil are impossible. Inasmuch, however, as structure controls within rather narrow limits the actual underground position of an oil accumulation, and in geologic practice the structure is determined as accurately as possible in advance of putting down a well, the structural requisite is generally known as the principle of the structural control of oil accumulation. The mode of occurrence of oil in an anticline is shown in Fig. 330.

If, because of insufficient pressure, free gas occurs with the oil (under heavy pressure all the gas would be dissolved in the oil), there will be

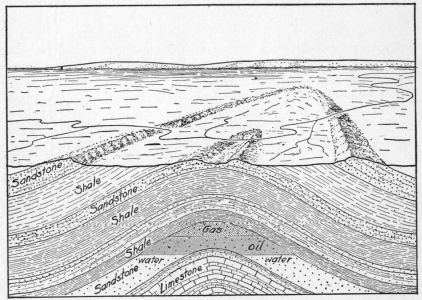

Fig. 330. — Occurrence of gas, oil, and water in an anticlinal structure.

this triple arrangement: gas fills the pore space in the reservoir rock in the arch of the anticline, below it oil fills the pore space in the reservoir rock, and below this occurs water, generally so charged with salts as to be termed a brine. The arrangement is thus according to specific gravity: the brine, which is heaviest, is at the bottom; and the gas, which is lightest, is at the top. The oil that fills the body of porous rock forms what in popular parlance is called the " oil pool."

If the sedimentary strata contain no water, the oil instead of occupying the upper parts of the anticlines occurs in the bottoms of the synclines. Recognition of the requisite conditions governing the accumulation of oil make it possible in a given territory to block out the impossibly and improbably oil-bearing areas. Areas of igneous and metamorphic rocks can contain no petroleum, and areas of non-marine strata, if not impossibly petroliferous, are at most improbably petroleum-bearing.

Life of an Oil Well. — The gas, oil, and salt water in an oil-bearing structure, such as shown in Fig. 330, have in the course of geologic time attained an equilibrium. As soon as the top of the structure is perforated by the drill this equilibrium is violently disturbed, and the disturbance spreads radially from the well. At first the well produces gas, then it becomes a gusher or flowing oil well, later it has to be pumped, and finally salt water appears with the oil, presaging the extinction of the well. The withdrawal of the gas causes the oil to move to the upper part of the structure, and the water follows up after the oil: not in all pools, but in many of them. Oil, being a fluid, migrates readily in the direction of decreased pressure. Consequently it recognizes no property lines, and if the pool is under divided ownership the first wells that tap the reservoir drain not only the oil within their own tracts but also, if situated near the property lines, the oil from the adjacent tracts.

Coarsely porous rocks yield their oil freely and give rise to extremely productive gushers. But they become exhausted rapidly — a fast life and a short one go together here. Finely porous rocks hold on to their oil tenaciously and so prolong the life of a well into old age. The record-breaking Mexican wells, which yielded as much as 260,000 barrels a day, drew their oil from limestones, which like most limestones contained solution channels and cavities; the oil therefore escaped with enormous rapidity and gave the wells their astounding yields, and for the same reason their period of production was short.

Function of Gas in Oil-Field Operation. — The chief gas associated with oil is methane, CH_4, the simplest of all the hydrocarbons. This gas and other allied gases collectively called " the gas " are dissolved in the oil under heavy pressure. The great importance of this natural gas in the efficient operation of an oil field is just beginning to be appreciated. In most fields it is the chief agent that brings the oil to the surface: it drives the oil to the well and lifts it to the surface; it reduces the viscosity of the oil and the tenacity with which it is held in the pores of the rocks. This tenacity is so great that after an oil field is " exhausted," that is, after it ceases to yield oil by pumping, 75 per cent or more of the oil is still underground. Less oil is left in the ground if the gas content is properly utilized. The more efficiently the gas is utilized the smaller the number of cubic feet of gas that are required to bring a barrel of oil to the surface.

Because of these important functions of the gas and because the withdrawal of the gas from any part of an oil pool eventually affects pressure conditions throughout the whole pool, it has been made unlawful in some

States to waste the gas content of an oil pool. An oil pool is a natural unit, and it is becoming apparent that to operate it most efficiently and to obtain the maximum recovery of oil it must be operated as a unit.

Geophysical Prospecting. — One of the most remarkable of the seven oil regions of the United States is the Gulf Coast field of Louisiana and Texas. The oil is associated with cylindrical or steeply conical masses of rock-salt which, forced to flow plastically under heavy pressure, have punched their way up from unknown depths through the overlying sedimentary strata. These masses are termed *plugs*, and most of them are a mile or so in diameter. The tops of some of the salt plugs are practically at the surface, but many of them are deep below the surface. Oil occurs in three kinds of structural traps: (1) cap rock, a peculiar rock made of calcite, gypsum, and anhydrite occurring as a capping over the tops of the salt plugs; (2) flanking sands, abutting upon and cut off by the salt plug; and (3) super-cap sands, the sandy strata that arch over the tops of the plugs, forming structural domes. Few of the salt-plug fields, however, produce oil from all three structures. The first of these oil fields to be brought in was the famous Spindletop, near Beaumont, Texas, discovered in 1901. Spindletop is a circular mound rising 65 feet above the otherwise level monotony of the Gulf coastal plain. The top of the salt plug is at a depth of 1100 feet, and the mound at the surface appears to have been due to a renewed upward push by the salt below. Many salt plugs, however, are without mounds or any other indication at the surface that they are present at depth. In recent years, geophysical methods have been employed with brilliant success in locating these hidden salt plugs. In essence the various geophysical methods depend on the fact that the physical properties of the salt differ greatly from those of the surrounding rocks. Use of the seismograph was introduced in the Gulf Coast region in 1924 and has probably been the most successful of the several geophysical methods employed, though the torsion balance, an extraordinarily sensitive instrument for measuring variations in the value of gravitational attraction, is more accurate for detailed work. The seismic method depends on the fact that the speed of earthquake waves is three times as fast through salt as it is through the adjacent strata. Artificial tremors are induced by the explosion of charges of dynamite, and the rate at which the waves travel is determined by appropriately located seismographs; those waves that travel for part of their course through a salt mass have the shortest travel-times. As a result of growing experience the methods are rapidly improving, and depths can be measured by the reflection of the waves. During the early years of seismic prospecting the effective working depth was 2500 feet, then it increased to 4500 feet, and lately to 7500 feet. The Gulf region is now being " re-shot " for the third and fourth times to locate the favorable oil-bearing structures formed by the deeper salt plugs. Whereas the discovery well at Spindletop was brought in at a depth of 1100 feet, oil is now being obtained from wells 6000 to 7000 feet deep, and exploratory wells have penetrated to depths of 7000 to 8000 feet. Geophysical methods were first used in the Gulf Coast region in 1924, and in the next four or five years as many domes were found as in the preceding thirty years.

The recent developments in seismic methods illustrate the reciprocal influence of pure and applied science. The seismograph was devised to study the transmission of earthquake waves, without thought of practical application. It was first used in the search for oil in 1924, and immediately methods and instruments began to improve at an accelerated rate. The technique thus developed in response to practical considerations is now being applied to such matters of theoretical interest as the determination of the thickness of glaciers in the Alps and of the ice sheet in Greenland.

ORE DEPOSITS

In addition to the mineral fuels, modern industry utilizes a large number of other mineral substances. At present the number reaches seventy-seven, but it will undoubtedly grow, for research is steadily finding or creating new uses for mineral products, and minerals considered today to be only of scientific interest may tomorrow become of economic importance.

It is customary to consider mineral deposits under the categories *metallic* and *nonmetallic*, on account of the very different natures, associations, and modes of origin of the two classes. The metallic, or more accurately, the metalliferous, include the deposits of the industrial metals and the precious metals — gold, silver, platinum, and allied metals; the nonmetallic include the mineral fuels, building stones, ceramic materials, gems, and a host of others. The nonmetallic substances mined in the United States exceed the metallic threefold in value of annual output, and the trend of the times is toward their greater and greater industrial utilization.

Primary Deposits

Definition of Ore. — An ore is a mineral aggregate from which one or more metals can be extracted at a profit. The essence of this definition is in the phrase " at a profit," for " ore " is an economic concept. Consequently many factors influence what is and what is not ore. When, as in 1931, the price of copper sank to 7 cents a pound, far below its long-time average of 13 cents, much copper-bearing material that had been ore fell out of the class of ore. On the other hand, the steadily increasing purchasing power of gold is restoring to the rank of ore much gold-bearing material that has not been ore during the last decade. Advances in metallurgical technique by making it profitable to work material of lower and lower grade also influence the status of what is or is not ore. The development of new uses can transform a worthless material into a valuable ore; for example, the discovery that the metal tungsten is one of the most useful steel-alloying elements has changed the status of its chief mineral from being considered an opprobrious impurity to a much-sought constituent.

Mineralogically, an ore consists of one or more metalliferous minerals inclosed in a matrix of worthless material. Technically this matrix consisting of mineral or rock matter is termed the *gangue*. The relative proportions of valuable constituent and gangue vary enormously; an iron ore of the highest grade consists solidly of the iron-bearing mineral magnetite, but iron ores at the lower limit of commercial availability consist of 30 per cent of magnetite mixed with 70 per cent of gangue. In contrast, most gold ores contain 0.001 per cent of gold disseminated through 99.999 per cent of gangue. In general, the amount of gangue in average ores largely exceeds the amount of valuable metalliferous material they contain. In the preliminary treatment of ores in metallurgical plants the prime purpose is to separate as cleanly as possible the metalliferous constituents from the gangue. As the result of this treatment, concentrates are produced which are much higher in metal content. The nature of the gangue influences the cost of concentration and subsequent treatment; hence the gangue is often as important as the metallic content in determining whether a material is ore. From many mining districts the concentrates are shipped to industrial centers for final treatment: zinc concentrate from Australia to Belgium, tin-bearing concentrate from Bolivia to Germany; literally from the ends of the Earth, and this movement of mineral commodities bulks large in international commerce.

The metallic content of the ores of the precious metals — gold, silver, and platinum — is measured in ounces per ton, though gold ore, because gold by legal enactment has the fixed value of $20.67 an ounce, is commonly cited as carrying so many dollars to the ton. The industrial metals are generally measured in per cents.

Occurrence and Origin of Ore Deposits. — Ore deposits as a rule do not occur singly but are grouped in small areas, and these mineralized areas determine where the world's mining districts are situated. Many of these districts produce predominantly one metal; indeed some districts produce only one metal. Hence mining districts are usually designated by their principal product, as the Rand gold district of South Africa, or the Butte copper district of Montana.

The habit of ore deposits to be localized in districts — their gregariousness as we may call it — is of advantage to man in many ways. Among these advantages is the fact that an intensive study of a district leads to a knowledge of the idiosyncrasies of its ore bodies that is of value in finding extensions of the known ore bodies and in finding the still undiscovered deposits; in fact, up to date this has been the most fruitful method so far developed in ore hunting.

Most mining districts are situated near, around, or on areas of igneous rocks. Indeed, this association is so common that, if igneous rocks do not occur in or near a mining district, it is thought by many that they are nevertheless present but concealed in depth; but this is probably an extreme view.

The geographic association of mining districts with igneous rocks early led to the idea that there is a fundamental relation between the occurrence of the igneous rocks and the origin of ore deposits. The fact that at Vesuvius and other volcanoes during times of heightened activity hot gases carrying iron, copper, and lead are given off and visibly form minerals, such as galena and hematite, suggested that the magmas from which the igneous rocks were formed supplied the metals in the ore deposits and that the metals were released from the magma at the time it solidified. The magma is the ore-bringer.

Most ore bodies formed in connection with igneous action are associated with plutonic rocks occurring as stocks and batholiths. Some occur in areas of volcanic rocks, but here the ore-forming solutions as well as the volcanic rocks themselves are both derivatives from a parent magma that solidified under plutonic conditions at a comparatively shallow depth, possibly a mile or two beneath the surface. In a few mining districts the ore deposits occur in volcanic necks. As a general rule the ore deposits genetically associated with stocks and batholiths have a greater vertical range than those associated with volcanic rocks: they persist to greater depths — at present the world's record for depth on an ore body of this origin is held by a gold mine in Brazil whose depth exceeds 7000 feet; whereas the deposits associated with volcanic rocks are likely to give out at depths of 500 to 1000 feet.

The solutions by means of which metals leave the magma are at high temperatures, so high that they are gaseous. As these solutions move upward through fissures toward the Earth's surface, they are steadily losing temperature, they are reacting with the wall rocks of the fissures, they are becoming admixed with more or less ground water, and the pressure on them is diminishing. As a result the composition of the solutions changes and certain constituents become insoluble and are deposited in the fissures. It is probable that the loss of temperature is the most potent factor in thus causing precipitation. As the solutions leave the magma they are gaseous, consisting mainly of steam, but during their journey upward they become condensed to water. Such hot-water solutions are the agents by which a majority of ore bodies have been formed, and the ores thus deposited are said to be of *hydrothermal* origin.

On this theory of origin every mineral deposit, if explored deeply enough, would be found to give out in depth; in other words, every vein or lode has roots. The theory explains readily the well-known fact that the interiors of large areas of intrusive igneous rocks (batholiths) are barren of mineral deposits. The large size of an area of exposed igneous rock is the result of widespread removal of the rocks that once extended as a roof over the igneous mass; consequently, as the top of a batholith is roughly dome-shaped, the greatest vertical thickness of rock has been removed from over the central portion of the area of igneous rock. In the interior, then, erosion has cut down deeply enough to remove even the roots of whatever veins were once present, toward the borders the roots remain, and at the borders and in the surrounding rocks the veins still have a considerable vertical range.

That veins persist downward in some batholiths, as at Butte, Montana, to depths exceeding 4000 feet, proves that the batholith had solidified to a depth of more than 4000 feet before this shell thus formed began to fracture and allow the magmatic gases to escape from the still-fluid magma beneath it. The fracturing that makes the channel-ways for the ascending solutions is likely to persist over a long time. Recurrent movements may reopen the veins, as already mentioned, and in many districts later fracturing has severed the veins and dislocated the segments. It is one of the tasks of structural geology to determine the laws that govern the formation of the channel-ways, without which there could be no mineral veins, and to find the faulted segments into which the veins have been severed.

Forms of Ore Bodies. — The shape or form of an ore body is of great practical importance, for it determines the way in which the ore body can be worked. A tabular mass of ore more or less sharply defined from the rock inclosing it is termed a *vein* (Fig. 331). The ideal vein is bounded by well-defined walls; the overhanging wall, as illustrated on p. 313, is the hanging wall, and the other, on which the miner obtains

his footing, is appropriately called the foot wall.   The ore breaks cleanly
from these walls.   It is tacitly part of the definition of a vein that if
the vein occurs in other than massive igneous rocks (such as granite)
it cuts across the structure of the inclosing rocks.   Beliefs in the characteristics of an ideal vein are of great practical significance, for they
have greatly influenced the mining laws of the United States; and

H. G. Ferguson, U. S. Geol. Survey.

Fig. 331. — Gold-bearing quartz vein.   Alleghany district, California.   The sharply
defined white quartz vein is well shown, together with some minor veinlets ramifying
through the adjacent wall rocks.

because the average vein departs widely from the ideal, these departures have caused and are still causing enormous difficulties in squaring
the legal view of what a vein should be with what nature has actually
formed.

Some veins are bordered by zones of mineralized rock rich enough to extract along with the vein filling. These mineralized zones as a rule shade off imperceptibly into rock too poor to mine. Consequently an ore body of this kind, instead of being bounded by well-defined walls, is bounded by " assay-walls," so called because continuous sampling and assaying to determine its metallic content are necessary in finding the limits of the ore body. Therefore such boundaries fluctuate with the price of the metal.

A *lode* consists of several veins spaced closely enough so that all of them, together with the intervening rock, can be mined as a unit. All the larger tabular ore bodies tend to be of this general character, and there is no sharp distinction between a vein and a lode.

Some ore bodies in sedimentary rocks conform to the bedding of the inclosing strata. Such ore bodies are either of sedimentary origin or of replacement origin (p. 97): genetically these two modes of origin are wholly unlike, and the distinction is of great practical importance although not always easy to make. If of sedimentary origin they are beds; if of replacement origin they are termed *bed veins*.

Emplacement of Ore Bodies. — Some ore bodies have been formed by the filling of cavities or openings in the crust, others have been formed by replacement, and others have been formed by a combination of both processes. Openings in the crust are made by fracturing and fissuring. As the walls of a fissure are not rigorously plane but are more or less irregular surfaces, movement along them relative to each other causes open spaces to form along the course of the fissure. These openings become the receptacles of vein matter, and the vein thus formed, when followed along its course or down its dip, will be found to expand and contract in width — " to swell and pinch," in the language of the miner. The abruptness of this swelling and pinching depends on the original irregularities in the fissure and determines how far the vein departs from the ideal tabular form. By renewal of movement along the vein the fissure may be reopened, and more vein matter deposited in the newly formed openings. In this way many veins have grown in size; the early formed portions of the vein are likely to become crushed during the later movements, and angular fragments of ore that was formed in the early stages may become incorporated in the ore deposited later. Thus the stages of growth of the vein are recorded within the vein, and a sequence in the order of deposition of the minerals can often be ascertained. These facts are not only of theoretical interest but also of practical consequence.

The vein-forming solutions that deposit the minerals in the openings along a fissure soak out into the wall rocks. There they bring about many changes, depending on their composition, on their temperature, and on the composition of the wall rocks. The effects may extend for a few inches up to hundreds of feet from the vein. From the study of these effects, conclusions can be drawn as to the composition and temperature of the ore-forming solutions.

Almost universally the ore-forming solutions in soaking into the wall rocks cause crystals of pyrite to grow in them. Nearly all ore-forming solutions carry dissolved sulphur, and when these solutions permeate the wall rocks this sulphur combines with the iron of whatever iron-bearing minerals are present to form pyrite, generally as well-crystallized cubes: the wall rock has been *pyritized*. This development of pyrite in the wall rock is a conspicuous, easily recognizable effect. Such pyrite is of replacement origin, as it has grown in the body of an old mineral as the result of the removal of part of the old mineral and the deposition of sulphur in the space thus made.

More interesting practically is the ability of the ore-forming solutions under some circumstances to transmute the wall rocks into ore. The vein is then bordered on one or both sides by a layer or layers of ore of replacement origin. The resulting ore body is therefore of dual origin: it was formed in part by the filling of open spaces and in part by replacement.

Many ore bodies are wholly of replacement origin. Limestone is the most common rock thus transformed into ore. In some ore bodies of this origin the evidence of replacement is astonishingly impressive. Although the ore consists solidly of sulphides — galena, sphalerite, and pyrite — it preserves faithfully the bedding and other sedimentary features of the vanished limestone: and on seeing such an ore body underground it is often difficult to believe that we are viewing an ore body and not merely country rock. In ore bodies of replacement origin, the ores in contrast to those in the fissure veins were formed by the ore-forming solutions dissolving the country rock and simultaneously depositing in the space thus formed an equal volume of ore. The thoroughness of replacement in many mining districts is impressive, but the immensity of the volume of rock removed during replacement is perhaps even more impressive. The process of replacement is of prime importance to an understanding of ore deposits.

Composition of Ores. — In the primary ores of copper, lead, zinc, and silver, the metals were originally deposited in compounds in which they are united with sulphur — in short, as sulphides. Galena (PbS) is the ultimate source of all the world's lead; sphalerite (ZnS) is the chief source of all our zinc; chalcopyrite ($CuFeS_2$) and other copper-bearing sulphides are the ultimate sources of our copper. Gold, it is true, is deposited as native metal, but it is almost invariably associated with pyrite (FeS_2), that most ubiquitous of all sulphides.

Certain important consequences follow this general rule that the primary ore bodies consist of sulphides. As soon as the ore deposits become exposed at the Earth's surface by the progress of erosion, the sulphides begin to oxidize — to unite with the oxygen of the atmosphere — and the oxidized products begin to unite with water and carbon dioxide. A host of new minerals is formed. Prominent among these changes are those that overtake the pyrite. Pyrite alters to rusty yellowish-brown limonite, which imparts to the outcrops of veins and lodes their characteristic iron-stained appearance. Not only is limonite formed from the pyrite, but powerful solvents, such as sulphuric acid and ferric sulphate, are generated, and as these solvents trickle downward they attack the other sulphides. They dissolve the silver and copper and cause them to move downward. As a result of these changes the ore body at the outcrop is likely to be vastly different from what it is in depth. It differs in appearance, in composition, and in metallic content.

These changes stop at or near the water table (p. 84), because movement of subsurface water is generally slow below the water table and the supply of oxygen therefore becomes scant. In humid regions the water table is near the surface; in arid regions it reaches depths as great as 2400 feet. As the position of the water table is influenced also by the relief of the land, the depth to which the oxidized zone extends is a function of climate and topography.

At the water table, then, the character of an ore is likely to change drastically. The metallurgical processes adapted to the oxidized ore may be wholly unsuited to the primary sulphide ore. Many a mine, equipped to treat the ore occurring near the surface, has failed from this cause alone. Moreover, the metallic content of an ore body is likely to become impoverished or enriched, depending on the nature of the chemical reactions that have taken place in the zone of oxidation. The explanation of why some ores are impoverished and others are enriched involves the application of chemistry to the problems of geology, but it would take us too far afield to discuss the details here.

Iron-Ore Deposits. — The ore deposits whose origin has been outlined in the preceding pages are concentrations of metals brought about by igneous activity. Other methods of concentration, however, are effective in producing ore deposits of economic value. These other methods can most readily be illustrated by means of the iron-ore deposits. Iron is by far the most useful of the metals, and fortunately its ores occur in greater abundance than those of all other metals. Part of this abundance is due to the fact that iron-ore deposits are formed in more ways than those of any other metal, but largely because many iron-ore deposits have been formed by sedimentation, a process that produces far larger ore deposits than any other process of concentration. If we consider that an iron-ore district containing a reserve of more than one billion (10^9) tons of ore is a district of first-magnitude reserves, then there are ten such the world over; and in at least seven of these ten the ores are of sedimentary origin.

It is occasionally said that aluminum in the future will supplant iron as an industrial metal. This assertion is based on the fact that aluminum averages 8.1 per cent of the Earth's crust, whereas iron makes up only 5.1 per cent. However, the processes by which aluminum has been concentrated into ore bodies are few, whereas many have been effective in assembling iron and moreover have operated on a grander scale. As a result the ores of iron are roughly 40 times as abundant as those of aluminum. Technically and economically it is the ores that are of decisive importance and not the average amounts of metal in the crust. For these and other reasons, chief among which is that " the services of iron, for which there are no substitutes, are well-nigh numberless," iron will remain supreme as an industrial metal.

In the following sketch of the various processes by which iron is assembled to form commercially valuable ore bodies, four types of deposits are described: first, deposits formed by concentration within molten magmas and thus originating at high temperature; second, those formed as a result of the iron being carried out of the magma by gaseous emanations, the iron having been rendered volatile by the presence of chlorine or some other agent, such as we have visible evidence of in the fumaroles at Vesuvius or in the Valley of Ten Thousand Smokes in Alaska; third, the deposits formed by sedimentation; and last, those in which the concentration has been effected by weathering.

Iron-ore bodies formed by concentration within molten magmas are rare. Probably the best-established examples, whose mechanism of concentration can most readily be visualized, are in the Bushveld, Union of South Africa. They are inclosed in gabbro as layers of magnetite resembling strata; they are up to 15 feet thickness and extend for hundreds of miles. At a certain stage while the gabbro magma was solidifying the magnetite began to separate out, and being heavier than the magma, the grains sank and accumulated in the form of a layer.

In some districts part of the iron of the magma escaped at the time the magma was solidifying, and if the magma was intrusive into limestones the iron-bearing emanations reacted with these limestones; in this way ore bodies of contact-metamorphic origin were formed, as outlined on p. 352. If the emanations do not encounter limestone, they are likely to migrate farther from the magmatic hearth, and as they move into an environment that is becoming progressively cooler with increasing distance from the magma, they give rise to different types of iron-ore deposits, distinguished by the fact that they were formed at progressively lower temperatures and carry minerals indicative of the conditions under which they were formed.

The *minette ores* of Lorraine in France are the most important ores of sedimentary origin. They consist of oölitic limonite in nearly horizontal beds interstratified with limestone, shale, and sandstone. Although nearly horizontal, they dip westward at a very low angle. They average 30 per cent of iron — a relatively low content, but because they contain sufficient calcite to form a slag in the furnace (they are " self-fluxing," in technical language), are near supplies of coking coal and also near consuming centers, they are of great commercial value. They contain nearly 2 per cent of phosphorus, ordinarily a highly undesirable impurity in an iron ore; but as a result of the development of the Thomas process of smelting in 1879, the phosphorus is eliminated in the form of a by-product valuable as fertilizer. In virtue of their sedimentary origin the ore bodies are of large areal extent and of constant composition; consequently the tonnage of ore can be estimated with far higher probability than can be done for ore of any other mode of origin. The reserves are estimated to contain 5000 million tons of ore.

The term minette, meaning " small mine," came to be applied to these ores in this way. At the outcrops the soluble gangue matter (calcite) of the ore as well as the deleterious phosphorus had been dissolved out; as a result the ore at the outcrop was enriched in iron and freed from an objectionable impurity. As soon as the water table was reached the primary ore was struck, lower in iron and high in phosphorus. Before 1879, that is, before the invention of the appropriate process to smelt phosphorus-bearing ores, the primary ores were worthless; hence the outcrop of the Lorraine ores was marked by a line of small inconsequential mines — minettes.

During the negotiations at the close of the Franco-Prussian war in 1871, Bismarck was advised by the Director of the Prussian Geological Survey to shift the proposed boundary of Lorraine westward to include the outcrop of the iron ore. This was accepted by the French, who were particularly anxious to obtain concessions of territory near Belfort. At that time neither the Germans nor the French understood the geology and origin of the Lorraine iron ores. The invention of the Thomas process in 1879 made the ores workable and immensely valuable, and the great iron industry of the German Empire was largely based on them. As development proceeded the geologic features of the deposits became clear, and it was seen that although the Germans had the outcrops of the deposits the gentle westward dip caused the iron-ore beds to extend under the soil of France, and that in fact a large fraction of the total reserves lay under French territory. An important iron industry was developed in France on the resources thus unexpectedly left to her. During the World War some of the fiercest, bloodiest drives of that war were undertaken by the Germans to undo the " error " of 1871. By the treaty of Versailles in 1919 *Lorraine annexée* was restored to France, and the entire iron field passed into her possession.

In eastern Cuba are large iron-ore deposits, in which the iron has been concentrated to commercial grade by the lateritic weathering of serpentine. The ore occurs on a plateau as a blanket 20 feet thick. In the cuts made by mining with steam-shovels the ore at the surface can be seen to grade downward into the unaltered serpentine from which it was derived. The serpentine contains 7 per cent of iron; and chemical weathering, by dissolving out almost all the constituents of the serpentine except the iron, has raised the iron content of the residual product to 50 per cent. Such lateritic ores are known to occur also in the Celebes and the Philippines.

In the Lake Superior region, from which the United States obtains 85 per cent of its supply of iron ore, the ore deposits are the results of a double concentration. First there was laid down by sedimentation an iron formation, consisting of thinly bedded strata of iron-bearing minerals alternating with siliceous strata. In the Mesabi district, which is the most productive iron district in the world, this iron formation averages 25 per cent in content of iron. This is too low in grade to be worked as ore. Fortunately, parts of the iron formation were reconcentrated by weathering, by which the gangue was removed and the iron minerals, because of their insolubility, were left behind. As a result of this purification the residual product contains 50 to 60 per cent of iron and is therefore valuable ore. This weathering took place not under present conditions of climate and topography but under those of remote geologic antiquity, of pre-Cambrian time.

In conclusion, then, we see that an extraordinary diversity of geologic processes has been effective in assembling iron into ore deposits of workable grade, and that to form some of these deposits a twofold concentration, first by sedimentation and second by weathering, was required.

Placers

General Features. — A *placer* is a deposit of sand or gravel containing particles of valuable mineral. Gold, tin (in the form of its oxide, cassiterite), platinum, and diamond are the substances commonly won from placers. Most placers are stream deposits; but a few are marine beach gravels, such as the famous gold placers of Nome, Alaska, one of which was the present beach of the Bering Sea, and the others were ancient beaches, formed when the Bering Sea had outlines somewhat different from those it has now.

Placers are so easily found and so readily worked, without special equipment or capital, that they have been sought from the beginning of history by the prospector and explorer. Gold placers have been the strongest incentive to this search, and most of our mining districts have been found by the placer miner. The richer placers are soon

G. K. Gilbert, U. S. Geol. Survey.

Fig. 332. — Hydraulic mining in the Sierra Nevada, California. At the time the picture was taken, the gold-bearing gravel was being swept by the jet of water into the head of the string of sluice boxes shown at the extreme left.

worked out, and attention then becomes directed to finding the bedrock sources from which the minerals in the placers were derived. If these sources prove to be deposits of economic size, they form the basis for a much more permanent industry; and the ephemeral placer-mining camp becomes transformed into the more staid lode-mining district.

Extraordinary ingenuity has been applied to the problem of working the leaner placers. So brilliant have been the results in the more advanced methods of placer mining — *hydraulicking* and *dredging* — that they represent the most efficient forms of mining, in the sense that lower-grade material can be worked by them than by any other method. In hydraulic mining a jet of water under heavy pressure is directed against a bank of gravel and the gravel thus loosened is swept by a current of water into a long sluice (Fig. 332); the heavy mineral — gold, platinum, or cassiterite — settles to the bottom and is caught by appropriate devices at the head of the sluice, and the lighter material, the gravel and sand, is carried through the sluice.   In thus concentrating the gold or other valuable material, the miner, using Nature's own method, has completed the concentration begun by Nature in forming the placer. In California, where hydraulic mining reached its highest development, gravel containing so little as 3 cents in gold to the cubic yard has been profitably worked.

In dredging, the digging apparatus and the entire concentrating plant are contained on a boat — the dredge.   The dredge floats on a pond; it digs and takes in the gravel at its forward end, and at the rear discharges the tailings — the gravel from which the gold, platinum, or cassiterite has been separated.   Thus the pond and dredge on it gradually travel up the valley.   Gold-bearing gravel averaging 10 cents in gold to the cubic yard can be worked at a profit by dredging.

At the present time 10 per cent of the world's annual output of gold, 70 per cent of its supply of tin, and nearly all its platinum are still derived from placers.

Origin of Placers. — As soon as ore bodies come into the zone of erosion, they are attacked by weathering.   If they contain sulphides, they are subject to a peculiarly active form of chemical weathering intensified by the sulphuric acid and other powerful solvents formed by the oxidation of pyrite and other sulphides.   Only the most resistant substances survive this attack.   After being set free from their matrix they eventually find their way by creep and rain wash into the streams.   Only the tougher materials withstand the pounding and abrasion to which they are subjected in the stream; the brittle minerals are pounded to minute particles and are swept downstream.   The valuable minerals in placers represent survivals of the fittest, where fitness is measured by resistance to chemical attack and to abrasion.   Hence it is easy to understand why the minerals commonly won from placers are gold, platinum, cassiterite, and diamond.

The gold and other valuable minerals occur in particles ranging from the minutest grains up to larger pieces termed *nuggets*.   According to the distance that these particles have been carried downstream from their source in bedrock, they are more or less water-worn.   Angular, jagged, " rough " gold occurs in placers near where it has been set free; smooth gold is found farther downstream.   It is somewhat surprising, however, to see within how short a distance from their bedrock source gold particles become smoothly water-worn. This is due partly to the softness of gold and partly to its great weight, which causes the grains and nuggets to move downstream slowly, with many a halt, and during their lagging progress downstream they are pounded and abraded by the passing gravel.

The lowermost few feet of gravel, those resting on bedrock, are much richer in gold than the upper layers of gravel. As the miner puts it, the "paystreak" rests on bedrock. In places enough gold occurs in cracks in the bedrock to make it profitable to mine several feet of the bedrock below the paystreak. Gold has a truly astonishing ability to sift down into the cracks, joints, and foliation planes of slates and schists.

The concentration of gold on bedrock is due in part to the churning action of streams during high-water stages. The gravel is locally scoured out to great depths during these stages (p. 57), and whatever gold was distributed through the scoured-out mass of gravel becomes concentrated on the channel thus formed; and as high water subsides, the scour channel becomes filled with barren gravel. Another method of concentration that causes the gold to move toward bedrock is that resulting from the downstream migration of the meander belt (p. 56).

It can be seen that a knowledge of the laws governing the transportation of detritus by streams and the laws of the origin of land forms is fundamental to an understanding of the formation of placers. In a region in the early stages of the cycle of erosion the streams are so actively engaged in downcutting that no gravels are laid down in their channels more than temporarily; hence such regions are unfavorable for the occurrence of placers. As a matter of experience it has been found that regions of uplifted and maturely dissected peneplanes are favorable for the development of gold placers. During the peneplane stage the gold is liberated from the veins and veinlets distributed throughout the region, and after the region is uplifted and the new cycle of erosion is well under way the gold becomes concentrated in the valleys carved in the old peneplane.

Placer deposits have formed at all times during the history of the Earth. Some of the older placers have been buried by later sedimentary rocks; others have been sealed beneath lavas that flowed down the old valleys in which the gravels were accumulating. In regions in which placers have been covered by flows of lava, the streams that formed the placers become dispossessed of their channels and seek new ones. In the course of time a complete revolution in the topography is effected, and the placers capped by the resistant lava flows become the divides between the existing streams. What were once the valley bottoms are now the mountain tops. Such dead rivers, whose gravels are sealed under lava flows, occur high above the present streams in various parts of the world, notably in the Sierra Nevada, where they have yielded much gold.

Although the finding of placers has generally been the prelude to the discovery of veins and lodes in bedrock, it by no means follows that rich placers are necessarily derived from rich deposits in bedrock. The contrary is almost true. For example, the larger part of the world's platinum has been won from placers in the Ural Mountains, but no workable primary deposits have been found. In its bedrock home the platinum is disseminated through large bodies of rock. The processes of forming placers are so efficient, however, that the small amount of platinum distributed through immense volumes of rock has become concentrated in the gravels of the streams draining the Ural Mountains. Cubic miles of rock were ground up by erosion, and the platinum in them has accumulated in workable amount in the stream beds. Similarly, rich gold-bearing gravels have accumulated in areas in which the gold occurs in bedrock in the form of small auriferous quartz veinlets, and the same disparity between the richness of the placers and the poverty of the bedrock sources is even more generally true of tin deposits and is reflected in the fact that 70 per cent of the annual supply of tin is still won from placers.

One of the richest gold-placer regions ever found was on the lower western slope of the Sierra Nevada. Its discovery in 1848 caused the greatest human migration in history. The gravels of the present streams have yielded $900,000,000. Their great richness was the result of a triple concentration of the gold. Near the end of Jurassic time the area of the present Sierra Nevada was intruded by a succession of great batholiths of granitic rock. During the solidification of the molten magmas, countless small gold-bearing veinlets were formed in the surrounding rocks. This was the first concentration of the gold. A long period of erosion then set in, during which the region was reduced almost to a peneplane. In the streams that flowed on this peneplane great masses of gravel accumulated, hundreds of feet thick in the larger valleys, and rich in gold in the layers resting on bedrock. The gold thus accumulated was the result of the second concentration. Great eruptions burst out and overwhelmed the streams with volcanic débris and sealed them under lava flows. The streams were forced out of their courses and began to dig new ones. Faulting along the eastern flank of the Sierra lifted the range high into the zone of erosion and tilted the western slope to the west, thereby enormously increasing the erosive powers of the westward-flowing streams. The great canyons that gash the western slope of the range were formed. Where the streams intersected the old river gravels, they robbed them of their gold, and to this store of easily won metal they added the gold that they obtained from the veins and veinlets in bedrock. As a result of these three stages of concentration the present streams of the Sierra Nevada acquired that richness which has made them famous the world over.

READING REFERENCES

1. Economic Aspects of Geology; by C. K. Leith. 431 pages. Henry Holt & Co., New York, 1921.

Written from the point of view that "there is no phase of geology which at some time or place does not have its economic application." Outlines the occurrence of the mineral resources; discusses the use of geology in the exploration and development of mineral deposits, and its bearing on valuation, taxation, mining laws, conservation, engineering construction, and other economic matters.

2. Introductory Economic Geology; by W. A. Tarr. 664 pages. McGraw-Hill Book Co., Inc., New York, 1930.

An introductory textbook, dealing with the distribution, mode of occurrence, uses, and origin of the common mineral substances.

3. Economic Geology; by H. Ries. 6th edition, 860 pages. John Wiley & Sons, Inc., New York, 1930.

4. Non-Metallic Mineral Products (Except Building Stones); by W. S. Bayley. 530 pages. Henry Holt & Co., New York, 1930.

5. Geology of Petroleum; by W. H. Emmons. 2d edition, 736 pages. McGraw-Hill Book Co., Inc., New York, 1931.

6. Petroleum and Coal: The Keys to the Future; by W. T. Thom, Jr. 223 pages. Princeton Univ. Press, Princeton, 1929.

Points out the great influence exerted by coal and petroleum on national policies. The occurrence and origin of the mineral fuels are briefly described, and the reserves of these fuels and their importance to the future of civilization are discussed.

APPENDIX A

MINERALS

INTRODUCTION AND DEFINITION

Minerals compose the rocks of which the Earth's crust is built. They are also the constituents of ore bodies and other deposits of economic value. Rocks are primary documents of geology, and in order to read these documents it is necessary to be able to recognize their constituents. A mineral can be defined as a naturally occurring substance that has a distinctive set of physical properties and a composition expressible by a chemical formula.

Minerals are composed of chemical elements. A few consist of single elements, such as native gold and silver, as these metals are termed when they occur in elementary form in nature, or diamond and graphite, both of which are crystalline forms of the element carbon. Diamond and graphite illustrate in the most striking way possible what is meant by a mineral; the two are of identical chemical composition, yet each has its own distinctive physical properties: diamond is transparent and is the hardest substance known, whereas graphite is opaque and is among the very softest of substances. Most minerals, however, are made up of two or more elements united in such a way that the product differs in its properties from any of the elements composing it.

There are 92 chemical elements, of which 90 have so far been discovered. Less than half of them are common, and it has been estimated that more than 99 per cent of the Earth's crust is composed of the 14 elements which, with their chemical symbols, are shown in the following table:

	Per Cent		Per Cent
Oxygen, O	46.46	Titanium, Ti	.62
Silicon, Si	27.61	Hydrogen, H	.14
Aluminum, Al	8.07	Phosphorus, P	.12
Iron, Fe	5.06	Carbon, C	.09
Calcium, Ca	3.64	Sulphur, S	.06
Sodium, Na	2.75	Chlorine, Cl	.05
Potassium, K	2.58	All others	.68
Magnesium, Mg	2.07	Total	100.00

Three elements together with their chemical symbols, not included in the preceding list, are added here because they occur in certain important ore-forming minerals. Each of these elements makes but a minute fraction of 1 per cent of the Earth's crust.

Copper, *Cu*
Lead, *Pb*
Zinc, *Zn*

The minerals formed by the various combinations among these 17 elements are very numerous, but those which are abundant are few in number.

CHARACTERS OF MINERALS

Chemical Composition

A few minerals have a fixed chemical composition; but most of them have a variable composition which, however, can be expressed by a chemical formula. Quartz, one of the most abundant of minerals, has a fixed composition, written SiO_2, which is a sort of chemical shorthand saying that one atom of silicon is united with two atoms of oxygen. Sphalerite, from which most of the world's zinc is obtained, is a mineral of variable composition, which is indicated by writing its formula thus: Zn,FeS — thereby showing that in this mineral an atom of iron can proxy for an atom of zinc.

The various minerals react differently to chemical reagents, and these reactions are one means of identifying minerals. It is beyond the scope of this discussion to explain how minerals are identified by their chemical behavior, but many textbooks of mineralogy treat the subject fully.

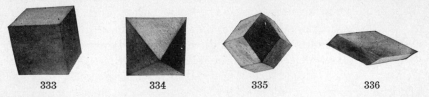

333   334   335   336

Fig. 333. — Model of a cubic crystal.
Fig. 334. — Top of an octahedron, showing four of the eight faces of the octahedron.
Fig. 335. — Dodecahedron, showing six of its twelve faces.
Fig. 336. — A rhombohedron.

Physical Characters

Crystals. — Nearly all minerals are *crystalline;* that is to say, the atoms of which they are built are organized in definite geometric arrangements, the so-called space-lattices. A few minerals are *amorphous* (noncrystalline). Under favorable conditions most minerals form *crystals*. Crystals are solids that are bounded by smooth plane surfaces called *faces*, whose arrangement is related to the internal structure of the mineral. As a rule, the crystals of any particular mineral have similar forms of crystallization. For instance, the mineral galena characteristically crystallizes in cubes (Fig. 333). Garnet is common either as dodecahedrons (Fig. 335) or trapezohedrons. These crystal forms are characteristic of these minerals, and their recognition greatly aids in identifying the minerals.

Structure of Minerals. — The *structure* of minerals generally refers to their outward shape and form. The following descriptive terms are used in this connection, some of which are self-explanatory: *crystallized*, occurring as crystals or showing crystal faces; *massive*, not bounded by crystal faces: the antithesis of crystallized; *columnar; fibrous; botryoidal*, consisting of small rounded forms like closely bunched grapes; *micaceous*, occurring in thin cleavable sheets; *granular*, in aggregates of coarse to fine grains; *compact; earthy; oölitic*, formed of small spheres which resemble fish roe.

Cleavage and Fracture. — The manner in which many minerals break is so characteristic that it is of great help in identifying them. If they break so that smooth plane surfaces are produced, they are said to have a *cleavage*. This cleavage invariably occurs along planes, but these planes may or may not be parallel to crystal faces. Some minerals have but one cleavage, others two, three, or even six different cleavage directions. The number of cleavage directions that a mineral has serves as an aid in determining the mineral. Good examples are the cubic cleavage of galena, whereby the mineral cleaves in three planes at right angles to one another, so that it breaks up into innumerable small cubes; the rhombohedral cleavage of calcite — three planes not at right angles, so that the resulting cleavage fragments are rhombohedrons (Fig. 336); and the cleavage of mica — in one direction only, the most remarkable example of cleavage in the whole mineral kingdom, by virtue of which the mica can be cleaved into sheets or folia of indefinite thinness.

If a mineral has no cleavage, then the nature of its broken surface — its *fracture* — is more or less distinctive. Various kinds of fracture are: *conchoidal*, if the surface of fracture is curved like the interior of a clam shell; *fibrous* or *splintery*, if it is like that of wood; *uneven* or *irregular*, if the surface is rough.

Color. — The color of a mineral is one of its most conspicuous physical properties. The color of some minerals is a definite and constant property and serves as a ready means of identification. For example, the golden-yellow of chalcopyrite, the lead-gray of galena, the black of magnetite, are striking properties of these minerals. Surface alterations are likely to change the color of a mineral, as is shown by the golden tarnish frequently seen on pyrite. In noting the color of a mineral a fresh surface should therefore be examined. Moreover, many minerals vary in color in the different specimens. This is due chiefly to a change in composition, such as an increase of iron content in sphalerite, with the consequent darkening of the color of the mineral; or to impurities, such as the red color given to quartz by an admixture of hematite. Other minerals, such as fluorite, show a wide range in color without perceptible changes in composition.

Color of Powder or Streak. — *The color of the streak* is an important aid in identifying minerals. The streak is a thin layer of the powder of the mineral obtained by rubbing the mineral on an unglazed porcelain plate known as a streak plate. The color of the streak may be similar to the color of the mineral or quite different. For example, some varieties of hematite are brilliantly black, but they give a red-brown streak, which positively identifies them as hematite.

Luster. — The *luster* of a mineral is due to the quality and intensity of the light it reflects. Luster must not be confused with color, for two minerals of the same color can have totally different lusters, just as a black paint with a shiny finish, such as an enamel, differs in appearance from a black paint with a dull finish because it reflects light differently. Descriptive terms are given to the different kinds of luster. A list that includes the more important is as follows:

Metallic. — Having the luster of a metal. Example: pyrite. Most minerals that give a dark or black streak have metallic luster.

Vitreous. — Having the luster of glass. Example: quartz.

Resinous. — Having the luster of yellow resin. Example: sphalerite.

Pearly. — Having the iridescence of pearl. Example: some varieties of dolomite.

Greasy. — Looking as if covered with a thin layer of oil. Example: some varieties of massive quartz.

Silky. — Like silk, as the result of a finely fibrous structure. Example: fibrous gypsum.

Adamantine. — Having a brilliant luster like that of a diamond.

Hardness of Minerals. — Minerals vary greatly in their hardness, and the determination of this property is an important aid in identifying them. The relative hardness of a mineral can be determined by comparing it with a series of minerals that has been chosen as a standard scale. The scale consists of the following minerals, each mineral being harder than those that precede it in the scale.

Scale of Hardness

1. Talc	4. Fluorite	8. Topaz
2. Gypsum	5. Apatite	9. Corundum
3. Calcite	6. Orthoclase	10. Diamond
	7. Quartz	

The relative hardness of a mineral in terms of this scale is determined by finding which of these minerals it can scratch and which it can not scratch. In determining hardness the following precautions must be observed. A mineral that is softer than another may leave a mark on the harder one which can be mistaken for a scratch. The mark can be rubbed off, however, whereas a true scratch is permanent. Some minerals are commonly altered on the surface to material much softer than the original material. The physical structure of a mineral may prevent a correct determination of its hardness. For instance, if a mineral is pulverulent, finely granular, or splintery in its structure, it can apparently be scratched by a mineral much softer than itself. It is always advisable when making the hardness test to confirm it by reversing the procedure, that is, by rubbing the unknown on the material of known hardness.

The following materials serve as additions to the above scale. The finger nail is a little over 2 in hardness, as it can scratch gypsum and not calcite. A copper coin is about 3 in hardness, as it can scratch calcite. The steel of an ordinary pocketknife is just over 5, and ordinary glass has a hardness of 5.5.

Specific Gravity. — The specific gravity of a substance is expressed as a number that indicates how many times heavier a given volume of the substance is than an equal volume of water. Minerals range in specific gravity between 1.5 and 20.0. The great majority range between 2.0 and 4.0. There are various instruments that enable one to determine the specific gravity of a mineral with accuracy, but ordinarily it is sufficient to judge the weight of a fair-sized piece in the hand. After some experience rather small differences in specific gravity can be detected in this way, and the specific gravity of a mineral can be approximately estimated.

Common Minerals

A few of the more common minerals are described on the following pages. The student should compare these descriptions with as many different specimens of the minerals as possible, and should note the form, color, and luster of each sample and make the simple tests for hardness, streak, and specific gravity.

Magnetite. — An oxide of iron, a combination of ferrous and ferric oxides, $FeO.Fe_2O_3$, or Fe_3O_4.

Physical Characters. — Black. Streak black. Hardness 6. Heavy. Strongly magnetic, hence its name. Granular or massive; fairly common in octahedral crystals (Fig. 334).

Occurrence. — Is a valuable iron-ore mineral, containing 72 per cent of iron. It is mined in the Adirondacks, New Jersey, Pennsylvania, and many other parts of the world. It is common as a minor rock constituent, particularly in the darker-colored igneous rocks. The black sand of the seashore is largely magnetite. In some places it occurs as a natural magnet, known as lodestone.

Hematite. — The ferric oxide of iron, Fe_2O_3.

Physical Characters. — Dark steel-gray to iron-black. Streak light to dark red-brown (Indian-red). Hardness 5.5 to 6.5. Granular; also micaceous. Rarely in crystals. Also earthy; in this form it is red.

Occurrence. — Hematite is widely distributed in rocks and is the most abundant ore mineral of iron. More than nine-tenths of the iron produced in the United States comes from this mineral. The chief districts are near the shores of Lake Superior in Michigan, Wisconsin, and Minnesota. Other important districts are in northern Alabama and eastern Tennessee. Earthy hematite is the pigment that gives many sandstones their red color. It is used also in red paints and as a polishing material, known as rouge.

Limonite. — Hydrous ferric oxide, $Fe_2O_3.H_2O$.

Physical Characters. — Dark-brown to nearly black. Streak yellowish-brown. Hardness 5 to 5.5. Medium heavy. Commonly as botryoidal and related forms having radiating fibrous structure; also in stalactitic forms resembling icicles; earthy. In recent years the tendency has been to restrict the term *limonite* to the amorphous and earthy forms and to call the crystalline forms *goethite*.

Occurrence. — A valuable source of iron. Limonite is a common mineral formed by the alteration of previously existing minerals containing iron. It occurs as a cellular mass known as *gossan*, forming the oxidized top of a sulphide vein, where it has accumulated by the oxidation of pyrite and other sulphides; as loose, porous bog-iron ore; associated with siderite as large deposits in limestone and other rocks. It gives brown, orange, and yellow colors to many weathered rocks, sedimentary strata, and soils.

Pyrite. — Iron sulphide, FeS_2.

Physical Characters. — Pale brass-yellow. Streak black. Hardness 6 to 6.5 (unusually hard for a sulphide). Heavy. Generally granular.

Common as crystals, especially as cubes whose faces are marked with fine parallel lines, or *striations*.

Occurrence. — The most common sulphide mineral. Occurs in many rocks and is an important vein mineral. May carry small amounts of gold or copper and so become an ore for both these metals. Is not used as an ore of iron, but as a source of sulphur in the manufacture of sulphuric acid. Its presence in building stones detracts from their value, as its oxidation produces not only iron-oxide stains but also sulphuric acid, which causes the stones to disintegrate.

Chalcopyrite (Copper Pyrite). — Copper-iron sulphide, $CuFeS_2$.

Physical Characters. — Golden-yellow; generally tarnished to bronze or iridescent colors. Streak greenish-black. Hardness 3.5, hence much softer than pyrite. Heavy. As a rule massive, rarely in crystals.

Occurrence. — An abundant and valuable ore-mineral of copper. Occurs widely distributed in vein deposits with many other sulphide minerals.

Sphalerite. — Zinc sulphide, ZnS. Generally contains a small amount of iron.

Physical Characters. — Commonly yellow-brown to dark-brown, being darker in the varieties containing more iron. Resinous to sub-metallic luster. Hardness 3.5 to 4. Heavy. White to yellow and brown streak, of lighter shade than the mineral itself. Perfect dodeca-hedral cleavage, having brilliantly flashing cleavage planes trending in six different directions. As a rule massive.

Occurrence. — The most important source of zinc. Widely distrib-uted, but generally in veins or irregular bodies in limestone. Associated generally with galena, pyrite, and chalcopyrite.

Galena. — Lead sulphide, PbS.

Physical Characters. — Lead-gray. Streak grayish-black. Hard-ness 2.5 (soft). Very heavy. Bright metallic luster. Perfect cleavage in three planes at right angles to each other, forming cubes. Occurs in natural cubic crystals (Fig. 312), but massive and granular aggregates are more common.

Occurrence. — The chief source of lead. Contains some silver and serves as an ore of that metal. Also commonly found with zinc min-erals.

Calcite. — Calcium carbonate, $CaCO_3$.

Physical Characters. — Generally white or colorless. Also variously tinted, gray, red, green, and blue. Usually opaque or translucent; rarely transparent. Hardness 3. Light in weight. Perfect cleavage in three planes at oblique angles to each other, giving rhombic-shaped faces (rhombohedral cleavage) (Fig. 336). In crystals generally of rhombohe-

dral form. Effervesces freely on application of a drop of cold acid. This
serves to distinguish calcite from dolomite, $CaMg(CO_3)_2$, another common carbonate, which does not effervesce under these conditions.

Occurrence. — A very common mineral. Is the chief constituent of
limestones and marbles. Also a very common vein mineral. Used in
the manufacture of lime, plasters, and cement, as a metallurgic flux, and
in chemical industries.

Dolomite. — Carbonate of calcium and magnesium, $CaMg(CO_3)_2$.
Physical Characters. — Generally white or gray; rarely flesh-colored.
Opaque to translucent. Hardness 3.5 to 4 (harder than calcite).
Perfect cleavage in three planes not at right angles to each other (rhombohedral cleavage). Light in weight. Vitreous to pearly luster.
Does not effervesce on application of a drop of cold acid unless the acid
is placed on a scratched or powdered surface. In this respect it differs
from calcite. In granular masses and in crystals, some of which have
curved faces.

Occurrence. — Composes rock masses such as dolomite limestone and
marble. Also as a vein mineral. In the rock form, used as a building
and ornamental stone, for the manufacture of some cements, as a source
of magnesia for refractory substances, and as agricultural lime.

Gypsum. — Hydrous calcium sulphate, $CaSO_4.2H_2O$.
Physical Characters. — Usually white or colorless. Hardness 2
(easily scratched with the finger nail). Light in weight. Has one very
perfect cleavage. In tabular diamond-shaped crystals or in granular
masses; also fibrous.

Occurrence. — Is a mineral widely distributed in sedimentary rocks,
commonly in thick beds. It is frequently interstratified with limestones
and shales. Generally occurs in association with salt beds. Is chiefly
used for the production of plaster of Paris.

Halite (Common Salt). — Sodium chloride, $NaCl$.
Physical Characters. — White or colorless. Hardness 2.5. Light in
weight. Perfect cleavage in three planes at right angles to one another
(cubic cleavage). Transparent to translucent. Salty taste. Generally in cubic crystals or in masses showing cubic cleavage.

Occurrence. — In thick beds interstratified with sedimentary rocks
and associated with gypsum. Used for culinary and preservative
purposes; also extensively in chemical industry.

Quartz. — Silicon dioxide, SiO_2.
Physical Characters. — Colorless or white; but many varieties are
colored by impurities, yellow, red, pink, amethyst, green, blue, brown,
black. Vitreous luster. Transparent to opaque. Hardness 7. Light
weight. Conchoidal fracture. Commonly in hexagonal crystals similar

to Fig. 337. The triangular faces at the ends of the crystals are usually smooth, whereas the rectangular faces between the ends are horizontally striated. Also massive.

Varieties. — There are many varieties of quartz to which different names are given. A few are as follows: *rock crystal,* colorless quartz, commonly in distinct crystals; *amethyst,* quartz colored purple or violet; *rose quartz,* usually massive with a pink color; *smoky quartz,* quartz with a smoky yellow to brown or almost black color; *chalcedony,* finely fibrous variety, translucent with a waxy luster; *agate,* a variegated chalcedony delicately banded with different colors; *jasper,* extremely fine-grained quartz colored red by admixed hematite.

Fig. 337. — Model of a quartz crystal.

Occurrence. — Quartz is one of the most common minerals. It occurs as an abundant constituent in many rocks. It is also the most common vein mineral. It makes up the largest part of most sands. It is widely used in its various colored forms as ornamental material. It is used for abrasive purposes, in the manufacture of glass, porcelain, in paints, scouring soaps, etc. As sand it is used in mortars and cements. Quartzite and sandstone — rocks made up largely of quartz — are used in building.

Garnet. — There are several garnets, which differ from one another in the elements they contain. They are all silicates with analogous formulas. The most common garnet contains ferrous iron and aluminum, $Fe_3Al_2(SiO_4)_3$. Other garnets contain magnesium, calcium, manganese, and ferric iron.

Physical Characters. — Color varies with the composition. Most commonly red or brown. Also yellow, white, green, black. Transparent to almost opaque. Hardness 7. Generally well crystallized, either in a form showing 12 rhombic-shaped faces (dodecahedron, Fig. 335) or 24 trapezium-shaped faces (trapezohedron).

Occurrence. — Garnet is a widely distributed mineral, occurring most commonly in metamorphic rocks. Used as an inexpensive gem stone and because of its hardness as an abrasive material.

Orthoclase (Potassium Feldspar). — Potassium-aluminum silicate, $KAlSi_3O_8$.

Physical Characters. — Colorless, white, gray, flesh-red; rarely green. Streak white. Hardness 6. Light in weight. Has two good cleavages making 90° angles with each other (whence the name of the mineral).

Occurrence. — The most common silicate. Widely distributed as a prominent rock constituent, occurring in rocks of many kinds, but most abundantly in granite and allied rocks. Also in large crystals and cleavage masses in what are known as pegmatite dikes. From these dikes it is quarried in large amounts for use in the manufacture of porcelain.

Plagioclase Feldspars. — Sodium-calcium-aluminum silicates.

Physical Characters. — Various shades of gray, less commonly white. Transparent to opaque. Hardness 6. Light in weight. Have two cleavages making nearly a 90° angle with each other, one of them (the basal cleavage) being better than the other. Commonly distinguished from orthoclase by the presence on the basal cleavage surfaces of a series of fine parallel lines termed striations, which resemble rulings made by a fine diamond point. Rarely as thin-bladed crystals with curved surfaces and a pearly luster.

Occurrence. — In much the same manner as orthoclase.

Muscovite (White Mica). — A complex silicate containing potassium and aluminum.

Physical Characters. — Has a perfect cleavage in one direction, which allows the mineral to be split into exceedingly thin sheets. These sheets are flexible and elastic. Transparent and almost colorless in thin sheets. In thicker blocks, opaque with light shades of brown and green. Hardness 2 to 2.5. Light in weight. Structure foliated in large to small sheets or scales.

Occurrence. — A common rock-making mineral. It occurs in granite together with quartz and feldspar, and with the same minerals in pegmatite dikes. It is characteristic of a series of rocks made up of abundant mica, in which it is arranged in parallel orientation, with the result that the rocks split in flakes and slabs parallel to the cleavage of the mica. These rocks are known as *mica schists.* Is used chiefly as an insulating material in the manufacture of electrical apparatus. Used as a transparent material in stove doors, etc. There are many other minor uses.

Biotite (Black Mica). — A complex silicate containing potassium, magnesium, iron, and aluminum.

Physical Characters. — Perfect micaceous cleavage. Cleavage sheets and flakes are flexible and elastic. Generally dark-green, brown, or black. Thin sheets usually have a smoky color (differing from the almost colorless muscovite). Hardness 2.5 to 3. Light in weight.

Occurrence. — An abundant rock-making mineral, common in granites and many gneisses and schists.

Chlorite. — A complex silicate containing magnesium and aluminum. A numerous group of minerals of similar characters which are called collectively the *chlorites* from their prevailing green color.

Physical Characters. — Perfect micaceous cleavage. Flakes are flexible but not elastic (differing thus from muscovite and biotite). Green of various shades. Hardness 2 to 2.5. Light in weight.

Occurrence. — A common rock-making mineral. The green color of many rocks is due to the presence of this mineral. This is particularly true of many schists and slates (green roofing slates).

Serpentine. — Magnesium silicate, $H_4Mg_3Si_2O_9$.

Physical Characters. — Olive-green or yellow-green to blackish-green. Luster greasy or wax-like; silky when fibrous. Hardness 2.5 to 5, generally 4. Light in weight. Usually massive but also fibrous or felted.

Occurrence. — A common mineral, widely distributed. Invariably an alteration product of some magnesian silicate, chiefly olivine. It is the chief constituent of the rock called serpentine, some varieties of which are used as ornamental stone. The fibrous variety known as *chrysotile* is the principal source of asbestos.

Olivine. — Silicate of magnesium and iron: $(Mg,Fe)_2SiO_4$.

Physical Characters. — Olive-green to yellowish-green; rarely brownish. Transparent to opaque. Hardness 6.5 to 7. Vitreous luster. Conchoidal fracture, causing it to look as if it were a green quartz.

Occurrence. — In basic igneous rocks — gabbros, peridotites, and basalts.

Pyroxene and Amphibole

These two abundant rock-making minerals are similar in some respects, and consequently it is difficult to discriminate them in most rocks, where good crystal forms are rare. However, it is well to study them separately under favorable conditions, in order to appreciate their differences as well as their points of similarity.

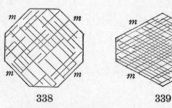

338   339

Fig. 338. — Cross-section of pyroxene perpendicular to the long axis of the crystal. The cleavage traces are parallel to the faces marked *m*. The alternate faces (those marked *m* and those unmarked) are nearly at right angles to each other.

Fig. 339. — Cross-section of amphibole perpendicular to the long axis of the crystal. The cleavage traces are parallel to the prism faces (*m*), which make angles of 56° and 124° with each other.

Pyroxene. — A silicate containing chiefly calcium and magnesium; also varying amounts of aluminum, iron, and sodium.

Physical Characters. — Light- to dark-green, varying with the amount of iron. Also nearly white or black. Commonly opaque. Hardness 5 to 6. Light in weight. In prismatic crystals with eight sides (Fig. 338); in reality square

prisms whose corners are truncated. The angle between alternate faces is therefore nearly 90°. These faces will fit into the corner of a box or tray. By means of these angles pyroxene can best be told from amphibole. Some specimens show a fair cleavage parallel with the faces lettered *m* in the figures, the angle between the cleavage faces being also nearly 90°.

Occurrence. — Pyroxene is a highly abundant rock-making mineral, occurring chiefly in the dark-colored igneous rocks. Rare in rocks that contain much quartz.

Amphibole. — Silicate of calcium and magnesium with varying amounts of aluminum, iron, and sodium. Similar to pyroxene.

Physical Characters. — Light- to dark-green, varying with amount of iron. Also nearly white or black. Commonly opaque. Hardness 5 to 6. Light in weight. Commonly in prismatic crystals with six sides. Fig. 339 shows that the angles between the faces lettered *m* are 124° and 56° (very different from the corresponding angles in pyroxene). Has a good cleavage parallel with the faces lettered *m*. The differing forms of the crystals, the differing cleavage angles, and the fact that amphibole has the better cleavage are the chief distinctions between amphibole and pyroxene. Amphibole as a rule has a higher luster and yields smoother, more continuous cleavage surfaces than does pyroxene. Some varieties of amphibole have long, needle-like crystals, resulting in a fibrous structure. Pyroxene does not occur in this form.

Occurrence. — Amphibole is an abundant rock-making mineral, occurring in both igneous and metamorphic rocks. Generally recognizable by its elongated bladed structure and good cleavage, which yields diamond-shaped cross-sections.

Hornblende is a common dark variety of amphibole.

Pyroxene and amphibole together with biotite are the common dark constituents of many rocks. The first two can be distinguished from biotite by the fact that they occur in prismatic crystals that can not be divided into thin elastic flakes; that is, they lack the perfect cleavage of the micas. If present as small grains in a rock, they lack the high luster characteristic of flakes of biotite. They can be told from chlorite by their much greater hardness as well as by their form and lack of micaceous cleavage.

APPENDIX B

ROCKS

Rocks are the principal constituents that make up the crust, or the Earth's outer " rocky " shell. Most rocks are aggregates of minerals. Consequently they range widely in appearance and other properties according to the minerals present, the number of kinds and their relative abundance, the size of the mineral grains, and the manner in which the minerals are associated. The kinds of rocks are many, but if classified according to the ways in which they come into existence, they fall into three major classes:

I. Igneous rocks, formed by the solidification of molten rock-matter, as exemplified by the rocks formed by the cooling of lava poured out from a volcano.

II. Sedimentary rocks, most of which were formed by their substance settling as sediment from a body of water.

III. Metamorphic rocks, which were formed from preëxisting rocks by developing new characters as the result of geologic processes acting on them within the Earth's crust.

Every rock carries within itself evidence of its mode of origin, and as one of the prime purposes of geology is to determine the constitution, structure, and history of the Earth's crust the recognition of rocks and the ability to read them is of fundamental importance.

CHARACTERS USED IN IDENTIFYING ROCKS

The properties most useful in identifying rocks are *structure, texture, hardness*, and *fracture*.

Structure is a term reserved for the larger features of rocks. A layered or laminated structure generally indicates sedimentary origin; if the rock contains numerous spherical or almond-shaped cavities or vesicles (formed by the expansion of gases in molten rock-matter) it has a *vesicular* structure and is of igneous origin. Other distinctive structures are referred to in the appropriate places.

Texture is the appearance of a rock as determined by the size, shape, and arrangement of its constituent mineral grains. The magnitude of the grains determines the *grain size* of the rock: if the grains are as large as peas, the rock is *coarse-grained* in texture; if they are the size of those in granulated sugar, the rock is fine-grained; and if they are so small that they can not be distinguished as individuals by the unaided eye and the rock seems to be a homogeneous substance, the rock is said to be *aphanitic*.

The shape and arrangement of the mineral grains with respect to one another produce the *fabric* of a rock. For example, a rock composed of grains approximately of one size has an *even-grained* or *equigranular* fabric, and a rock in which the grains are of differing sizes has an *inequigranular* fabric. There are various fabrics, many of which are distinctive of the rocks in which they occur. Inasmuch as texture is the conjoint effect of grain size and fabric, it has become customary to use texture for grain size, for fabric, or for their conjoint effect.

Certain textures are of definite help in identifying rocks. The texture of a granite, which is so distinctive that it is termed the *granitic texture*, proves not only that the rock is of igneous origin, but that it was formed under conditions of slow undisturbed cooling. A glassy texture also proves that the rock is of igneous origin, but that, unlike granite, it was formed by the sudden solidification of molten rock-matter, for glasses are the result of the extremely rapid chilling of molten rock-matter. The *clastic texture*, which occurs in rocks made up of fragments of minerals more or less rounded, is characteristic of many sedimentary rocks. Other textures are described in connection with particular rocks.

Hardness is of service in distinguishing between certain kinds of rocks. Many rocks resemble limestone, but the test for hardness with the knife-point serves at once to distinguish a limestone, whose hardness is 3, from the much harder rocks that resemble it.

Fracture is a less useful property. However, a semi-conchoidal fracture yielding shell-like fragments characterizes shales, and the tendency of most metamorphic rocks to split into slabs or thin flakes is a valuable aid in their recognition.

IGNEOUS ROCKS

Since the rocks derived from molten rock-matter vary in texture and in composition, these two variables can be used as factors in classifying the igneous rocks. By employing texture as the first criterion for setting the igneous rocks in order, we obtain at once five major classes:

I. *Even-granular*, in which all the minerals are of about the same size and are large enough to be identified by the eye alone or aided by a pocket lens.

II. *Porphyritic-granular*, in which certain minerals — the phenocrysts — by virtue of their large size contrast conspicuously with those which surround them, thus forming a porphyry having an even-granular groundmass.

III. *Porphyritic-aphanitic*, in which the conspicuous crystals — the phenocrysts — are set in an aphanitic groundmass.

IV. *Aphanitic*, in which none of the constituents are distinguishable.

V. *Glassy*, in which few or none of the constituents have crystallized.

These five classes are termed *massive* rocks, and for the sake of completeness Class VI, *fragmental*, is added to include the pyroclastic products of volcanic eruptions (p. 269).

This order from Class I to Class V marks in a general way the decreasing amount of easily recognizable minerals in rocks: in Class I, all the constituents can be easily distinguished as individual grains by the unaided eye; in II, the phenocrysts can be easily distinguished, but the constituents of the groundmass less readily; in III, the phenocrysts alone are distinguishable; and in IV, none of the constituents can be recognized.

Each of the major classes is then subdivided on the basis of composition — on the kinds of minerals present and the proportions in which these minerals occur. It is to these subdivisions that the actual rock names are given. For example, an even-granular rock that is composed of feldspar and quartz and generally also a dark mineral, as a rule biotite, is called *granite*.

By applying these principles, the following classification of igneous rocks is obtained, as shown in the accompanying table.

Remarks on the Table. — The glassy rocks, which are rare, and the tuff and breccia, which are described on page 269, being left out of account, the following remarks may prove of service in understanding the classification of igneous rocks shown in the table.

All rocks in the same horizontal column have the same texture.

All rocks in the same vertical column have essentially the same chemical composition; for example, granite, granite porphyry, and rhyolite are alike in chemical composition. In physical appearance, however, they differ notably: a granite differs somewhat from a granite porphyry, and vastly from a rhyolite. Yet it is easily possible to assemble a series of specimens that will bridge by imperceptible gradations the vast gap between granite and rhyolite. The differences between granite, granite porphyry, and rhyolite are mainly the results of different rates of cooling of magmas of identical composition. When this magma cools slowly within the crust it forms granite, whereas the same magma, if erupted on the Earth's surface where it would be drastically chilled, would solidify as rhyolite. In the same way a magma that would yield diorite in depth would, if erupted at the surface, solidify as andesite; and a magma that yields gabbro in depth solidifies as basalt on the Earth's surface. These facts can be epitomized thus: rhyolite is the extrusive equivalent of granite; andesite is the extrusive equivalent of diorite; and basalt is the extrusive equivalent of gabbro.

TABLE OF IGNEOUS ROCKS

Major Classes (based on texture)	Subdivisions of Major Classes (based on mineral composition)			
	Light-colored minerals, chiefly feldspar, predominate		Dark minerals predominate	Dark minerals entirely
I Granular (with grains interlocking)	Granite (has quartz)	Diorite (has no quartz) (See note below)	Gabbro Dolerite (grain size is intermediate between that of gabbro and basalt)	Peridotite Hornblendite Pyroxenite
II Granular (as above) and porphyritic	Granite Porphyry (has quartz)	Diorite Porphyry (has no quartz)	Gabbro Porphyry	
III Porphyritic, with aphanitic groundmass	Rhyolite (contains phenocrysts of quartz)	Andesite	Basalt	
IV Nonporphyritic, aphanitic	Felsite			
V Glassy	Obsidian Pitchstone Pumice		Basalt Glass	
VI Fragmental	Volcanic tuff and breccia			

Note: *Syenite* is briefly mentioned in the text.

The rocks in which the light-colored minerals predominate are light in color and light in weight, *i.e.*, they are of low specific gravity. The rocks in which the dark (ferromagnesian) minerals predominate are dark in color and heavy in weight. The range in specific gravity — from 2.67

for the average granite to 3.0 for gabbro — is not large, but is sufficient after experience to serve as an aid to identification.

Although in the table each rock has been placed in a separate compartment, in nature no rock variety is as sharply delimited from its neighbors as it seems to be in the table. For example, there are transitional varieties between granite and diorite and between granite and granite porphyry. No hard and fast boundaries set off any of the so-called rock species. These facts often make it difficult to classify a given rock. Further difficulties are presented by the finer-grained rocks, especially the aphanitic group. When the accurate identification of a rock becomes a matter of high importance, recourse is had to the microscope.

DESCRIPTION

Even-granular Rocks

The even-granular rocks are the results of slow cooling, or of slow cooling combined with high gas content. Typically, then, they occur in deep-seated intrusive bodies, especially in batholiths (p. 240). In such deep-seated masses cooling was necessarily long protracted, and the pressure was sufficient to keep the gases within the magma and to allow them to exercise their power of promoting coarse crystallization. Hence these rocks are often called *deep-seated rocks* or *plutonic rocks* in fanciful reference to the realm in which they originated. There is a correlation between the coarseness of grain and the depth at which the rock was formed, but only a rough correlation, on account of the disturbing influence of gas content.

Granite. — As may be seen from the scheme of classification, *granite* is composed largely of quartz and feldspar (mainly of the variety orthoclase). It contains also as a rule some mica, generally the black mica biotite; less commonly it contains hornblende, or hornblende and biotite together. All these component minerals are roughly of the same size, and hence granite is said to be even-granular, or equigranular. The minerals separated from the magma in a definite order: first the dark minerals, hornblende and biotite; then followed by the feldspars; and last the quartz. The dark minerals, being the first to crystallize, were not hampered in their growth by the presence of any neighbors, and so are generally in the form of sharply defined crystals; and the feldspars, having begun to grow later, are less well crystallized, for where they abutted upon the earlier-formed dark minerals their freedom to grow was hampered. As the quartz was the last mineral to separate from the magma, it had to take what space was left, and it is therefore molded around the earlier minerals and occupies the angular interspaces between them. This habit of the quartz produces an intimately interpenetrating and interlocking arrangement. This interlocking equigranular texture is so characteristic of granites that it is often called for short the *granitic texture*. It serves to distinguish rocks of Class I from all others.

The average granite contains 60 per cent of feldspar, 30 per cent of quartz, and 10 per cent of dark minerals. There are many varieties of granite, based on color, texture, and composition. Its common occurrence is shown in the fact that there are few States in the Union or Provinces in Canada that do not contain exposures of granite; and its use as a building stone and for other purposes is well known.

Diorite. — *Diorite* is an equigranular igneous rock composed of feldspar and one or more dark minerals, in which the feldspar is more abundant than the dark minerals. The feldspar is mainly plagioclase, but unless the characteristic striations on the cleavage planes of the plagioclase can be seen it is generally difficult to recognize this fact with the unaided eye. The dark minerals may be biotite, hornblende, or pyroxene, occurring either singly or together.

Syenite is much like granite in composition, but it differs in containing little or no quartz and hence is here classed with diorite. It is not a common rock, nor does it as a rule occur in large masses compared with the enormous bodies of granite.

Gabbro. — *Gabbro* differs from diorite in that the feldspar is subordinate and the dark minerals predominate. Hornblende, pyroxene, and olivine are the common dark minerals, occuring singly or together; biotite, though present in some gabbros, is distinctly uncommon. Because of the prevalence of dark minerals, gabbros are dark and of high specific gravity. *Dolerite* is a convenient term for the basic rocks that in grain size are intermediate between basalts and gabbros.

Peridotite. — *Peridotite* is composed wholly of ferromagnesian minerals, with olivine predominating. It is not common and occurs as minor intrusive bodies — dikes, sills, and stocks (p. 235). It is interesting and important, however, as being the source of ores of chromium, nickel, and platinum, and of the diamond. It is generally dark or black, and heavy from the large amount of iron-bearing minerals present. The diamonds of South Africa are very minor components of rock of this kind, filling volcanic pipes, and they occur also in similar intrusions in Arkansas.

A notable feature of peridotite is its tendency to alter to a dark-green rock, serpentine. In this change the minerals of the peridotite combine with some 14 per cent of water, and this added water causes a large expansion of volume, which in turn causes much internal movement in the attempt of the mass to accommodate its increased volume. As a result the serpentine, or " serpentinized peridotite " is traversed by countless smooth shiny surfaces known as *slickensides* (p. 313). There are few peridotite masses the world over that are not more or less serpentinized.

Pyroxenite, as its name implies, is composed wholly of pyroxene, and *hornblendite* consists entirely of hornblende. As a rule these rocks form bodies of small size; nevertheless, in places, as at the remarkable platinum deposits recently discovered in South Africa, pyroxenite occurs in vast volume.

Porphyritic-granular Rocks

The distinguishing feature of rocks of this class is that they contain phenocrysts imbedded in a groundmass so coarse-grained that its component minerals can be recognized by the unaided eye. The phenocrysts in most of these porphyries are abundant, making up half or more of the bulk of the rock. If the volume of the phenocrysts exceeds 75 per cent, the porphyry becomes indistinguishable from the corresponding granular rock.

The porphyries are common as minor intrusive bodies: as dikes, sills, volcanic necks, stocks, and laccoliths (p. 237). They do not occur as batholiths.

Granite Porphyry, Diorite Porphyry, etc. — The typical *granite porphyry* contains conspicuous crystals of feldspar, quartz, and biotite set in a granitic groundmass. As its name implies, its composition is like that of granite; it differs from granite in having phenocrysts, and on the average the grain of the groundmass is finer than the grain of the average granite.

Diorite porphyry differs from granite porphyry in the absence of quartz phenocrysts and the great prevalence of striated feldspar.

Porphyritic-aphanitic Rocks

The rocks of this class are generally of volcanic origin. Extruded upon the Earth's surface, the magmas from which they were formed have cooled rapidly. They are characterized by the occurrence of porphyritic crystals set in a groundmass that is either so fine-grained as to be irresolvable by the unaided eye or else is partly or wholly glassy.

Rhyolite. — *Rhyolite* represents the aphanitic lava form of the magma that at depth consolidates as granite. It contains phenocrysts of feldspar, quartz, and biotite, and rarely of hornblende. The number of these phenocrysts varies within the widest bounds, so that there is a complete transition from non-porphyritic to highly porphyritic rhyolite.

If the amount of the phenocrysts exceeds 25 per cent of the volume, the rock is by some called a *rhyolite porphyry*. The colors range from white to gray, pink, red, and purple. Rhyolites and andesites with inconspicuous phenocrysts or with few or no phenocrysts are termed *felsite*.

Andesite. — *Andesites* are of many colors, but in general they are darker than the rhyolites; dark-gray is common. They are transitional on the one hand into rhyolites; on the other, into basalt. The average or typical andesite occupies the intermediate position. The darker andesites are of basaltic appearance, but unlike basalts their freshly broken thin edges are translucent when held in bright light. The phenocrysts in andesites commonly consist of striated feldspar and one or more dark minerals (hornblende, pyroxene, or biotite). Quartz phenocrysts are absent (distinction from rhyolite). Andesites crowded with prominent phenocrysts are by some called *andesite porphyries*.

Andesite and andesite porphyry are enormously abundant among the extrusive rocks of the globe. They are the chief products of the volcanoes that form the " circle of fire " surrounding the Pacific Ocean. In fact, it was because of their prevalence in the *Andes* of South America that they were given their name. In virtue of their great abundance and differences in color, texture, and mineral composition the variety of andesitic rocks is legion.

Felsite. — The difficulty of discriminating between rhyolites and andesites that are devoid of phenocrysts makes it necessary to use an elastic noncommittal name. For the light-colored rocks of this class, namely those which are white, light to medium gray, light-pink to dark-red, pale yellow or brown, purple, or light-green, rather than dark-green, dark-gray, dark-brown, or black, the term *felsite* is convenient.

Basalt. — Lavas that are dark-gray, dark-green, brown, or black are termed *basalt*, the common extrusive equivalent of the basic magmas. Basalts are either compact or vesicular. If the vesicles have become filled with some mineral, such as calcite, chlorite, or quartz, the fillings are called *amygdules* and the rock is termed an *amygdaloidal basalt*. Many basalts are without phenocrysts, but others contain abundant conspicuous phenocrysts, consisting of feldspar, olivine, or pyroxene, or some combination of these. Therefore, in the Table of Igneous Rocks basalt is shown to fall in both Classes III and IV. The phenocrysts are hard and have straight, clean-cut boundaries, whereas amygdules are generally soft and have irregular, roundish or elliptical boundaries.

Basalt is by far the most voluminous of the extrusive rocks. The enormous tracts in western America, India, and elsewhere that have been flooded by outpourings of basalt are mentioned in Chapter XI.

Dolerite is the name given to the coarser-grained basalts, in which the grains are so well developed that the constituent minerals are nearly or quite recognizable. There is no hard and fast line between basalt and dolerite on the one hand and dolerite and gabbro on the other.

Glassy Rocks

Volcanic glasses occur as thin crusts on the surfaces of lava flows, or as lava flows which have cooled rapidly. Most of the glasses are the products of the chilling of silicic magmas (p. 248). Brilliantly lustrous volcanic glass is called *obsidian,* and the duller and more pitchy variety is *pitchstone.* Pumice is frothed glass. Natural glasses, like the obsidian of Obsidian Cliff, Yellowstone Park, commonly contain crystallized minerals in the form of small spheres which, having a radiating or spoke-like structure, are known as *spherulites.*

Obsidians are generally dark-colored to black, and yet many of them correspond in chemical composition to rhyolite and granite. Hence they seem to contradict the rule that nearly all rocks of siliceous composition are light-colored. However, if a piece of black obsidian is chipped to a thin edge it transmits the light and loses much of its dark appearance. The deep coloring is the result of the uniform distribution throughout the glass of a relatively small amount of dark material.

Basalt glass is of rare occurrence. Its formation requires extremely rapid chilling of basaltic magma.

SEDIMENTARY ROCKS

Sedimentary rocks are formed principally in two ways. Some are formed by the accumulation of fragments derived from older rocks: detritus consisting of rock and mineral particles is carried away from its source rocks by water, wind, or ice, is eventually deposited, and becomes hardened into rock. *Detrital rocks* thus formed are classified according to the size of the constituent grains of detritus. The second principal class of sedimentary rocks is formed by the withdrawal of material dissolved in the sea (and to a lesser extent in lakes), either in the form of the shells of organisms or as chemical precipitates; rocks of this origin are classified according to composition.

By far the most abundant sedimentary rocks are shale, sandstone, limestone, and conglomerate.

DESCRIPTION

1. Conglomerate consists of gravel that has become firmly cemented. The pebbles in it are more or less rounded, having become water-worn by abrasion during stream transportation or by buffeting by waves in the shore zone. They consist of rocks of any kind, but generally of some durable material, such as quartz and quartzite.   The filling in the inter-spaces between the pebbles consists of sand and a cement, which may be silica, clay, iron oxide, or calcium carbonate.

Breccia is like conglomerate, except that most of the fragments, instead of being water-worn pebbles, are angular, with sharp edges and unworn corners.   There is no sharp demarcation between breccia and conglomerate, since the distinction between them rests on the shape of the constituent fragments, which ranges from complete angularity through subangularity to complete roundness.   Breccias in brief are angular detrital rocks; those that are firmly cemented alluvial deposits are termed *fanglomerates* (p. 204), and those of glacial origin are termed *tillites* (p. 133).

2. Sandstone.

Color. — A wide range of colors: gray, yellow (buff and tawny), red, and brown are most common, but green and other tints occur.

Physical Characters. — Consists of firmly cemented sand grains. Coarse sandstones grade into conglomerates; on the other hand, fine-grained sandstones grade into shale, the lower limit of grain size for a sandstone being that at which the individual grains are not distinguishable by the unaided eye.   The grains are chiefly particles of quartz or of other durable material.   The substance filling more or less completely the interspaces between the grains is the *cement*.   The strength and durability of a sandstone depend on the nature of its cement, and the porosity depends on the extent to which the spaces between the grains have been filled.   The kind of cement differs in different sandstones, as in conglomerates.   A siliceous cement produces the strongest and most durable sandstones.

Sandstones when fractured break around the grains instead of through them, because the grains are stronger than the cement; therefore the broken surfaces have a gritty feel.   In quartzites (p. 359), however, the grains are so firmly cemented that fracturing takes place across the grains instead of around them.

Arkose is a variety of sandstone in which grains of feldspar are abundant.   The feldspar can be recognized by its cleavage planes, which reflect flashes of light as the specimen is turned from side to side while being examined.   If an arkose contains a large amount of feldspar, it closely resembles a granite.   The two can be distinguished, however, by the fact that in the arkose the quartz is in angular or subangular particles, instead of being molded around the feldspar as it is in granite.

3. Shale and Mudstone.

Color. — Gray in various shades perhaps most common; but red and pink in many shades, brown, buff, green, and black are also common.

Physical Characters. — Shale is so fine-grained as to appear homogeneous to the unaided eye. Is soft enough to be easily scratched. Typical shale has a smooth and almost greasy feel; but a small amount of fine sand in its composition will make it somewhat gritty. True shale has a semi-conchoidal fracture, causing it to split into shell-like fragments parallel to its bedding.

Rock of the same general character as shale but without its capacity to split parallel to the bedding is termed *mudstone.*

Shale and mudstone are essentially clays or muds that have been converted into rock. They are therefore high in clayey constituents and are said to be *argillaceous* rocks (Latin *argilla,* clay).

4. Limestone.

Color. — Variable, but grays are most common.

Physical Characters. — Limestones range from aphanitic varieties, so fine-grained as to appear homogeneous, to fragmental and granular varieties. The aphanitic varieties are made up of chemically precipitated calcium carbonate, or of microscopic shells, or of a mixture of both. In coarse-grained limestones, whole or fragmentary shells can readily be seen with the unaided eye. If the shells are abundant and loosely cemented, the rock is termed *coquina.* Some limestones show on their freshly fractured surfaces distinct cleavage planes of calcite.

Limestones necessarily have the same hardness as that of their chief constituent calcite (hardness = 3), and hence can be scratched easily. Limestones effervesce vigorously with dilute acid, owing to the violent liberation of carbon dioxide gas.

Many limestones are impure, as the result of admixture with clay or fine sand. By increasing amounts of impurities they grade into shale on the one hand, and into sandstone on the other.

Chalk is a variety of incoherent limestone — incoherent because weakly cemented. It is as a rule white or creamy white.

Marl is a mixture of calcium carbonate and clay. It is a loose friable rock, which effervesces readily with acid.

5. Dolomite is like limestone in many ways, but is slightly harder and does not effervesce in cold acid except on scratched or bruised surfaces, *i.e.,* where the rock has been powdered. The texture ranges from aphanitic to visibly crystalline. Some dolomites have a coarsely porous structure.

Dolomite, like limestone, is a carbonate rock, but limestone is composed of calcium carbonate ($CaCO_3$), whereas dolomite is composed of calcium-magnesium carbonate — $CaMg(CO_3)_2$.

METAMORPHIC ROCKS

A metamorphic rock is the product of the transformation of a previously existing rock. Such transformations occur in response to changes in the geologic environment to which the preëxisting rock was subjected within the Earth's crust. The resulting metamorphic rock may retain vestiges of the original characters of the rock from which it was derived, but generally the transformation has been so thorough that the original characters have vanished and the metamorphic product is to all appearance a new rock.

Most metamorphic rocks have a more or less parallel arrangement of their component minerals. If these minerals are in part at least of flaky habit, they confer on the rock the capacity to split readily parallel with the direction in which the flakes are oriented. This tendency of a rock to split parallel to a plane is termed *foliation* (Latin *folium*, a leaf) because the rocks breaks into thin leaves or slabs. All rocks having such a foliation are conveniently grouped together as *foliates*. The notable foliation-producing minerals are the micas (muscovite and biotite), chlorite, and to a lesser extent amphibole, which because of its needle-like habit produces a less well-defined foliation.

The kinds of metamorphic rocks are many, but only those occurring most abundantly are described here. The explanation of the origin of metamorphic rocks is given in Chapter XIV.

DESCRIPTION

1. Gneiss.

Physical Characters. — Gneiss has a coarsely granular texture, and a streaky, roughly layered appearance due to the alternation of lenses or layers of unlike mineral composition. Most varieties contain mica, whose flakes have a parallel arrangement. The rock splits parallel to the direction marked by the mica. Gneisses are *coarse-grained* foliates.

Kinds of Gneiss. — Probably the commonest kind is *mica gneiss*, characterized by abundant content of black mica. In some varieties both black and white mica occur together.

Gneiss containing conspicuous prisms of hornblende which are more or less in parallel alignment is called *hornblende gneiss.* Many gneisses are obviously partly transformed granites and are therefore termed *granite gneisses.* In some granite gneisses the parallel arrangement of the mica was acquired during flowage while the rock was still partly molten; such gneisses are termed *primary gneisses* to distinguish them from the gneisses of metamorphic origin.

2. Schist.

Physical Characters. — Schist differs from gneiss in having a closely spaced foliation, as a result of which it splits readily into thin flaky slabs or plates. There is no demarcation between gneisses, which are coarse-grained foliates, and schists, which are finer-grained foliates. In schists the minerals are large enough to be recognized by the unaided eye, a feature that distinguishes them from the still finer-grained foliates termed phyllites.

Kinds of Schist. — Schists are generally known by the mineral responsible for the foliation. Thus *mica schist* is rich in mica (biotite, muscovite, or both). Chlorite is the foliation-making mineral in *chlorite schist,* hornblende in *hornblende schist,* and talc in *talc schist.*

As schists invariably split parallel with the plane in which the foliation-making minerals are oriented, these minerals seem to make up most of the rock; only by examining a schist on cross-fracture, *i.e.,* at right angles to the foliation, can it be seen that the schist is composed of other minerals, most commonly quartz. Many schists contain distributed through them crystals, somewhat simulating the phenocrysts of igneous rocks. A pink or red garnet commonly occurs in this fashion in mica schists; such rocks are called garnet-mica schists.

3. Phyllite.

Physical Characters. — Phyllites are intermediate in appearance between schists and slates. They are finer-grained than the schists, so that the minerals of which they are made are not discriminable by the unaided eye. They differ from slates in having a higher, glossy luster. Some phyllites, otherwise much like slates in appearance, contain scattered, large, well-defined crystals of garnet and other minerals.

Phyllites grade on the one hand into schists and on the other into slates. Rocks in the transition ranges are described by such terms as phyllitic schists or phyllitic slates, as the case may be.

4. Slate.

Physical Characters. — Slate is a homogeneous rock, so fine-grained that no mineral grains can be seen. Most slates are blue-black, a shade so typical as to be called slate-colored, but many are red, green, gray, or black. Slate splits with a foliation so perfect that it yields slabs having plane surfaces, almost as smooth as the cleavage planes of minerals; hence this variety of foliation is termed *slaty cleavage.* In roofing slates the cleavage attains its finest development and causes them to split into plane-parallel slabs of any desired degree of thinness. Slaty cleavage has no necessary relation to the bedding of the slate in which it occurs: in some slates it is parallel to the bedding but in most slates it intersects the bedding at angles ranging up to 90°.

Slates grade on the one hand into phyllites, and on the other into shales. The distinguishing differences from shales are as follows:

Surfaces of shale are generally dull, whereas slate has considerable luster. Slate is on the average somewhat harder than shale, although the difference is slight. Most slates ring when struck a light blow, and sonorousness is a time-honored test of the quality of a roofing slate. Slates when split yield approximately plane surfaces, whereas shales have a semi-conchoidal or " shelly " fracture.

5. Marble.

Color. — Marble is commonly gray or nearly white, but many other tints occur, and many marbles are streaked or splotched irregularly.

Physical Characters. — Marble is the metamorphic equivalent either of limestone or of dolomite. The ordinary variety is composed of calcite and therefore effervesces readily when touched with cold dilute hydrochloric acid, but dolomite marble effervesces only if the acid is applied to a fresh scratch.

In geologic usage the term marble is reserved for those metamorphosed limestones that are visibly crystalline. In commercial practice, however, any limestone or marble that will take a polish is called a marble. All varieties of marble are soft enough to be scratched easily (hardness about 3).

Although marbles are metamorphic rocks, few of them are foliated.

6. Quartzite.

Physical Characters. — Quartzite consists chiefly of quartz, and therefore has a hardness of 7. The grains of quartz of which it is composed are so firmly cemented that when the rock is fractured the fracture passes through the grains — not around them, as it does in sandstone. Most quartzites have been formed by the metamorphism of sandstones, but some sandstones have been so firmly cemented by silica that they too fracture through the grains and hence are called quartzites. Quartzites of metamorphic origin no longer show the sand grains of which the sandstone was composed, and tend to have a glassy appearance. Like marbles, most quartzites are massive and do not have the foliation so characteristic of most metamorphic rocks.

APPENDIX C

TOPOGRAPHIC MAPS

Topography is the configuration of the land. A *topographic map* is a representation of a land area, greatly reduced, showing the positions of hills, valleys, streams, lakes, and other features, the exact shapes of hills and valleys, the differences in elevation between them (*relief*), and the steepness of their slopes. The map employs conventions to show the topographic features of the area and the positions of roads, towns, and other works of man. In order to use a topographic map intelligently it is necessary to know what the conventions signify, and to be able to form in the mind's eye a picture of the land area represented.

Orientation. — Lines of latitude and longitude are usually selected as the boundaries of a topographic map. Most maps therefore represent unit areas known as *quadrangles*, and are standardized as to form and orientation. The map is oriented so that its top lies to the north. The lines of longitude (*meridians*) that limit the map on the east and west extend geographically north and south. On the other hand the lines of latitude (*parallels*) that limit the map on the north and south trend due east and west. Since meridians are not parallel but converge to a point at each pole, maps having meridians as east and west boundaries are not true rectangles.

The geographic north pole and the north magnetic pole do not coincide; therefore a line (determined by a compass needle) drawn from most points on the Earth's surface toward the magnetic pole diverges either to the right or to the left of true or geographic north. The amount of this divergence in any region is the *magnetic declination* and is usually indicated on the lower margin of the map by the angle between two converging lines.

Conventions. — All water features such as streams, lakes, swamps, and the sea are represented on a topographic map in blue, the works of man (*culture*) in black, and the relief of the land in brown. Special conventions for various features on both land and water are explained in detail on the back of the map sheet.

Scale. — The *scale* of a map indicates the proportion between distance on the ground and the corresponding distance on the map. For example, a scale of 1 inch to 1 mile means that two points on the ground exactly 1 mile apart will appear on the map exactly 1 inch apart. A common scale used internationally is 1 to 1,000,000, in which one unit on the map represents one million units on the ground. This scale (expressed as the fraction $\frac{1}{1,000,000}$ is too small for most purposes, and therefore larger multiples of it are used. The scales $\frac{1}{125,000}$ and $\frac{1}{62,500}$, both extensively used for topographic maps in the United States, are respectively 8 and 16 times $\frac{1}{1,000,000}$.

A graphic scale in miles and kilometers and a fractional scale are placed along the lower margin of every topographic map so that distances on a horizontal plane can be readily measured on the map by reference to those scales.

Relief; Contour Lines. — The vertical dimension is shown by *contour lines* (often called simply *contours*), which are printed in brown. The difference in elevation between each two successive contours on any map is known as the *contour interval*, and this is indicated on the lower margin along with the scale.

Each contour line passes through points that have the same altitude above mean sea level. Therefore if one starts at a certain altitude on an irregular surface, and walks in such a way as to go neither uphill nor downhill, but always on a level, he will trace out a path that corresponds to a contour line. Obviously such a path will not be straight but will curve around hills, bend upstream in valleys, and swing outward around spurs. Viewed broadly, every contour must be a closed curve, just as the shoreline of an island or of a continent returns upon itself, however long it may be. Actually there are many contours that are closed curves even upon a relatively small map, such as those marking the higher elevations of isolated hills, but many more do not close within a designated area These extend to the borders of the map and join with the contours on adjacent maps.

In order to form a more definite concept of a contour line, one may picture an island in the sea crowned by two prominent, isolated hills, with much steeper slopes on one side than on the other, and with an irregular shoreline. The shoreline is a contour line (the zero contour) because the surface of the water is horizontal. If the island is pictured as submerged until only the two isolated peaks project above the sea, and then raised above the sea 50 feet at a time, the successive new shorelines will form a series of contour lines separated by 50-foot contour intervals. At first, two small islands will appear, each with its own shoreline, and the contour marking their shorelines will have the form of two closed curves. When the main mass of the island rises above the water the remaining shorelines or contours will pass completely around the land mass. The final shoreline is represented by the zero contour, which now forms the lowest of a series of contours separated by vertical distances of 50 feet.

As the island is raised, the successive new shorelines are not displaced through so great a horizontal distance where the slope is steep as where it is more gradual. In other words, the water retreats through a shorter horizontal distance in falling from one level to the next along the steep slope than along the gentle slope. When these successive shorelines are projected upon the flat surface of a map they will therefore be crowded where the slope is steep and farther apart where it is moderate. In order to facilitate reading the contours on a map, certain contours (usually every fifth line) are strengthened and numbered in brown.

It is customary to print the exact elevations of certain points on a map. These are either prominent relief features such as mountain peaks, or permanent bench marks, marked " B.M.," followed by the elevation in feet, printed in brown. Such figures must not be confused with the figures showing the elevations of contours. The latter are always multiples of the contour interval and are placed between broken ends of the contour they designate.

Depression-Contours. — Because the contours that represent a depression without an outlet resemble those of an isolated hill, it is necessary to give them a distinctive appearance. Depression-contours therefore are marked on the downslope side with short transverse lines termed *hachures*. The contour interval employed is the same as in elevation-contours.

Ideal Example. — The illustrations (Figs. 340, 341) show the relation between the surface of the land and the topographic map representing it. The sketch (Fig. 340) represents a stream valley between two hills, viewed from the south. In the foreground is the sea, with a bay sheltered by a recurved spit. The valley is flanked by terraces in which small streams have excavated gullies. The hill on the east has a rounded summit and sloping spurs separated by steep narrow valleys. The spurs are truncated at their lower ends by a wave-cut cliff, at the base of which is a beach. The hill on the west rises abruptly above the valley by a steep scarp, and descends gently westward, trenched by a few shallow gullies.

The map (Fig. 341) represents each of these features by contours directly beneath its proper position in the sketch. The contour interval selected is 20 feet.

Construction and use of Topographic Maps

Most of the governments of the world construct topographic maps for both civil and military purposes. In North America the majority of the government topographic maps are made by the United States Geological Survey and the Geological Survey of Canada, respectively. The construction of an accurate topographic map requires much time and pre-

Modified after U. S. Geol. Survey.

Fig. 340. — Ideal landscape sketch.

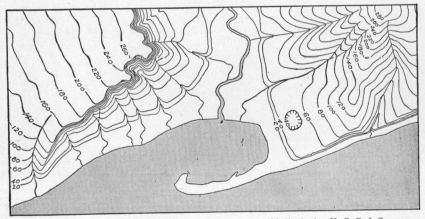

Modified after U. S. Geol. Survey.

Fig. 341. — Contour map of the landscape shown in Fig. 340.

cise work, as it is necessary to determine a large number of exact elevations and positions before the contours can be drawn and other important data entered on the map. It is not surprising therefore that more than half of the continent remains to be mapped topographically, although in some of the States mapping has been completed, and in each of the other States and Provinces at least some work has been done.

The geological surveys aim to complete maps for the entire area of the United States and Canada.

A good topographic map serves many useful purposes. It enables the engineer engaged in the construction of roads, railroads, dam-sites, power-transmission lines, pipelines, and other similar projects, to outline, before he leaves his office for the field, some of the problems to be solved in an area in which he is going to work. It forms the most acceptable base for the construction of geologic maps with their manifold scientific and practical applications, and it is helpful to the prospector, the camper, and the motorist going out into areas new to them. In fact, the ability to read a topographic map quickly and accurately is a valuable asset to anyone who, for work or for pleasure, has to do with the land.

APPENDIX D

TIME–SCALE OF EARTH HISTORY

(Total time represented, 1,500,000,000 + years)
(Time since beginning of the Cambrian, 500,000,000 years)

Major Divisions of Time	Subdivisions of Time			Important Crustal Revolutions	Dominant Life
CENOZOIC	Quaternary	Recent			Man
		Pleistocene (latest ice age)			
	Tertiary	Pliocene		Intense folding in the Alps, in the Himalayas, and in western North America	Warm-blooded animals and flowering plants
		Miocene			
		Oligocene			
		Eocene		Folding in the Rocky Mountain region	Reptiles and first modern floras
MESOZOIC	Cretaceous			Folding in lands bordering the Pacific Ocean	
	Jurassic				Reptiles and medieval plants
	Triassic				
PALEOZOIC	Permian			Folding in the Appalachian region, in Europe and in other continents	Earliest land animals and the first forests
	Pennsylvanian	Carboniferous			
	Mississippian				
	Devonian			Folding in western Europe and eastern North America	
	Silurian				Shelled invertebrates and the first fishes
	Ordovician				
	Cambrian				
PRE-CAMBRIAN — PROTEROZOIC	Keweenawan			Some folding and intrusion of granite	Primitive invertebrates, chiefly without shells
	Huronian				
PRE-CAMBRIAN — ARCHEOZOIC				Widespread folding, metamorphism, and intrusion of granite	Most primitive life, probably minute and soft-tissued
	Timiskaming				
				Folding and local intrusion of granite	
	Keewatin				
				Undeciphered record	

NOTE: Heights of spaces in table are *not* proportional to lengths of time intervals.

INDEX

Asterisks refer to illustrations

495